ASCENT
CENTER FOR TECHNICAL KNOWLEDGE

Autodesk® Civil 3D® 2021
Fundamentals for Surveyors

Learning Guide
Imperial Units - 1ˢᵗ Edition

AUTODESK.
Authorized Publisher

ASCENT - Center for Technical Knowledge®
Autodesk® Civil 3D® 2021
Fundamentals for Surveyors
Imperial Units - 1st Edition

Prepared and produced by:

ASCENT Center for Technical Knowledge
630 Peter Jefferson Parkway, Suite 175
Charlottesville, VA 22911

866-527-2368
www.ASCENTed.com

Lead Contributor: Jeff Morris

ASCENT - Center for Technical Knowledge (a division of Rand Worldwide Inc.) is a leading developer of professional learning materials and knowledge products for engineering software applications. ASCENT specializes in designing targeted content that facilitates application-based learning with hands-on software experience. For over 25 years, ASCENT has helped users become more productive through tailored custom learning solutions.

We welcome any comments you may have regarding this guide, or any of our products. To contact us please email: feedback@ASCENTed.com.

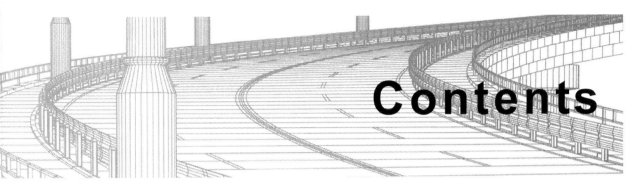

Contents

Preface ix

In This Guide xiii

Practice Files xv

Chapter 1: The Autodesk Civil 3D Interface 1-1

   1.1 Product Overview 1-2

   1.2 Autodesk Civil 3D Workspaces 1-3
      Start Tab 1-4

   1.3 Autodesk Civil 3D User Interface 1-7

   Practice 1a Overview of Autodesk Civil 3D and its User Interface 1-13

   1.4 Autodesk Civil 3D Toolspace 1-17
      Prospector Tab 1-18
      Settings Tab 1-20
      Survey Tab 1-21
      Toolbox Tab 1-22

   1.5 Autodesk Civil 3D Panorama 1-24

   Practice 1b Autodesk Civil 3D Toolspace 1-26

   1.6 Autodesk Civil 3D Templates, Settings, and Styles 1-33
      Drawing Settings in Detail 1-33
      Styles 1-44
      Managing Styles 1-52

   Practice 1c Autodesk Civil 3D Styles 1-57

   Chapter Review Questions 1-66

   Command Summary 1-68

Chapter 2: Survey Setup 2-1

2.1 Survey Workflow Overview 2-2

2.2 Collecting Field Data 2-4

2.3 Introduction to the Survey Toolspace 2-6

2.4 Survey User Settings vs. Drawing Template 2-7
    Drawing Template 2-7
    Survey User Settings 2-7

2.5 Templates 2-9

2.6 Survey Figures 2-10
    Drawing Settings 2-11
    Figure Styles 2-11
    Figure Prefix Database 2-13

Practice 2a Creating a Civil 3D Drawing Template 2-14

2.7 Points Overview 2-22
    Point Marker Styles 2-24
    Point Label Styles 2-28

Practice 2b Point Marker and Label Styles 2-35

2.8 Description Key Sets 2-42

Practice 2c Creating a Description Key Set 2-46

2.9 The Survey Database 2-50

Practice 2d Create a Survey Database 2-57

Chapter Review Questions 2-62

Command Summary 2-64

Chapter 3: Entering Linework 3-1

3.1 Survey Workflow Overview 3-2

3.2 Lines and Curves 3-3

Practice 3a Input the Project Boundary 3-7

3.3 Online Maps Service 3-11

3.4 Traverse Editor 3-15
    Manually Entering COGO Data 3-15
    Traverse Editor Options 3-17

3.5 Traverse Adjustment 3-20
    Adjusting a COGO Traverse 3-20

Practice 3b Traverse Editor and Adjustment 3-25

Chapter Review Questions 3-34

Command Summary 3-35

Chapter 4: Field Book Files 4-1

4.1 **Survey Networks** 4-2

4.2 **Importing a Field Book** 4-4

Practice 4a Importing a Field Book 4-7

4.3 **Traverse Basics** 4-14
   Open Traverse 4-14
   Closed Traverse 4-14
   Closed Connected Traverse 4-14
   Traverse Data in a Field Book 4-15

4.4 **Defining a Traverse** 4-16
   Traverse Editor 4-16
   Least Squares Traverse 4-16
   Adjustment Reports 4-17

Practice 4b Creating a Network Traverse 4-18

4.5 **Multiple Network Surveys** 4-28
   Survey Points 4-28
   Closed Connected Traverse 4-29
   Field Book Edits 4-29
   Network Groups 4-30

Practice 4c Closed Connected Traverse 4-33

4.6 **Working with Figures** 4-42

Practice 4d Field Book Edits, Styles, and Figure Prefixes 4-45

Chapter Review Questions 4-50

Command Summary 4-51

Chapter 5: Points with Connective Codes 5-1

5.1 **Field Codes** 5-2

5.2 **Survey Data - Figures** 5-6

Practice 5a Importing Data - Figures 5-7

5.3 **Figure Prefix Database** 5-16

Practice 5b Importing Data - Figures, Parcels 5-17

5.4 **Survey Data - Line Code** 5-21

5.5 **Adjusting Figures** 5-25

Practice 5c Line Code 5-27

5.6 **Translating a Survey Database** 5-34

Practice 5d Translating Survey Database 5-35

Chapter Review Questions 5-44

Command Summary 5-45

Chapter 6: Points 6-1

6.1 Point Settings 6-2

6.2 Creating COGO Points 6-4

6.3 Transparent Commands 6-5

Practice 6a Creating Autodesk Civil 3D Points 6-7

6.4 Importing and Exporting Points 6-12
  Importing Points 6-12
  Duplicate Point Numbers 6-14
  Transforming Points on Import or Export 6-16

Practice 6b Importing and Exporting Points Part I 6-18

Practice 6c Importing and Exporting Points Part II 6-22

6.5 Point Groups 6-28
  Defining Point Groups 6-28
  Updating Out of Date Point Groups 6-31
  Overriding Point Group Properties 6-31
  Point Groups Display Properties 6-32
  Survey Point Groups 6-34

Practice 6d Creating Point Groups 6-35

6.6 Reviewing and Editing Points 6-40
  Repositioning Point Objects and Labels 6-41

Practice 6e Manipulating Points 6-44

6.7 Locking/Unlocking Points 6-46

Practice 6f Point Locking and Editing 6-48

6.8 Point Reports 6-51
  Reports Manager 6-51
  Point Editor Reports 6-52

Practice 6g Point Reports 6-54

6.9 Filtering a Survey Database 6-56

Practice 6h Filter a Survey Database 6-61

Chapter Review Questions 6-64

Command Summary 6-65

Chapter 7: Surfaces 7-1

7.1 Surface Process 7-2

7.2 Surface Properties 7-8

7.3 **Surface Data** **7-11**
Contours 7-11
DEM Files 7-14
Drawing Objects 7-14
Point Files 7-14
Point Groups 7-14
Point Survey Queries 7-15
Figure Survey Queries 7-15

Practice 7a Creating an Existing Ground Surface **7-16**

7.4 **Breaklines and Boundaries** **7-19**
Breaklines 7-20
Boundaries 7-24

Practice 7b Add Additional Data to an Existing Ground Surface **7-26**

7.5 **Surface Editing** **7-35**
Line Edits 7-36
Point Edits 7-36
Simplify Surface 7-37
Smooth Contours 7-38
Smooth Surface 7-39
Copy Surface 7-39
Surface Paste 7-40
Raise/Lower Surface 7-40
Adjusting Surfaces Through Surface Properties 7-41

7.6 **Surface Analysis Tools** **7-42**
Viewing a Surface in 3D 7-42
Quick Profile 7-43

Practice 7c Surface Edits **7-44**

7.7 **Surface Labels** **7-54**
Contour Labels 7-55
Spot and Slope Labels 7-55

7.8 **Surface Analysis Display** **7-56**
Analysis Settings 7-58
Analysis Data Display 7-59

Practice 7d Surface Labeling and Analysis **7-60**

Chapter Review Questions **7-66**

Command Summary **7-68**

Chapter 8: Field to Finish **8-1**

8.1 **Field to Finish Overview** **8-2**

8.2 **Fieldwork Standards** **8-3**

Practice 8a Fieldwork Review **8-4**

8.3   Civil 3D Settings 8-8

Practice 8b Civil 3D Settings Review 8-9

8.4   Survey Toolspace 8-13

Practice 8c Survey Toolspace Review 8-14

8.5   Drawing Production 8-17

Practice 8d Drawing Production 8-18

8.6   Project Workflow 8-30

Appendix A: Additional Tools A-1

A.1   Least Squares A-2

Practice A1 Creating a Least Squares Survey A-4

A.2   Creating a Least Squares Input File A-8
        Adjustment Analysis A-9
        Blunder Detection Analysis A-10
        Updating the Survey A-12

Practice A2 Creating a Least Squares Input File and
Adjustment A-13

A.3   Querying Survey Database Points with the Survey
Command Window A-17

Appendix B: Connecting to Geospatial Data B-1

B.1   Introduction to the Planning and Analysis Workspace B-2
        Map Workflow B-2

B.2   Coordinate Systems B-4

Practice B1 Start a New Project B-7

B.3   Geospatial Data Connection B-10
        Connect to GIS Data B-10
        Autodesk Connector for ArcGIS B-14
        Stylize GIS Data B-15
        Draw Order B-18

Practice B2 Connect to GIS Data B-19

B.4   Create a Surface from GIS Data B-23
        Contour Issues B-26
        Minimizing Flat Triangle Strategies B-27
        Draping Images on a Surface B-28

Practice B3 Create a Surface from a Shape File B-29

Chapter Review Questions B-34

Command Summary B-35

Appendix C: Additional Surface Tools **C-1**

C.1 Surface Volume Calculations..**C-2**
Volumes Dashboard...C-2
Bounded Volumes..C-2
Volume Reports C-3
Grid Volume or TIN Volume Surface..C-3
3D Solid Surface from TIN Surface...C-4

Practice C1 Create a 3D Solid **C-6**

C.2 Point Cloud Surface Extraction **C-8**
Attach Point Cloud C-8
Point Cloud Transparency...C-11
Cropping Point Clouds C-11
Surfaces from Point Clouds C-13

Practice C2 Create a Point Cloud Surface **C-18**

Index **Index-1**

Preface

The *Autodesk® Civil 3D® 2021: Fundamentals for Surveyors* guide is for surveyors and survey technicians that do not necessarily need all of the functionality that is taught in the *Autodesk Civil 3D: Fundamentals* guide. This guide equips the surveyor with the basic knowledge required to use Autodesk Civil 3D efficiently in a typical daily workflow. You will learn how to import converted field equipment survey data into a standardized environment in Autodesk Civil 3D and to use the automation tools to create an Existing Conditions Plan.

Data collection and traverses are also covered. Other topics that help in increasing efficiency include styles, correct AutoCAD® drafting techniques, the methodology required to create linework effectively for variables used in defining symbology, surfaces, categorizing points, and using online maps.

Topics Covered

- The Autodesk Civil 3D interface
- Points overview and styles
- Importing points and coordinate transformations
- Creating points and drafting
- Point groups, grips, and reports
- Point security and editing
- Introduction to data collection in the field
- Introduction to Civil 3D Survey and automated linework
- Survey networks
- Coordinate Geometry Editor for entering traverse information or legal descriptions
- Surface overview
- Surface editing
- Surface labels and analysis

Prerequisites

- Access to the 2021.0 version of the software, to ensure compatibility with this guide. Future software updates that are released by Autodesk may include changes that are not reflected in this guide. The practices and files included with this guide might not be compatible with prior versions (e.g., 2020).

- Experience with AutoCAD® or AutoCAD-based products and a basic understanding of Surveying is recommended.

Note on Software Setup

This guide assumes a standard installation of the software using the default preferences during installation. Lectures and practices use the standard software templates and default options for the Content Libraries.

Students and Educators Can Access Free Autodesk Software and Resources

Autodesk challenges you to get started with free educational licenses for professional software and creativity apps used by millions of architects, engineers, designers, and hobbyists today. Bring Autodesk software into your classroom, studio, or workshop to learn, teach, and explore real-world design challenges the way professionals do.

Get started today - register at the Autodesk Education Community and download one of the many Autodesk software applications available.

Visit www.autodesk.com/education/home/

Note: Free products are subject to the terms and conditions of the end-user license and services agreement that accompanies the software. The software is for personal use for education purposes and is not intended for classroom or lab use.

Lead Contributor: Jeff Morris

Specializing in the civil engineering industry, Jeff authors training guides and provides instruction, support, and implementation on all Autodesk infrastructure solutions.

Jeff brings to bear over 20 years of diverse work experience in the civil engineering industry. He has played multiple roles, including Sales, Trainer, Application Specialist, Implementation and Customization Consultant, CAD Coordinator, and CAD/BIM Manager, in civil engineering and architecture firms, and Autodesk reseller organizations. He has worked for government organizations and private firms, small companies and large multinational corporations and in multiple geographies across the globe. Through his extensive experience in Building and Infrastructure design, Jeff has acquired a thorough understanding of CAD Standards and Procedures and an in-depth knowledge of CAD and BIM.

Jeff studied Architecture and a diploma in Systems Analysis and Programming. He is an Autodesk Certified Instructor (ACI) and holds the Autodesk Certified Professional certification for Civil 3D and Revit.

Jeff Morris has been the Lead Contributor for *Autodesk Civil 3D: Fundamentals for Surveyors* since 2019.

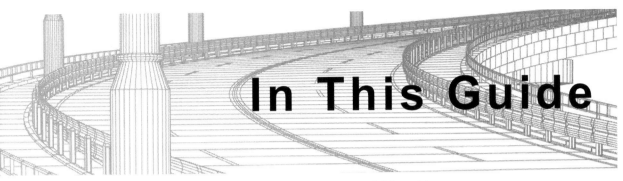

In This Guide

The following highlights the key features of this guide.

Feature	Description
Practice Files	The Practice Files page includes a link to the practice files and instructions on how to download and install them. The practice files are required to complete the practices in this guide.
Chapters	A chapter consists of the following - Learning Objectives, Instructional Content, Practices, Chapter Review Questions, and Command Summary.
	• **Learning Objectives** define the skills you can acquire by learning the content provided in the chapter.
	• **Instructional Content**, which begins right after Learning Objectives, refers to the descriptive and procedural information related to various topics. Each main topic introduces a product feature, discusses various aspects of that feature, and provides step-by-step procedures on how to use that feature. Where relevant, examples, figures, helpful hints, and notes are provided.
	• **Practice** for a topic follows the instructional content. Practices enable you to use the software to perform a hands-on review of a topic. It is required that you download the practice files (using the link found on the Practice Files page) prior to starting the first practice.
	• **Chapter Review Questions**, located close to the end of a chapter, enable you to test your knowledge of the key concepts discussed in the chapter.
	• **Command Summary** concludes a chapter. It contains a list of the software commands that are used throughout the chapter and provides information on where the command can be found in the software.
Appendices	Appendices provide additional information to the main course content. It could be in the form of instructional content, practices, tables, projects, or skills assessment.

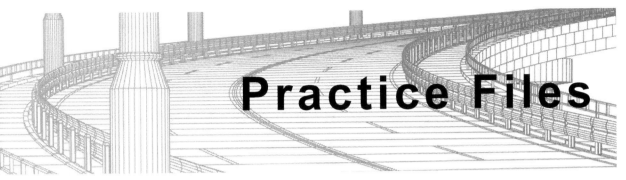

Practice Files

To download the practice files for this guide, use the following steps:

1. Type the URL **exactly as shown below** into the address bar of your Internet browser, to access the Course File Download page.

   Note: If you are using the ebook, you do not have to type the URL. Instead, you can access the page simply by clicking the URL below.

   ## https://www.ascented.com/getfile/id/hesperia

   Note: If you are completing the optional point cloud practice in Appendix C, you will need to download the point cloud file from the URL below.

   ## https://www.ascented.com/getfile/id/ovina

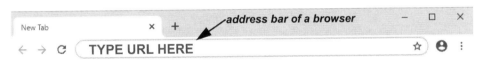

2. On the Course File Download page, click the **DOWNLOAD NOW** button, as shown below, to download the .ZIP file that contains the practice files.

3. Once the download is complete, unzip the file and extract its contents.

   The recommended practice files folder location is:
   C:\Civil 3D for Surveyors

   Note: It is recommended that you do not change the location of the practice files folder. Doing so may cause errors when completing the practices.

Stay Informed!

To receive information about upcoming events, promotional offers, and complimentary webcasts, visit:

www.ASCENTed.com/updates

The Autodesk Civil 3D Interface

In this chapter, you will learn about the Autodesk® Civil 3D® software interface and terminology. You will learn how to navigate the available workspaces and the Toolspace and how to work in a dynamic model environment. You will also learn how to use styles across multiple models to ensure that your drawings adhere to specific standards.

Learning Objectives in This Chapter

- Switch between the Autodesk Civil 3D tools, 2D drafting and annotation tools, 3D modeling tools, and planning and analysis tools by changing the workspace.
- Locate the basic features and commands of the Autodesk Civil 3D software interface, which include the ribbon, Drawing Window, Command Line, and Toolspace.
- Access commands by right-clicking on an object or collection of objects in the *Prospector* and *Settings* tabs in the Toolspace.
- Access predefined reports and create custom reports to be able to share useful engineering data about AEC objects in a drawing.
- Create and assign object and label styles to correctly display Autodesk Civil 3D objects for printing and other purposes.

1.1 Product Overview

The Autodesk Civil 3D software supports a wide range of Survey and Civil Engineering tasks. It creates intelligent relationships between objects so that design changes can be updated dynamically.

- The Autodesk Civil 3D software uses dynamic objects for points, alignments, profiles, terrain models, pipe networks, etc. Objects can update when data changes. For example, if an alignment changes, its associated profiles and sections update automatically. Commands can be safely undone in the software without the graphics becoming out-of-date with survey and design data.

- These objects are style-based and dynamic, which streamlines object creation and editing.

- Autodesk Civil 3D objects (surfaces, alignments, etc.) are often stored directly inside drawing files. The exception to this is when you are working with the Autodesk Data Management System (Vault), data shortcuts, or a survey database.

- The Autodesk Civil 3D software supports a multiple document interface. This means that you can have multiple drawing files open in the same instance of the Autodesk Civil 3D software at the same time.

- The Autodesk Civil 3D software can be launched by selecting its icon on the desktop or by accessing the command through the Start menu. Depending on the installed version of the software, the icon indicates Imperial or Metric. Once launched, the software initiates with the standard Autodesk Civil 3D profile. Your CAD or BIM Manager can customize the shortcut to have the software launch with project-based settings, which is accomplished by using a custom profile.

1.2 Autodesk Civil 3D Workspaces

When the Autodesk Civil 3D software is launched for the first time, a *Let's Get Started* window displays, as shown in Figure 1–1. This window is used to verify your Autodesk Civil 3D license. There are three options for communicating your license information:

- **Sign In:** Use your Autodesk Subscription account information to verify your purchase.

- **Enter a Serial Number:** Manually enter your software serial number and software key.

- **Use a Network License:** Point the software to your network license server to use the software license.

Figure 1–1

Start Tab

By default, the *Start* tab is continually available even when a drawing file is open. It enables you to complete several actions, as shown in Figure 1–2:

- Open existing files (1)

- Create new drawings from template files (2)

- Review and open recent documents (3)

- Browse to BIM 360 (4)

- Access Learning Videos and Tips (online) (5)

- Access various online tools and support (6)

- See the File Type (either local or cloud-based) (7)

- Select the search columns to display (8)

For more information on BIM 360 Collaboration with Civil 3D, see the ASCENT guide BIM 360: Fundamentals.

Hint: In order to open BIM 360 cloud-based drawings, you need to have access to BIM 360.

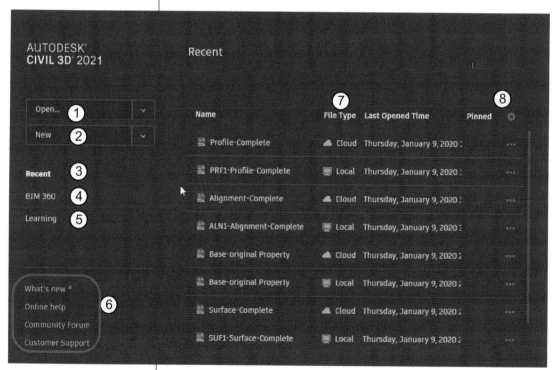

Figure 1–2

The *Start* tab is persistent even when other drawings are open. This makes it easier and faster to open or start new drawings.

It is recommended that you stay in the Autodesk Civil 3D workspace most of the time. As a review, AutoCAD® Workspaces are saved groupings of menus, toolbars, and palettes, which can be customized as required for specific tasks. You can modify the default Workspaces supplied with the Autodesk Civil 3D software or create your own. In this material, you work with the Civil 3D workspace, which includes a complete list of Autodesk Civil 3D-specific ribbons, drop-down menus, and tools.

You can change Workspaces using the Workspaces switching icon in the lower right corner of the Status Bar, as shown in Figure 1–3. You can also modify them using the **CUI** command.

Figure 1–3

Each of the ribbons from the workspaces are shown in order in Figure 1–4 and include the following:

- **Civil 3D workspace:** Contains tools used to create AEC objects, such as surfaces, alignments, profiles, corridors, grading objects, etc.

- **Drafting & Annotation workspace:** Contains tools that are commonly used in the standard AutoCAD software, such as those in the *Home* tab>Draw and *Home* tab>Modify panels.

- **3D Modeling workspace:** Contains standard AutoCAD 3D modeling tools for designing 3D solids, mesh surfaces, etc.

- **Planning and Analysis workspace:** Contains tools found in the AutoCAD® Map 3D® software that help you attach and analyze GIS data for more efficient planning of projects before starting your design.

Civil 3D workspace

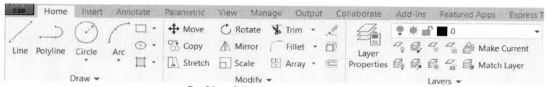

Drafting & Annotation workspace

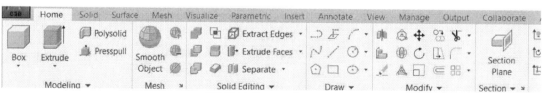

3D Modeling workspace

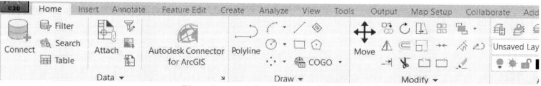

Planning and Analysis workspace

Figure 1–4

1.3 Autodesk Civil 3D User Interface

The Autodesk Civil 3D software user interface is shown in Figure 1–5.

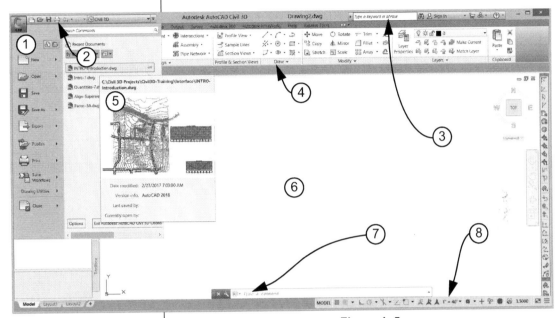

Figure 1–5

1. Application Menu	5. Tooltips
2. Quick Access Toolbar	6. Drawing Window
3. InfoCenter	7. Command Line
4. Ribbon	8. Status Bar

1. Application Menu

The *Application Menu* provides access to commands, settings, and documents, as shown in Figure 1–6. With the Application Menu, you can:

- Browse the menus available in the Autodesk Civil 3D software.

- Perform a search of menus, menu actions, tooltips, and command prompt text strings.

- Browse for recent documents, currently open documents, and commands you have recently executed.

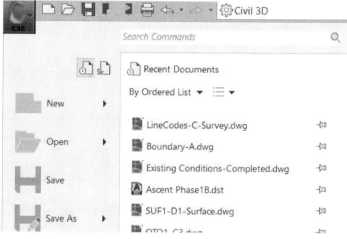

Figure 1–6

2. Quick Access Toolbar

The *Quick Access Toolbar* provides access to commonly used commands, such as **Open**, **Save**, **Print**, etc. You can add an unlimited number of tools to the Quick Access Toolbar by clicking the down arrow on the right, as shown in Figure 1–7.

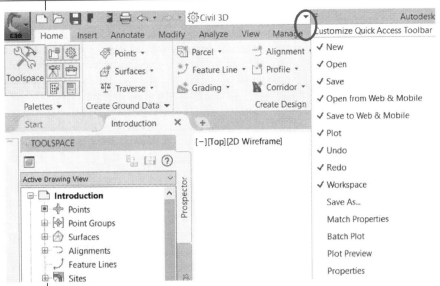

Figure 1–7

3. InfoCenter

The *InfoCenter* enables you to quickly search for help. You can specify which Help documents to search, and collapse or expand the search field (as shown in Figure 1–8) to save screen space. You can also sign in to the A360 service, where you can share files with other design team members using the cloud.

provides the ability to connect to the Autodesk App Store to find additional efficiency enhancing applications.

Figure 1–8

4. Ribbon

The *ribbon* provides a single, compact location for *commands* that are relevant to the current task. It contains tools in a series of *tabs* and *panels* to reduce clutter in the application and maximize drawing space. Selecting a tab displays a series of panels. The panels contain a variety of tools, which are grouped by function, as shown in Figure 1–9.

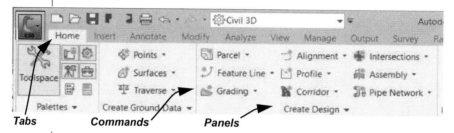

Figure 1–9

Clicking the drop-down arrow expands the panel to display additional tools, as shown in Figure 1–10. Clicking an arrow pointing to the bottom right opens the tool's dialog box, which contains additional options.

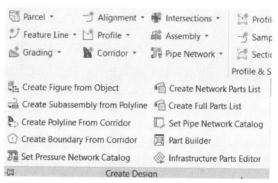

Figure 1–10

You can minimize the ribbon by clicking the arrow successively, as shown in Figure 1–11.

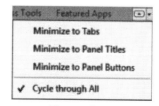

Figure 1–11

There are two classifications of ribbons: static and contextual.

- **Static ribbons:** Displays the most commonly used tabs, panels, and commands.

- **Contextual ribbons:** Displays the tabs, panels, and commands that are only applicable to the selected object. An example of a contextual ribbon is shown in Figure 1–12.

AEC Ribbon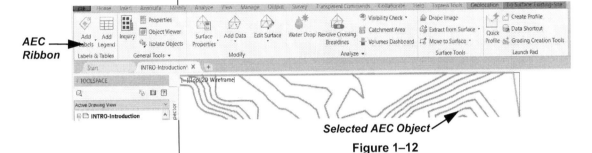

Selected AEC Object

Figure 1–12

5. Tooltips

Tooltips display the item's name, a short description, and sometimes a graphic. They provide information about tools, commands, and drawing objects, as shown in Figure 1–13.

Tooltips can be turned off and a display delay can be set in the Options dialog box> Display tab.

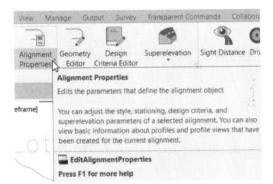

Figure 1–13

6. Drawing Window

The *Drawing Window* is the area of the screen where the drawing displays.

7. Command Line

The *Command Line* is a text window that is located at the bottom of the screen and displays command prompts and a history of commands, as shown in Figure 1–14.

To toggle the Command Line display on or off, press <Ctrl>+<9>.

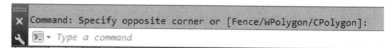

Figure 1–14

8. Status Bar

The *Status Bar* enables you to change many of AutoCAD's drafting settings, such as Snap, Grid, and Object Snap. Not all of the available tools are shown by default (i.e. Coordinates). To toggle on more available tools in the Status Bar, click

 (Customization), as shown in Figure 1–15.

Customization

Figure 1–15

Practice 1a

Overview of Autodesk Civil 3D and its User Interface

Practice Objective

- Locate the basic features and commands of the Autodesk Civil 3D software interface, which includes the ribbon, Toolspace, Drawing Window, and Command Line.

In this practice, you will become familiar with Autodesk Civil 3D's capabilities and learn about its interface.

Task 1 - Set up the practice.

In this task, you will add a folder shortcut in the pane on the left side of the dialog box. This enables you to quickly access the practice files folder in the Open dialog box.

1. If required, launch the Autodesk Civil 3D 2021 Imperial application.

2. In the *Start* tab, click (Open), or expand (Application Menu) and select **Open**.

3. In the Select File dialog box, browse to the *C:\Civil 3D for Surveyors\Working* folder, as shown in Figure 1–16.

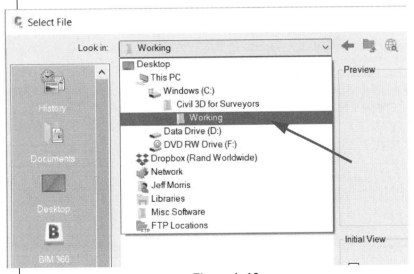

Figure 1–16

4. Expand the Tools drop-down list and select **Add Current Folder to Places**, as shown in Figure 1–17.

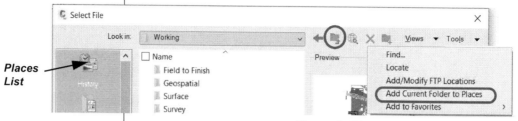

Places List

Figure 1–17

5. After you create the new entry in your *Places*, use the up arrow (as shown above in Figure 1–17) to go up one folder. (As an alternative to adding an entry via the drop-down list as you did in the previous step, you could drag and drop the *Working* folder to the Places List from this level.)

6. Browse to the *References\DWG* folder.

7. Select **Introduction.dwg** and then select **Open.**

*If prompted to save the changes to your Places List, click **Yes**.*

8. In the Status Bar, confirm that **Civil 3D** is the active Workspace. The Workspace icon is located in the Status Bar (at the bottom right of the interface) and in the Quick Access Toolbar (at the top left of the interface), as shown in Figure 1–18.

Figure 1–18

By default, the Toolspace is docked to the left side of your drawing window.

9. Locate the Autodesk Civil 3D Toolspace (as shown in Figure 1–19). If you cannot find it, click ✻ (Toolspace) in the *Home* tab>Palettes panel.

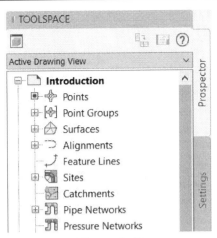

Figure 1–19

10. Save the drawing as **Intro-A.dwg**. To do this, expand

    ![C3D] (Application Menu) and select **Save As**. Browse to the
    C:\Civil 3D for Surveyors\References\DWG folder, and then
    in the *File Name* field, type **Intro-A**. Click **Save**.

Task 2 - Review Autodesk Civil 3D's Dynamic Object Model.

Alternatively, select the View tab>Views panel, expand the Named Views drop-down list, and select Aln-Profile.

1. In the top-left corner of the drawing window, select **Top**,
   expand Custom Model Views and select **Aln-Profile**, as
   shown in Figure 1–20. This will zoom into a preset view of the
   alignment and the surface profile to the right.

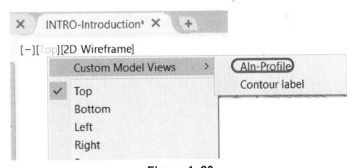

Figure 1–20

If the alignment labels display, they also update.

2. Select the **Jeffries Ranch Rd** alignment to activate its grips, as shown in Figure 1–21. (If you have difficulty selecting the alignment, you might need to set the draw order so that it is on top of all of the other objects.) Select the eastern grip and reposition it to the east. The alignment and profile both update.

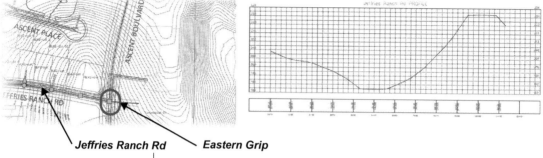

Jeffries Ranch Rd   *Eastern Grip*

Figure 1–21

3. Hover the cursor near the alignment in its new position. The station, offset, and surface elevation information display through tooltips.

4. Close the drawing without saving.

1.4 Autodesk Civil 3D Toolspace

The Autodesk Civil 3D software uses a Toolspace to manage objects, settings, and styles. Each tab uses a hierarchical tree interface to manage objects, settings, and styles. Branches in these hierarchical trees are referred to in the Autodesk Civil 3D software as *collections*. The Toolspace is an interactive data management tool.

Toolspace operates similar to an AutoCAD tool palette in that it can be resized, set to dock or float, and when floating can be set to auto-hide. The Toolspace is shown floating on the left in Figure 1–22 and docked on the right in Figure 1–22.

Right-clicking on a collection or on an individual object provides many commonly used commands in the shortcut menus.

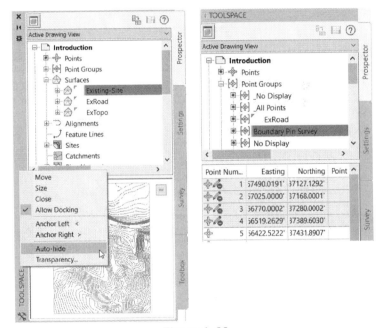

Figure 1–22

- The Toolspace can be closed by selecting the **X** in the upper left or right corner.

- Once closed, it can be opened by clicking (Toolspace) in the *Home* tab>Palettes panel.

Prospector Tab

The Toolspace>*Prospector* tab, lists the Autodesk Civil 3D objects that are present in open drawings and other important information. Its hierarchical structure dynamically manages and displays objects and their data. As objects are created or deleted, they are removed from the *Prospector* tab. A drop-down list at the top contains the following options:

- **Active Drawing View:** Displays only the Autodesk Civil 3D objects that are present in the active drawing. If you switch to another drawing, the tree updates to reflect the currently active drawing.

- **Master View:** Displays a list of all open drawings and their objects, project information, and a list of drawing templates. The name of the active drawing is highlighted.

The Toolspace>*Prospector* tab is shown in Figure 1–23.

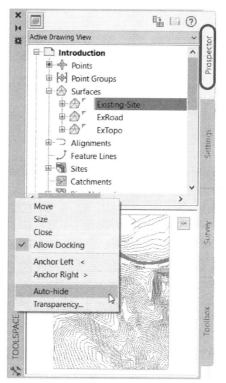

Figure 1–23

- To toggle the display of the Toolspace>*Prospector* tab on or off, click (Prospector) in the *Home* tab>Palettes panel.

- Each object type (Points, Point Groups, Alignments, Surfaces, etc.) is allotted a collection, and objects present in a drawing are listed below the respective collection.

- The bottom of the Toolspace>*Prospector* tab displays a list view of items in the highlighted collection or a preview of an object that has been selected in the Toolspace>*Prospector* tab.

- The icon at the top of the Toolspace>*Prospector* tab controls how items in the Prospector tree display. Icons next to objects provide additional information about the object. A list of common icons is as follows:

Icon	Description
▢	Toggles the Toolspace item preview on or off.
▦	Opens (or closes) the Panorama window. This window only opens if vistas are available to be displayed in the Panorama.
?	Opens the Autodesk Civil 3D Help system.
⌀	Indicates that the object is currently locked for editing.
▽	Indicates that the object is referenced by another object. In the Toolspace>*Settings* tab, this also indicates that a style is in use in the current drawing.
↗	Indicates that the object is being referenced from another drawing file (such as through a shortcut or Vault reference).
!	Indicates that the object is out of date and needs to be rebuilt, or is violating specified design constraints.
◣	Indicates that a vault project object (such as a point or surface) has been modified since it was included in the current drawing.
◢	Indicates that you have modified a vault project object in your current drawing and that those modifications have yet to be updated to the project.

Settings Tab

The Toolspace>*Settings* tab is used to configure how the Autodesk Civil 3D software operates and the way Autodesk Civil 3D objects are displayed and printed, as shown in Figure 1–24.

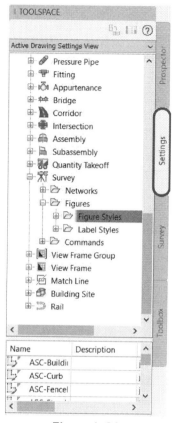

Figure 1–24

Different settings are accessed by right-clicking on the name of a drawing file or on one of the collections located inside the tab.

The collections (such as the *Parcel* collection shown in Figure 1–24) can contain object styles, label styles, command settings, and related controls.

Changes to settings affect all lower items in the tree. For example, assigning an overall text height in the drawing's Edit Label Style Defaults dialog box applies that height to all other settings and styles in the drawing. Applying the same setting in the *Surface* collection's Edit Label Style Defaults only applies the text height to the surface label styles. (Lower items in the tree and styles can be set to override these changes individually as required.)

- All drawing settings originate from the template used to create an Autodesk Civil 3D drawing.

- To toggle the display of the Toolspace>*Settings* tab on or off, click 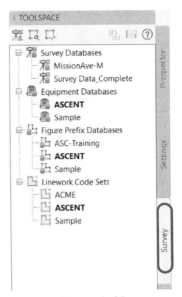 (Settings) in the *Home* tab>Palettes panel.

Survey Tab

The Toolspace>*Survey* tab is used to manage survey observations data, as shown in Figure 1–25. Selecting this tab enables you to create a survey database, a survey network, points, and figures, and import and edit survey observation data.

To toggle the Toolspace>Survey tab display on or off, click

 (Survey) in the Home tab>Palettes panel.

Figure 1–25

Toolbox Tab

The Toolspace>Toolbox tab can be toggled on and off by clicking

 (Toolbox) in the Home tab>Palettes panel.

The Toolspace>*Toolbox* tab is used to access the Reports Manager and to add custom tools to the Autodesk Civil 3D interface, as shown in Figure 1–26.

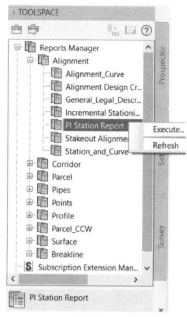

Figure 1–26

The Reports Manager, the only set of tools that displays in the toolbox by default, enables you to generate a large variety of survey and design reports. For example, to launch a Stakeout Alignment Report, right-click on it in the *Alignments* collection and select **Execute**.

The icons in the upper left area of the Toolspace>*Toolbox* tab enable you to:

	Open the Edit Report Settings dialog box, in which you can assign settings for all report types. These settings include items, such as the name to display in the report.
	Open the Toolbox Editor, in which you can add custom reports and other tools.

Once a report has been executed, it can be saved in multiple formats, including .HTML, .DOC, .XLS, .TXT, and .PDF. To save it in a format other than the default .HTML, expand Files of type and select the type of file required, as shown in Figure 1–27.

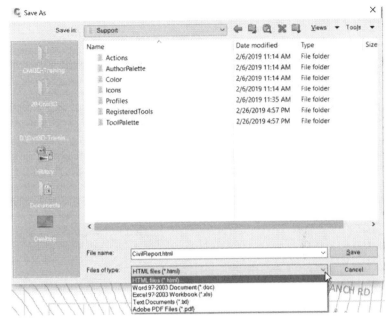

Figure 1–27

1.5 Autodesk Civil 3D Panorama

The Autodesk Civil 3D software includes a multi-purpose grid data viewer called the *Panorama window*. It is similar to an AutoCAD tool palette in that it can be docked or floating, and set to auto-hide. Each tab in the Panorama is called a *Vista*. The Panorama can be opened from the Autodesk Civil 3D Toolspace by clicking 🔲 (Panorama), and can be closed by selecting the **X** in the upper left or right corner of the window. You can only display the Panorama after launching a command that uses it, such as **Edit Points** (right-click on a point group in the Toolspace>*Prospector* tab in the Toolspace to access this option). The Panorama can display many different kinds of data, each in its own Vista, such as point properties, alignment, and profile data, as shown in Figure 1–28.

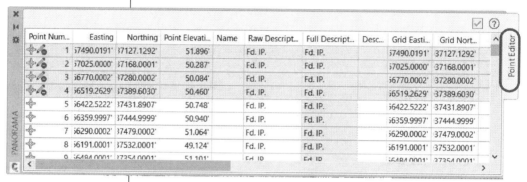

Figure 1–28

The Panorama can also display a special Vista called the *Event Viewer*, as shown in Figure 1–29. The *Event Viewer* opens prompting you about the status of the performed action. If every thing was successful, it displays a white circle containing a blue **i**, indicating that it is for informational purposes only. When there are items of interest or an item needs attention, a yellow triangle containing a black **!** (exclamation point) displays.

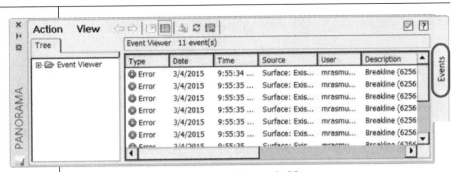

Figure 1–29

When the Autodesk Civil 3D software encounters a processing error, such as when surface breaklines cross or a road model passes over the edge of the existing ground surface, a red circle containing a white **x** displays, as shown in Figure 1–30. When working through a large number of events, you can use **Action>Clear All Events** to clear all of the old entries in the Panorama.

Figure 1–30

If a Panorama contains multiple Vistas, selecting the green checkmark only closes the current Vista. To close (hide) the Panorama, click the **X** in the top right or left corner.

If you have multiple monitors, the Panorama can be moved to your secondary monitor, where it can remain open without obstructing your main tasks.

In the Toolspace (in the top right corner) there is a persistent Panorama visibility toggle that displays regardless of which tab is active, as shown in Figure 1–31. If the Panorama tool is open, this toggles its visibility.

Figure 1–31

Practice 1b

Autodesk Civil 3D Toolspace

Practice Objective

*   Access commands and change the drawing using the Autodesk Civil 3D Toolspace.

In this practice, you will explore the tabs in the Autodesk Civil 3D Toolspace.

Task 1 - Review the Toolspace>Prospector tab.

1. Open **Introduction.dwg** from the *C:\Civil 3D for Surveyors\References\DWG* folder.

2. Ensure that the Autodesk Civil 3D Toolspace displays.

3. In the Toolspace, select the *Prospector* tab to make it active.
    *   Note: The tabs are listed vertically along the right side of the Toolspace.

If the Toolspace is not displayed, click

(Toolspace) in the Home tab>Palettes panel.

4. Select the **+** signs to open the collections and the **-** signs to close them. Items displayed in the Toolspace>*Prospector* tab are the design data (also known as AEC objects) currently in the drawing file (such as points, alignments, and surfaces).

5. Collections, such as *Points*, do not have a **+** or **-** sign because they are not intended to be expanded in the tree view of the Toolspace>*Prospector* tab. Select the **Points** collection and the list view displays in the Preview area, describing the Autodesk Civil 3D points that are currently in the drawing file.

6. Under the *Surface* collection, look for the surface called **ExTopo**. Expand its branch and the *Definition* area inside it. Highlight the items below (breaklines, boundaries, etc.) and note the components displayed in the list view.

7. With the **ExTopo** breaklines highlighted in the list view, right-click on *Ridge* and note the commands available in the shortcut menu, as shown on the left in Figure 1–32. Select **Zoom to**.

Similar right-click menus are available for nearly all of the objects displayed in the Toolspace>Prospector tab.

8. Expand the Point Groups and select the **Boundary Pin Survey** point group. In the Preview area at the bottom, press <Shift> to select point numbers **2** and **3**, as shown on the right in Figure 1–32. Right-click and select **Zoom To**. Although the points are not displayed, the software stores where they reside in the drawing.

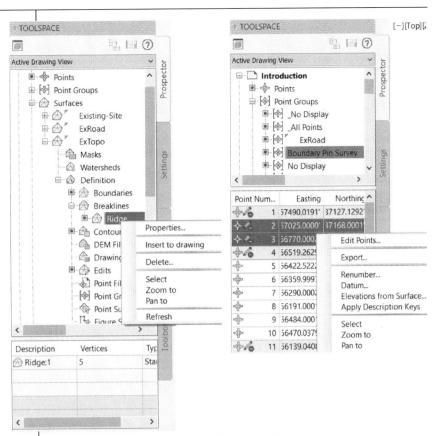

Figure 1–32

Task 2 - Review the Toolspace>Settings tab.

1. Select the Toolspace>*Settings* tab, as shown in Figure 1–33.

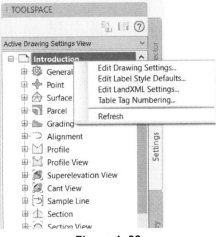

Figure 1–33

2. In the Toolspace>*Settings* tab, right-click on the drawing's name (**Introduction.dwg**, at the top) and select **Edit Drawing Settings**.

3. In the Drawing Settings dialog box, select the *Units and Zone* tab, as shown in Figure 1–34.

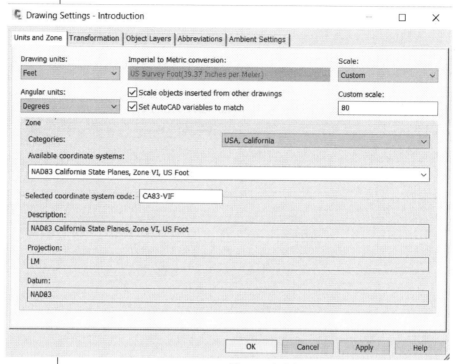

Figure 1–34

4. Expand the Scale drop-down list and select **1"=40'**.

5. Note the coordinate systems that are available in the *Zone* area, such as **CA83-VIF**, **NAD83 California State Planes**, **Zone VI**, and **US Foot**.

6. Click **OK** to close the dialog box.

Because Autodesk Civil 3D labels are annotative, the label annotation size has changed to match the new Drawing Scale.

7. You can also change the Model Space display scale using the **Annotation** icon in the Status Bar. Change it to read **1"=80'**. Note that as you change the scale, all of the labels also change in size, as shown in Figure 1–35.

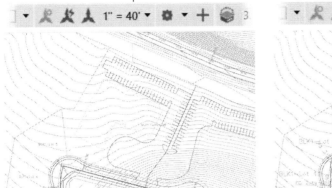

Figure 1–35

8. You can change the display of the contours by changing the style of the surface. In the drawing, select the surface object (click on a contour) so that the contextual tab displays in the ribbon, as shown in Figure 1–36.

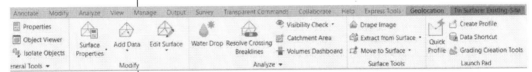

Figure 1–36

Alternatively, you can right-click and select ***Surface Properties***.

9. In the Modify panel, click (Surface Properties).

10. In the *Information* tab, select the drop-down arrow for the surface style, as shown in Figure 1–37. Select any of the predefined styles and click **Apply** to apply the selected style to the surface to preview the results before they display in the dialog box.

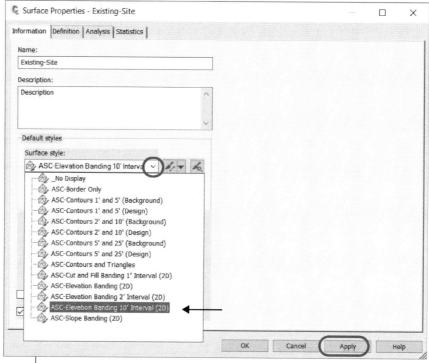

Figure 1–37

11. Click **OK** to exit the Surface Properties dialog box.

Task 3 - Review Autodesk Civil 3D's Reports Manager.

1. In the Toolspace>*Toolbox* tab, expand **Reports Manager>Alignment**. Right-click on **PI Station Report** and select **Execute**, as shown in Figure 1–38.

*As a shortcut, you can double-click to launch the **Report** without having to select the **Execute** command.*

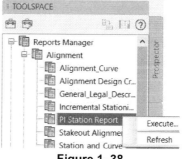

Figure 1–38

2. Accept all of the defaults and click **Create Report**. The report displays, as shown in Figure 1–39.

Alignment PI Station Report

Client:
Mr. Student
Need to know Inc.
Address 1
Date: 5/17/2019 6:25:17 AM

Prepared by:
Mr. Surveyor
ASCENT
123 Main Street

Alignment Name: Ascent PI
Description:
Station Range: Start: 0+00.00, End: 6+98.38

PI Station	Northing	Easting	Distance	Direction
0+00.00	2,036,643.0632'	6,256,521.2052'		
			353.170'	N1° 18' 05"E
3+53.17	2,036,996.1421'	6,256,529.2258'		
			381.930'	S75° 03' 44"E
6+98.38	2,036,897.6924'	6,256,898.2491'		

Alignment Name: Jeffries Ranch Rd
Description:
Station Range: Start: 0+00.00, End: 11+30.01

PI Station	Northing	Easting	Distance	Direction
0+00.00	2,036,671.1106'	6,255,943.0293'		
			235.765'	S85° 04' 23"E
2+35.77	2,036,650.8613'	6,256,177.9234'		

Figure 1–39

3. Review the report and close the Internet browser.

4. In the Create Reports dialog box, click **Done**.

5. In the Toolspace>*Toolbox* tab, expand the *Surface* collection. Select **Surface Report**, right-click, and select **Execute**, as shown in Figure 1–40.

Figure 1–40

6. From the list, select only the Existing-Site surface, then click **OK**. Type a file name for the saved report or accept the default. Expand the Files of type drop-down list, select **.HTML**, and click **Save**. The report displays in your standard Internet browser, as shown in Figure 1–41. Review and close the report.

Your Company Name

123 Main Street

Suite #321

City, State 01234

Surface Report
Project Name: C:\Civil 3D for Surveyors\References\DWG\Introduction.dwg
Report Date: 4/30/2020 3:11:57 PM

Client: Client Company
Project Description:
Prepared by: Preparer

Linear Units: USSurveyFoot	Area Units: squareFoot	Volume Units: cubicYard

Surface: Existing-Site
Description: Description

Area 2D: 4816206.212	Area 3D: 4861183.063
Elevation Max: 310.000	Elevation Min: 115.000
Number of Points: 22267	Number of Triangles: 43179

Figure 1–41

1.6 Autodesk Civil 3D Templates, Settings, and Styles

A drawing template (.DWT) contains all blocks, Paper Space title sheets, settings, and layers for a new drawing. As with the AutoCAD software, a template file in the Autodesk Civil 3D software is the source file from which new drawings acquire their settings, units, layers, blocks, text styles, etc., and therefore, enforces standardization.

With the Autodesk Civil 3D software, in addition to the AutoCAD components noted, the drawing template is also the source for specific Autodesk Civil 3D styles and settings. As you learn, Autodesk Civil 3D styles and settings (Feature and Command) have a profound impact on the appearance of objects, labels, and tables. These styles and settings also act as the primary mechanism that controls the behavior and default actions. If you work primarily with one coordinate system, then you can set your template to that coordinate zone to save you time when starting a new drawing, as well as ensuring that the drawing is set to the correct coordinate system.

Selecting the correct template for your intended design and standards needs is a significant component of fully using the benefits that the Autodesk Civil 3D software offers. Therefore, it is highly recommended that all styles and settings be configured in the template file before you use the Autodesk Civil 3D software in a project.

To use the Autodesk Civil 3D software efficiently and effectively, you need to configure styles and settings to control the object display. All of these styles and settings affect the final delivered product and enable you to deliver a product with consistent quality.

To create a template file, use the **Save As** command and in the Save As dialog box, change the *File of Type* to **DWT**.

Drawing Settings in Detail

The values in Drawing Settings influence every aspect of the drawing environment. Each tab has values affecting a specific drawing area. For example, layer naming properties, coordinate systems, default precisions, input and output conventions, abbreviations for alignment, volume units, etc. After the Autodesk Civil 3D software is correctly configured, you should only need to access the first two tabs for your everyday work.

To access the Drawing Settings, in the Toolspace>*Settings* tab, select and right-click on the drawing name (at the top), and select **Edit Drawing Settings**.

Units and Zone

In the Drawing Settings dialog box, the *Units and Zone* tab (as shown in Figure 1–42) sets the Model Space plotting scale and coordinate zone for the drawing. The scale can be a custom value or selected from a drop-down list. A zone is selected from a drop-down list of worldwide categories and coordinate systems.

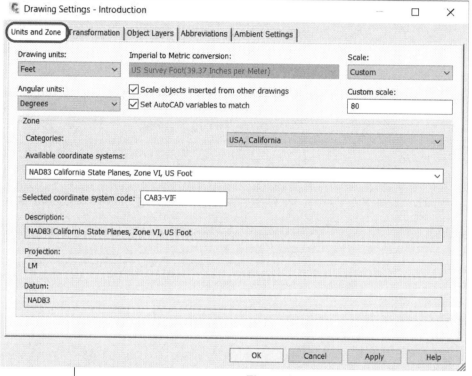

Figure 1–42

If you work predominantly in one Coordinate Zone, you can set your template to that zone.

A drawing which has been assigned a coordinate system enables points to report their grid coordinates, longitude, and latitude. Conversely, when assigning a coordinate system, grid coordinates and Longitude and Latitude data can create points in a drawing.

When plotting from the *Model* tab, the drawing scale in the upper right corner is the scale at which you would prefer the drawing to be printed. When in the *Model* tab, changing this scale automatically updates all Autodesk Civil 3D annotations that are scale-dependent. (Autodesk Civil 3D annotations are automatically resized for correct plotting in each viewport that displays them based on that viewport's scale.) If there are any AutoCAD annotative objects (i.e., text, dimensions, hatching, linetypes, blocks, etc.) that are set to your chosen scale, they are also resized.

*Refer to the AutoCAD Help if you need more information on variables such as **ltscale**, **msltscale**, and **psltscale**.*

Changing the drawing scale does not automatically change the **ltscale** variable. It is recommended that you set **ltscale** to **1** and ensure that **msltscale** and **psltscale** are also set to **1**. If this is not the case, you need to assign this variable manually.

You can also set the drawing scale by assigning a different annotation scale in the Status Bar, as shown in Figure 1–43. In layouts you can change either the VP Scale or Annotation Scale and have both update.

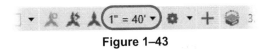

Figure 1–43

Transformation

During the life of a project, there can be reasons to change local point coordinates to a coordinate system. The values in the *Transformation* tab (as shown in Figure 1–44) transform local coordinates to a State Plane Coordinate system, UTM system, or other defined planar system.

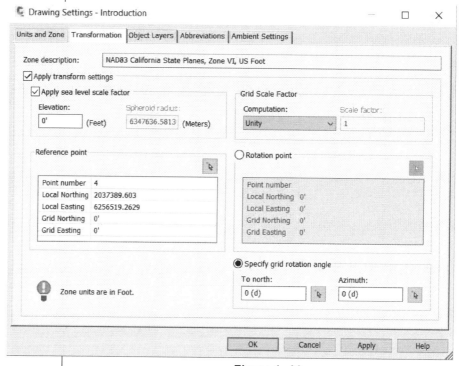

Figure 1–44

Object Layers

The *Object Layers* tab (shown in Figure 1–45) assigns layer names to Autodesk Civil 3D objects. A modifier, which can be a prefix or a suffix, is associated with each layer's name. The value of the modifier can be anything that is typed into its *Value* field. Traditionally, the value is an * (asterisk) with a separator (a dash or underscore). The Autodesk Civil 3D software replaces the asterisk with the name of the object of the same type. For example, the base surface layer name is **C-TOPO** with a suffix modifier of -* (a dash followed by an asterisk). When a surface named **Existing** is created, it is placed on the layer **C-TOPO-EXISTING**, and when a surface named **Base** is created it is placed on the layer **C-TOPO-BASE**.

The last column of the *Object Layers* tab enables you to lock the values. When a value is locked at this level, the Autodesk Civil 3D software does not permit it to be changed by any lower style or setting.

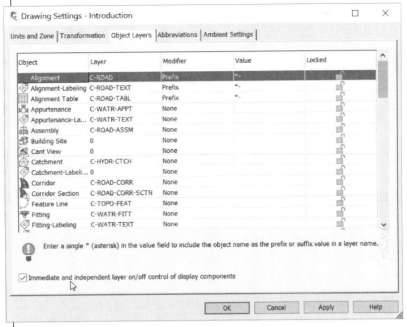

Figure 1–45

To change the listed object layers, double-click on a layer name. In the Layer Selection dialog box (shown in Figure 1–46), select the layer from the list. If the layer does not exist, click **New** in the Layer Selection dialog box. This opens a second dialog box, in which you can define a new layer for the object type.

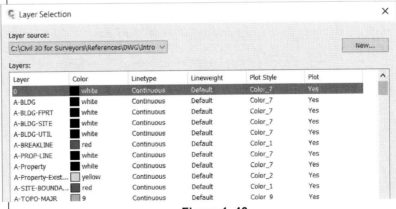

Figure 1–46

Abbreviations

The *Abbreviations* tab (shown in Figure 1–47) sets standard values for reports referencing alignment or profile data. Some entries in this panel have text format strings that define how the values associated with the abbreviation display in a label.

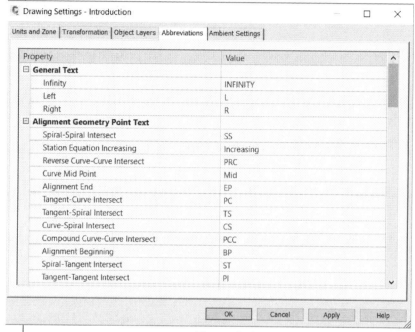

Figure 1–47

Ambient Settings

In the *Ambient Settings* tab (shown in Figure 1–48), the values influence prompting and reports. For example, the *Direction* area affects the prompting for direction input: **Decimal Degrees**, **Degrees Minutes and Seconds** (with or without spaces), or **Decimal Degrees Minutes and Seconds**. Any value set at this level affects everything (labels and commands) in the drawing.

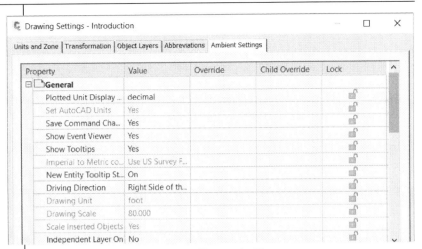

Figure 1–48

Edit Label Style Defaults

The values assigned in the Edit Label Style Defaults dialog box (shown in Figure 1–49) control text style, plan orientation, and the basic behavior of label styles. Similar to Feature Settings, this dialog box is available at the drawing level and at the individual objects level. Editing Label Style defaults at the drawing level affects all label styles in the drawing. Editing them at the object level (such as surfaces) only affects that object's labels.

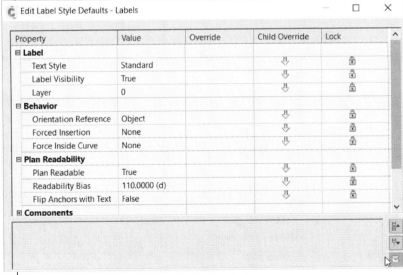

Figure 1–49

In the *Label, Behavior,* and *Plan Readability* areas, the values affect the overall visibility of labels, their default text style, label orientation, and the rotation angle that affects plan readability.

The values in the *Components, Leader,* and *Dragged State Components* areas affect the default text height for the label, colors for the text, leader, surrounding box, and type of leader. There are also several settings defining what happens to a label when you drag it from its original position.

Edit Autodesk LandXML Settings

The LandXML Settings dialog box (shown in Figure 1–50) provides settings that control how Autodesk LandXML data is imported and exported from the Autodesk Civil 3D software. Autodesk LandXML is a universal format for storing Surveying and Civil Engineering data that enables you to transfer points, terrain models, alignments, etc., between different software platforms. For more information, see *www.landxml.org* and the Autodesk Civil 3D Help system. The dialog box can be opened by right-clicking on Drawing Name in the Toolspace>*Settings* tab and selecting **Edit LandXMLSettings**.

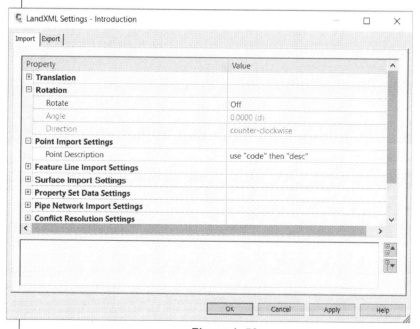

Figure 1–50

Feature Settings

In the Toolspace>*Settings* tab, each object type collection has an Edit Feature Settings dialog box, as shown for Surface in Figure 1–51. Its main function is to assign default naming values, initial Object and Label styles, and overriding the default values found in Edit Drawing Settings for that object type. You can access the feature settings by right-clicking on the object tree in the Toolspace>*Settings* tab and selecting **Edit Feature Settings**.

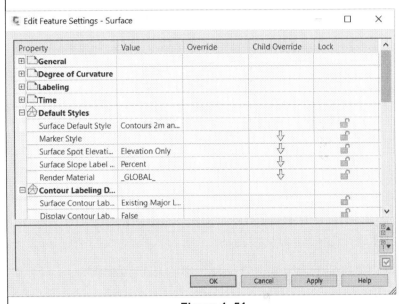

Figure 1–51

Command Settings

Similar to feature settings, in the Edit Command Settings dialog box (shown in Figure 1–52), you can set the default object and label styles used when creating objects with a specific command. Each object type contains a unique set of commands. Typical values in these dialog boxes include the naming format template (surface 1, parcel 1, etc.), design criteria (minimum area, frontage, length of vertical curve, and minimum horizontal curve), etc.

To open the dialog box, expand a collection in the Toolspace> *Settings* tab until the commands display. Right-click on the command to which you want to assign default settings and select **Edit Command Settings**.

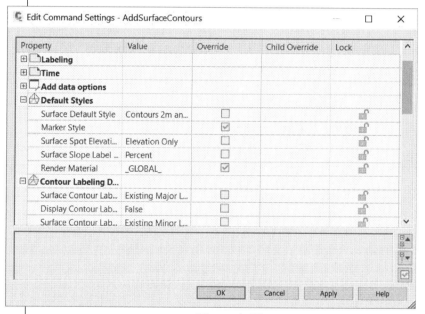

Figure 1–52

Hint: Style and Setting Overrides

In the Edit Label Style Defaults, Feature Settings and similar dialog boxes, a downward pointing arrow in the Child Override column indicates that a setting or style lower in the settings tree has a different value than the one displayed. Selecting the arrow (which creates a red **x** over the icon) and clicking **OK** removes the variant settings and makes all lower settings and styles match those assigned in the dialog box. This can be a quick way of standardizing multiple settings dialog boxes and styles at the same time.

For example, in the Surface Label Style defaults window (shown in Figure 1–53), some surface label styles are assigned a layer other than 0 and a visibility of false, because an arrow is present in the *Child Override* column. Since an arrow is not shown for the Text Style property, all surface label styles are using a text style of **Standard**.

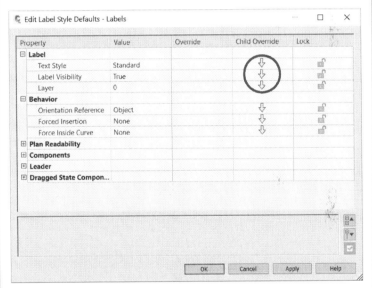

Figure 1–53

The *Override* column indicates whether a value in this window is overriding a higher settings dialog box. Clicking the **Lock** icon prevents you from changing that value in a lower setting's dialog box or style

Styles

Styles are preconfigured groups of settings specific to an individual object type or label that make the objects display and print the way that you want. For example, in the list of surface styles shown in Figure 1–54, each surface style is configured differently to display different features, such as contours at different intervals and on the correct layers. The display of a terrain model can be changed by swapping one surface style for another. Styles enable an organization to standardize the look of their graphics by providing preconfigured groupings of display settings.

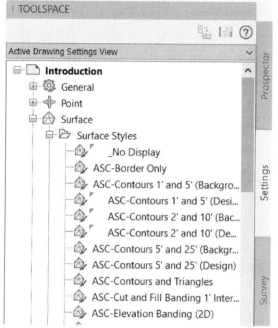

Figure 1–54

The two categories of styles you work with most often are Object Styles and Label Styles. Some objects have table styles as well. Object styles control how Autodesk Civil 3D objects (points, surfaces, alignments, etc.) display, what combination of components the object displays, which layers they display on, and many other settings. Label Styles are similar except that they control the text and other annotations associated with the objects.

For example, an alignment object style specifies many settings including the layers on which to draw tangents and curve segments (which might be different) and which symbols to add at certain points as required (such as a triangle at the PI point). Alignment label styles include major and minor station labels, the display of station equations, design speeds, and similar annotation. By separating object and label styles, you can mix and match the right combination for a specific object.

Styles are the lowest items in the Toolspace>*Settings* tree and are typically dependent on other settings above them. If a style is given a unique setting, different from feature settings or label style defaults (such as a different text height), then that style is considered to have an override.

Styles in Depth

Styles are central to the Autodesk Civil 3D software. Their flexibility enables an organization to create a unique look for their drawings. By changing the assigned style, you can change the composition of a profile view, as shown in Figure 1–55.

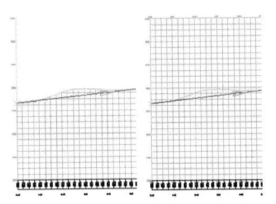

Figure 1–55

In the Toolspace>*Settings* tab, an object type branch identifies each style type and lists its styles below each heading. An example is shown in Figure 1–56.

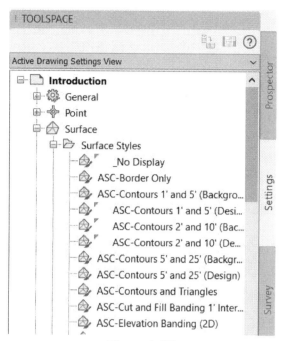

Figure 1–56

Object Styles

Object Styles stylize an object's data for display. To edit a style, in the Toolspace>*Settings* tab, right-click on the style and select **Edit**. Most of the work for all object styles is done in the *Display* tab. For certain objects, other tabs might need to be modified.

For example, in the Surface Style dialog box, the *Display* tab enables you to toggle on or off triangles, borders, contours, and other items, as well as define the layer, color, linetype, etc. that are assigned, as shown in Figure 1–57. The *Contours* tab sets the contour interval, smoothing, and other settings, as shown in Figure 1–58.

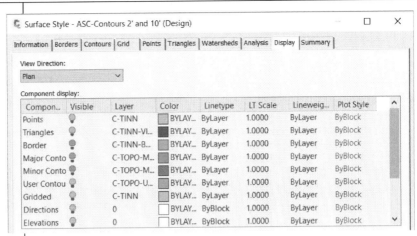

Figure 1–57

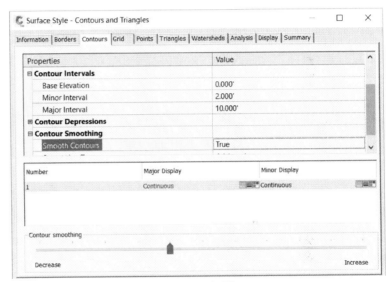

Figure 1–58

From the default Autodesk Civil 3D template, the respective Parcel Style dialog boxes for Open Space, Road, or Single Family (shown in Figure 1–59) define how the segments and hatching are displayed by assigning different layers for the components. The other tabs are rarely used for the Parcel styles.

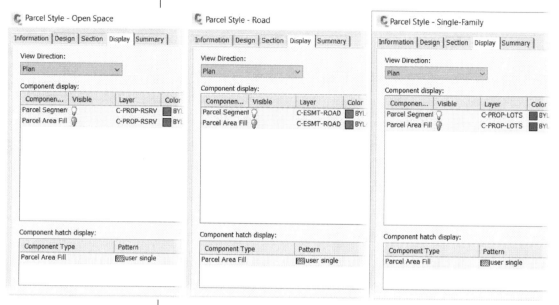

Figure 1–59

An object style represents a specific task, view, type, or stage in a process. For example, a surface style for developing a surface, reviewing surface properties, or documenting surface elevations as contours for a submission. For Parcels, styles represent a type such as open space, commercial, easement, single family, etc. One style can cause an object to look different in various views. For instance, you might want to display both the point and the label in the plan view but only the point marker in a model (3D view). As shown in Figure 1–60, there are four view directions to consider when creating an object style.

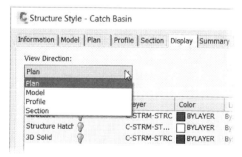

Figure 1–60

Label Styles

Label styles produce annotation of critical values from existing conditions or a design solution. A label annotates a contour's elevations, a parcel's number and area, an horizontal geometry point's station on an alignment, etc.

A label style can have text, vectors, AutoCAD blocks, and reference text. The content of a label depends on the selected object's components or properties. For instance, a Line label can annotate bearing, distance, and coordinates, and use a direction arrow. A Parcel Area label can contain a parcel's area, perimeter, address, and other pertinent values. A surface label can include a spot elevation and reference for an alignment's station and offset.

- To access the values of a label style, in the Toolspace>*Settings* tab, select the style, right-click on its name, and select **Edit**.

- A style's initial values come from Edit Label Style Defaults and the style's definition.

- All labels use the same interface.

- The object properties available for each label vary by object type.

Each label style uses the same tabbed dialog box. The Information tab describes the style and who defined and last modified its contents. The values of the *General* tab affect all occurrences of the label in a drawing. For example, if Visibility is set to False, all labels of this style are hidden in the drawing. Other settings affect the label's text style, initial orientation, and reaction to a rotated view.

The *Layout* tab lists all of a label's components. A label component can be text, line, block, or tick. The Component name drop-down list (shown in Figure 1–61) contains all of the defined components for the style. When selecting a component name in the drop-down list, the panel displays information about the component's anchoring, justification, format, and border.

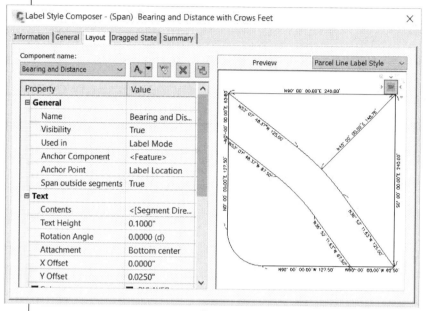

Figure 1–61

When defining a new text component, you assign it an object property by clicking 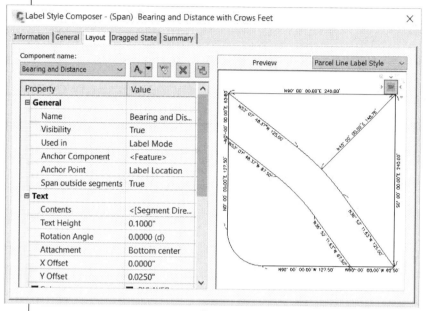 (Browse) for Contents. This opens the Text Component Editor dialog box, as shown in Figure 1–62. The Properties drop-down list displays the available object properties. The number and types of properties varies by object type. For example, a parcel area label has more and different properties than a line label does. Once a property has been selected, units, precision, and other settings can be set to display the property correctly in the label. Click next to Properties to add the property to the label layout area.

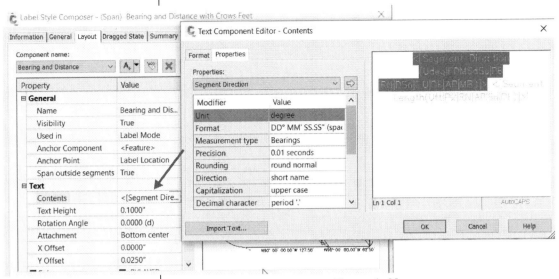

Figure 1–62

The values in the *Dragged State* tab define a label's behavior when it is dragged to a new location in the drawing.

The key to having the label display correctly when it is not in the dragged state, is to line up the Anchor Point of the component with the **Attachment** option for the text. Each has nine options from which to select. The options are shown in Figure 1–63.

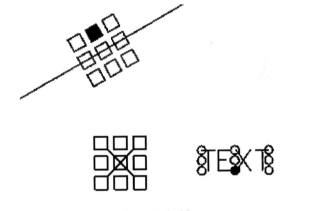

Figure 1–63

Aligning the square hatched Anchor Point with the circular hatched attachment option results in the text centered above the object similar to the bearing distance label shown in Figure 1–64.

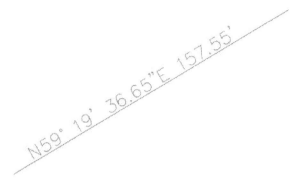

Figure 1–64

Managing Styles

There are three methods of managing styles in a drawing: **Import**, **Purge**, and **Reference**. These commands are located in the *Manage* tab>Styles panel.

Import

The **Import** styles command ( ) enables you to import the styles from a source drawing into the current drawing using the Import Civil 3D Styles dialog box, shown in Figure 1–65. The dialog box lists the styles that are available for import, and displays the style differences between the source and current drawing.

Each style collection lists three subcategories:

- Styles to be added
- Styles to be deleted
- Styles to be updated

When you use the **Import** command, the styles in the design file are overwritten. However, if the styles change in the .DWG or .DWT source file that you imported, the styles in the design file do not automatically update.

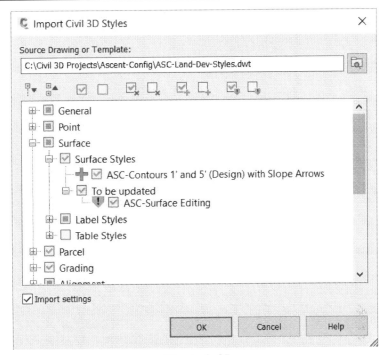

Figure 1–65

Drag and Drop Method

Another method for importing styles is the Drag and Drop method. This is the preferred method when only a few specific styles need to be imported into your current drawing. The steps are as follows:

1. Ensure that both the source drawing (where the style resides) and the destination drawing (where you want to import the style into) are open in Civil 3D.
2. In the Toolspace of the destination drawing, go to the *Settings* tab and set your display option to **Master View,** as shown in Figure 1–66.

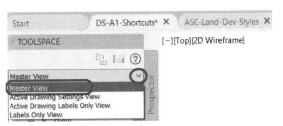

Figure 1–66

3. On the *Settings* tab, note that your current drawing is in bold. Click the minus symbol (-) next to the drawing name to collapse its branch, revealing the other drawing you have open.

4. If required, click the plus symbol (+) to expand the branch of the drawing that contains the styles you need.

5. Browse to the style you require, then click and drag it into your current drawing's drawing area, as shown in Figure 1–67.

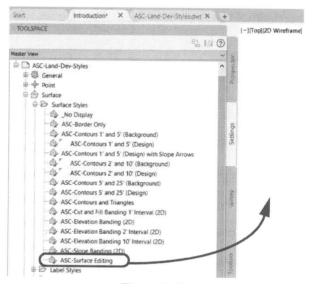

Figure 1–67

6. Repeat these steps, for other styles you wish to import, on an individual basis.

Purge

The **Purge** styles command ( ) enables you to purge all of the selected unused styles in a drawing. The purging information displays in the Style Purge Confirmation dialog box, shown in Figure 1–68. A prompt displays in the Command Line when there are no unused styles in the drawing.

Typically, you need to run the **Purge** command more than once, as there are some styles that are used as parents to other styles. By repeating the command, you can ensure that the nested styles are also purged.

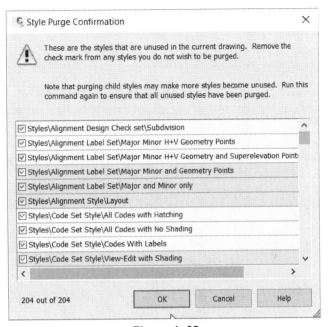

Figure 1–68

Reference

The **Reference** styles command (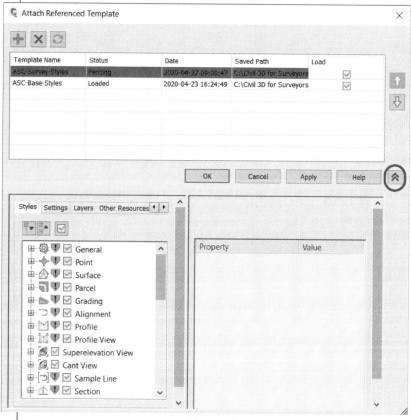) enables you to attach one or more .DWG or .DWT files to your design file. Styles that are in the attached files override styles with the same name in the design drawing. If the styles change in the attached .DWG or .DWT file, the styles in the design file also change.

Using the **Reference** styles command enables you to maintain a consistent style across multiple drawings, and can be used to implement and maintain an organization-wide CAD standard. Figure 1–69 shows the Attach Referenced Template dialog box.

*   When multiple style templates are attached, you can set the priority using the arrows on the right of the Attach Referenced Template dialog box.

*   You can choose which objects are to be referenced from the attached template by clicking the double down arrow symbol

    ( ) in the lower right corner.

Figure 1–69

Practice 1c | Autodesk Civil 3D Styles

Practice Objectives

- Create an object and label style to be used in the drawing.
- Import object and label styles to be used in the drawing and purge any styles not being used.

In this practice, you will create Autodesk Civil 3D styles, import styles, and purge styles for both objects and labels.

Task 1 - Create an object style.

1. Continue working in the drawing from the last practice. If you closed it, open **Introduction.dwg** from the *C:\Civil 3D for Surveyors\Working\Interface* folder.

2. Select the Toolspace>*Settings* tab to make it active.

The tabs are listed vertically along the right side of the Toolspace.

3. Click the **+** sign next to **Parcel**, and then click the **+** sign next to **Parcel Styles**. Note that five parcel styles are already in the drawing, but a new one needs to be created to designate blocks.

4. Right-click on **Parcel Styles** and select **New**. In the *Information* tab, type **ASC-Blocks** in the *Name* field.

5. In the *Display* tab, highlight both the **Parcel Segment** and **Parcel Area Fill** (press <Shift> to select both). In the *Layer* column, click **0**.

6. In the Layer Selection dialog box, click **New** to create a new layer. Name the layer **C-PROP-BLOK** and set its *color* to **blue**, as shown in Figure 1–70.

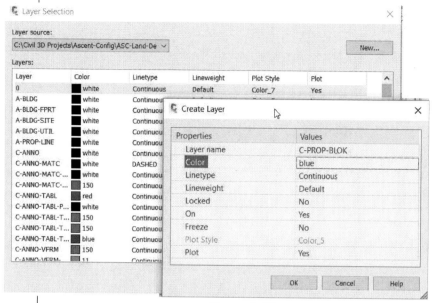

Figure 1–70

7. Click **OK** to exit the Create Layer dialog box.

8. In the Layer Selection dialog box, select the new **C-PROP-BLOK** layer and click **OK** to exit the Layer Selection dialog box.

9. Verify that the light bulb is toggled on for the **Parcel Segment** visibility and toggled off for the **Parcel Area Fill** visibility, as shown in Figure 1–71.

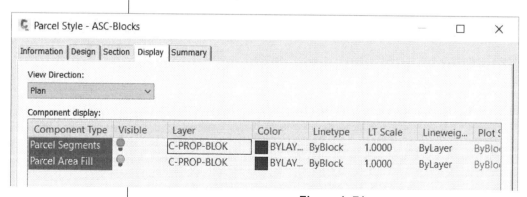

Figure 1–71

10. Click **OK** to exit the Parcel Style dialog box.

Task 2 - Work with a label style.

1. Ensure that the Toolspace>*Settings* tab is active.

2. View the label style default. In the *View* tab>Views panel, expand the Named Views drop-down list and select **Contour label**. The display zooms to a preset view of the contour labels, as shown in Figure 1–72.

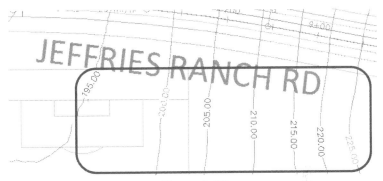

Figure 1–72

Note that the labels are not rotated to the correct drafting standards. The contour label style being used is rotating the text so that it remains plan readable (so they do not display upside down). The highlighted labels are rotated more than 90 degrees from horizontal. This is caused by the *Readability Bias* setting being larger than 90 degrees. This setting controls the viewing angle at which the contour text should be flipped.

3. If required, you can change the setting in this specific contour label style only. To assign this new value to all of the surface label styles, in the Toolspace>*Settings* tab, right-click on the *Surface* collection and select **Edit Label Style Defaults**.

4. Under the Plan Readability property, set the *Readability Bias* to **91°**, as shown in Figure 1–73, and click **OK**.

Property	Value	Override	Child Override	Lock
⊞ **Label**				
⊞ **Behavior**				
⊟ **Plan Readability**				
Plan Readable	True		⇩	🔓
Readability Bias	91.0000 (d)		⇩	🔓
Flip Anchors with Text	False		⇩	🔓
⊞ **Components**				
⊞ **Leader**				
⊞ **Dragged State Compone...**				

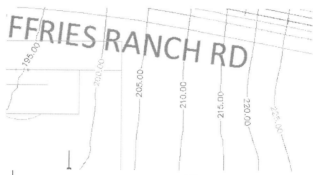

Figure 1–73

5. In the Toolspace>*Settings* tab, click **+** next to **Surface**, and then click **+** next to **Label Styles and Contour**. Right-click on Existing Major Labels and select **Edit**.

6. In the *Layout* tab, click [...] (Browse) next to Contents to open the Text Component Editor. Delete all of the information in the content area to the right.

7. In the Properties drop-down list, select **Surface Elevation**, change the *Precision* to **1**, and click ⇨ to place it in the content area, as shown in Figure 1–74.

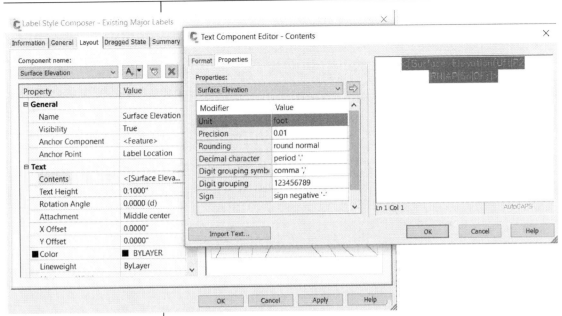

Figure 1–74

8. Click **OK** to exit the Text Component Editor dialog box. Click **OK** again to exit the Label Style Composer dialog box.

9. Repeat Steps 5 to 8 to change the **Existing Minor Labels** style in the same way.

10. Save the drawing.

Task 3 - Drag and drop styles.

1. Open the **ASC-Land-Dev-Styles.dwg** template file from the *C:\Civil 3D for Surveyors\Ascent-Config* folder.

2. Note the tabs across the top of the drawing area, one for each file you have open. Click on the *Introduction* tab to make that drawing your active drawing.

3. Go to the *Settings* tab and set your display option to **Master View**, as shown in Figure 1–75.

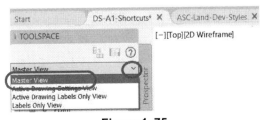

Figure 1–75

4. On the *Settings* tab, note that **Introduction** (your active drawing) is in bold. Click the minus symbol (-) next to the drawing name to collapse its branch.

5. If required, click the plus symbol (+) next to the **ASC-Land-Dev-Styles** drawing to expand the branch.

6. Browse to *Surface\Surface Style* and select the **ASC-Surface Editing** style.

7. Click and drag it into your current drawing's drawing area, as shown in Figure 1–76.

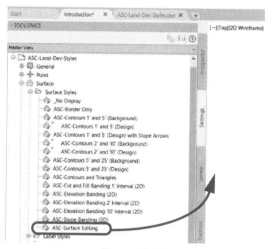

Figure 1–76

8. Expand the branch of the **Introduction** drawing and verify that the new **ASC-Surface Editing** style is listed under *Surface\Surface Style.*

9. Change the surface style to the *ASC-Surface Editing* style by changing the surface properties. Note the point markers, triangles, and slope arrows shown in Figure 1–77.

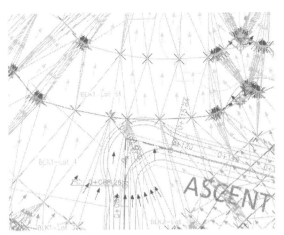

Figure 1–77

10. Save the drawing, but do not close it.

Task 4 - Import and purge styles.

1. In the *Manage* tab>Styles panel, click (Import).

2. Select and open the **ASC-Land-Dev-Styles.dwg** file from the *C:\Civil 3D for Surveyors\Ascent-Config* folder.

3. Expand *Surface Styles* and verify that **Contours 1' and 5' (Design) with Slope Arrows** is selected, as shown in Figure 1–78.

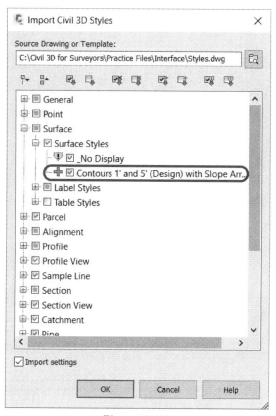

Figure 1–78

4. Click **OK** in the Warning dialog box regarding overwriting duplicate styles. Click **OK** in the Message dialog box.

5. Change the surface style to the newly imported style by changing the surface properties. Note the slope arrows shown in Figure 1–79.

Figure 1–79

6. In the *Manage* tab>Styles panel, click  (Purge).

7. Clear any styles that you do not want to purge and click **OK**.

8. Save and close the drawing.

Chapter Review Questions

1. Which workspace should you be in if you want to create an AEC object (surfaces, alignments, profiles, etc.)?

   a. 2D Drafting and Annotation

   b. 3D Modeling

   c. Civil 3D

   d. Planning and Analysis

2. What does the Toolspace>*Prospector* tab do?

   a. Sets the layers for AEC objects.

   b. Lists the AEC objects and provides access to their information.

   c. Sets the workspace in which you want to work.

   d. Enables you to connect to GIS data from a number of sources.

3. What does the Toolspace>*Settings* tab do?

   a. Sets the layers and display styles for AEC objects.

   b. Creates templates from which new drawings are based.

   c. Creates new drawings with references to data.

   d. Generates Sheets for printing purposes.

4. How do you open the Edit Drawing Settings dialog box?

   a. Type **CUI** in the Command Line to open the Customize User Interface dialog box.

   b. **Application menu>Drawing Utilities**.

   c. In the Toolspace>*Prospector* tab, right-click on the drawing name.

   d. In the Toolspace>*Settings* tab, right-click on the drawing name.

5. What is the main function of the Panorama window?

   a. Setting up styles for AEC objects.

   b. Reviewing and editing tabular AEC object data.

   c. Pan inside the drawing.

   d. Look at the AEC objects in 3D views.

6. How do you force the styles in a design file to update every time the CAD Manager makes a change to the styles in the organization CAD Standards template file?

a. In the *Manage* tab>Styles panel, click (Reference)

b. In the *Manage* tab>Styles panel, click (Purge)

c. In the *Manage* tab>Styles panel, click (Import).

d. You have to create a new style manually because there is no way to force an update to styles in an existing drawing.

Command Summary

Button	Command	Location
	Close	• **Drawing Window** • **Application Menu** • **Command Prompt:** close
	Close Current Drawing	• **Application Menu**
	Import Styles	• **Ribbon:** *Manage* tab>Styles panel • **Command Prompt:** importstylesandsettings
	Manager Reference Styles	• **Ribbon:** *Manage* tab>Styles panel • **Command Prompt:** AttachReferenceTemplate
	Open	• **Quick Access Toolbar** • **Application Menu** • **Command Prompt:** open, <Ctrl>+<O>
	Prospector	• **Ribbon:** *Home* tab>Palettes panel • **Command Prompt:** prospector
	Settings	• **Ribbon:** *Home* tab>Palettes panel • **Command Prompt:** settings
	Style Purge	• **Ribbon:** *Manage* tab>Styles panel • **Command Prompt:** purgestyles
	Surface Properties	• **Contextual Ribbon:** *Surface* tab>Modify panel • **Command Prompt:** editsurfaceproperties
	Survey	• **Ribbon:** *Home* tab>Palettes panel • **Command Prompt:** survey
	Toolbox	• **Ribbon:** *Home* tab>Palettes panel • **Command Prompt:** toolbox
	Toolspace	• **Ribbon:** *Home* tab>Palettes panel • **Command Prompt:** toolspace

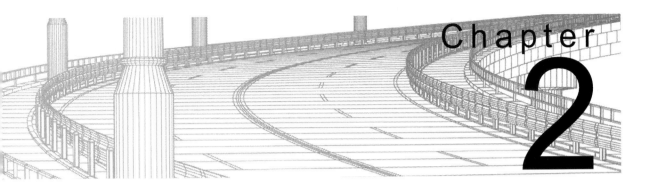

Survey Setup

Autodesk® Civil 3D® has a dedicated Toolspace for surveying that has unique capabilities. The Toolspace enables survey data to be processed external to the drawing in a special database. In this chapter, you will learn how to prepare the settings for the Survey data in the Autodesk Civil 3D software. This will enable you to import survey data by creating a figure database and figure styles, along with point styles, point label styles, and the description keys. Next, you will learn how to successfully create a new survey database for storing survey data.

Learning Objectives in This Chapter

- Create a drawing template.
- Display the Survey Toolspace and content that is listed under each of its trees.
- Create a figure prefix database for stylizing linework automatically on importing field book or ASCII files.
- Create a point marker style to ensure that the correct symbol is assigned to specific points.
- Create a point label style for annotating groups of points with the required information.
- Create description key sets.
- Create survey equipment databases.
- Create a new survey database in the required working folder.

2.1 Survey Workflow Overview

This guide focuses on automated **Field to Finish** tools that aid in creating an accurate and efficient *Existing Conditions Plan*. These tools create a correct existing topography, property lines, right-of-way, and center line locations.

Workflow

The three distinctive phases of a survey workflow are as follows:

- Phase 1: Prepare for survey data
- Phase 2: Obtain and create survey data
- Phase 3: Adjust, analyze, and output survey data

These phases are shown in Figure 2–1.

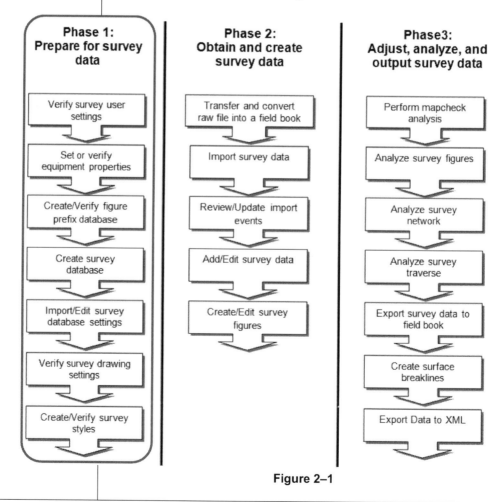

Figure 2–1

The first stage in standardizing the survey workflow is to research, understand, establish, and implement the resources available to you. When using the data collector, you need to determine the final format required for the data.

In addition, the Autodesk® Civil 3D® Styles and Settings must be set up in advance and saved as a Template (*.DWT) for the required automation to work correctly. This chapter focuses on that phase.

Some factors that need to be addressed so that you can maximize your productivity when using the automation, tools, and extensions in the Autodesk Civil 3D software are as follows:

- Are the survey field crews responsible for reducing their field notes on site?

- What software is used to analyze the survey data, if not the Autodesk Civil 3D software?

- Is the data analyzed before it is imported into the Autodesk Civil 3D software?

- What type of data format is being used?

- Are point code descriptions and line code connectives used?

- When should you import points into the drawing using the Toolspace>*Prospector* tab or the Survey Database?

- Are the figure commands placed before or after the code?

- Does the field crew know the correct keystrokes to enter into the data collector and how that input affects the linework, symbology, or breaklines for the office surveyors and draftsman?

2.2 Collecting Field Data

Before collecting field data, it is important to determine which file formats can be used when importing survey data. Both field books and point text files can be used. Depending on which ASCII format is used, point descriptions are coded differently in the field. The following three survey data files can be imported into the Autodesk Civil 3D software:

- Point files

- Point files with connective codes

- Field book files

Point Files

Point files consist of a simple ASCII file containing the point number, northing, easting, elevation, and description, as shown in Figure 2–2. This format has been commonly used since the early days of CAD. Surveyors reduced their survey notes, modified the data as required, and output the point file that was imported into a CAD program.

```
304,620965.9041,1906975.735,51.6471,BRUSH COTTONWOOD 5.2
305,620950.2947,1906966.547,52.2897,BRUSH DOGWOOD 1.2
306,620951.2129,1906947.254,52.8633,BRUSH COTTONWOOD 1.6
307,620891.4575,1907051.619,54.2706,BRUSH DOGWOOD 3.7
308,620947.5148,1907001.198,51.6455,BRUSH COTTONWOOD 2
309,620929.0278,1907005.972,52.2365,BRUSH DOGWOOD 3.2
310,620918.3755,1907041.441,53.0132,CTREE PINE 2.3
311,620924.0094,1907055.064,52.4753,CTREE FIR 1.4
312,620929.4085,1907070.096,52.3893,CTREE PINE 1.4
313,620939.2678,1907131.87,49.9998,DTREE CHERRY 1.7
314,620938.7983,1907117.777,50.5543,CTREE FIR 2.7
315,620893.9387,1907123.407,54.4338,DTREE APPLE 4.5
316,620843.4236,1906905.9,56.0765,CTREE FIR 3.7
317,620943.8604,1906915.226,54.2207,CTREE PINE 3.4
318,620959.5893,1906922.546,53.786,DTREE CHERRY 2.7
```

Point Description

Figure 2–2

Point Files with Connective Codes

A point file with connective codes contains the point number, northing, easting, elevation, description, and line connective codes, as shown in Figure 2–3. Line connective codes are appended to the point description. The connective code is a line command code that indicates whether the line is a beginning, continuation, end, curve segment, or line segment.

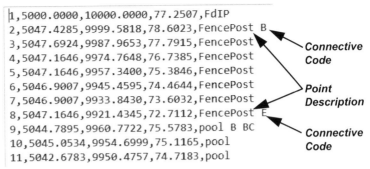

Figure 2–3

In the Autodesk Civil 3D software, the syntax of the field code corresponds to a previously defined linework code set. The correspondence between the field codes and the linework code set permits the following:

- Automatic assignment of point properties, such as **Layer**, **Symbol**, and **Label**.

- Automatic assignment of line feature properties, such as **Layer**, **Color**, **Linetype**, and **Lineweight**.

- Line connectivity between the surveyed points.

Field Book Files

A field book file typically contains all of the data that was used during the survey field pickup by a total station (e.g., setups, backsites, instrument height, prism height, turned angles, side shots, etc.). The difference between a field book file and a point file with connective codes is that, in the field, the connective code is added as a note which is separate from the point description. However, the point description and the connective codes must match, as shown in Figure 2–4.

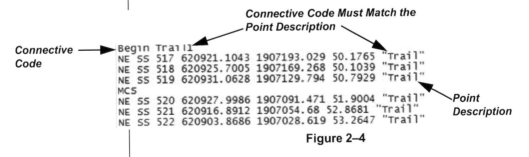

Figure 2–4

2.3 Introduction to the Survey Toolspace

The Survey Toolspace displays a panel through which all surveys are processed. Survey uses graphics to display field book imports, figure and network previews, and points. If you toggle off these graphics, you can process a survey without a drawing being open. If you want to display these graphics, you need to have a drawing open. Survey prompts you to open a drawing if you do not have one open.

The Survey Toolspace contains Survey settings, Equipment defaults, Figure Prefixes, and Linework Code Sets. Survey settings can be on a local or network folder. Using a network folder is recommended to ensure that all users can access the setting files and to standardize the file values.

How To: Display the Survey Toolspace

Click ![Survey Toolspace icon] (Survey Toolspace) in the *Home* tab>Palettes panel, as shown in Figure 2–5.

Figure 2–5

Typical Survey Database Settings

Surveys are either in a predefined Coordinate system or an assumed coordinate system (e.g., 5000 for Northing and 5000 for Easting, Elevation set to 100). Either of these coordinates systems are typed in a data collector at the first survey control found by the field crew. In the Autodesk Civil 3D software, these different settings can be stored as definitions that are assigned when creating a database, or are assigned by editing a survey's setting.

2.4 Survey User Settings vs. Drawing Template

Drawing Template

The Autodesk Civil 3D drawing template contains all of the settings and configurations contained within the Toolspace>*Settings* tab. Any drawing originating with a specific template adopts these settings.

If a reference template is attached to a drawing (or another template), then many of the styles and settings in the Toolspace>*Settings* tab are controlled through the reference template.

Survey User Settings

The settings within the Toolspace>*Survey* tab are not drawing specific. Rather, they are user specific, and reside in designated folders. This ensures that the Survey User Settings are persistent regardless of which drawing is active. Survey user settings are specific to the Windows user login account, and only affect the survey features, not project or drawing data.

You access the *Survey User Settings* by clicking 🀫 (Survey User Settings) in the top left corner of the Toolspace>*Survey* tab, as shown in Figure 2–6.

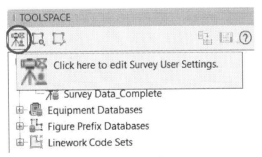

Figure 2–6

The following are controlled through the *Survey User Settings*, in addition to a variety of other settings:

- Survey Database Defaults

- Equipment Defaults

- Linework Processing Defaults

- Figure Defaults

You set the specific paths for these settings and their defaults as shown in Figure 2–7.

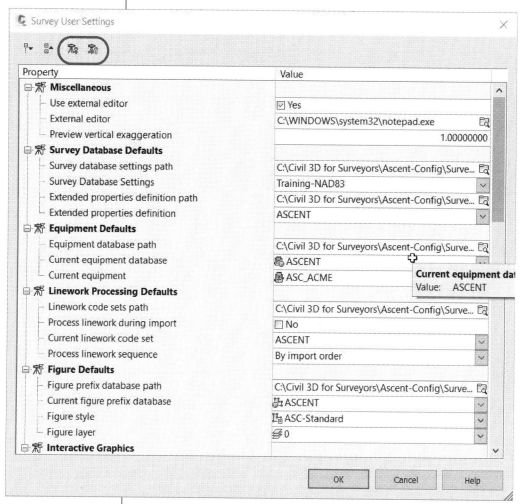

Figure 2–7

Once the settings are established, you can export these settings to a file. Click (Export Settings) and enter the path and file name.

You can then import these settings on other computers by clicking (Import Settings) and selecting the path and file name. This sets all of the *Survey User Settings* to the values stored in the file.

2.5 Templates

A drawing template (.DWT extension) contains all blocks, Paper Space title sheets, settings, layers, Autodesk Civil 3D styles, and content-specific settings for a new drawing.

Creating Template Files

To use the Autodesk Civil 3D software efficiently and effectively, you need to configure styles and settings to control the object display. All of these styles and settings affect the final delivered product and enable you to deliver a product with consistent CAD standards. Once all of the styles required for a set of drawings have been created, saving the file as a template enables you to use the same styles over and over in various projects. To create a template file, use the **Save As** command and in the Save As dialog box, change the *File of Type* to **DWT**.

For more information on Layer Reconciliation, consult the AutoCAD Help feature.

After giving the file a name, the Template Options dialog box opens as shown in Figure 2–8. This dialog box enables you to enter a description, set the measurement units, and save new layers as reconciled or unreconciled.

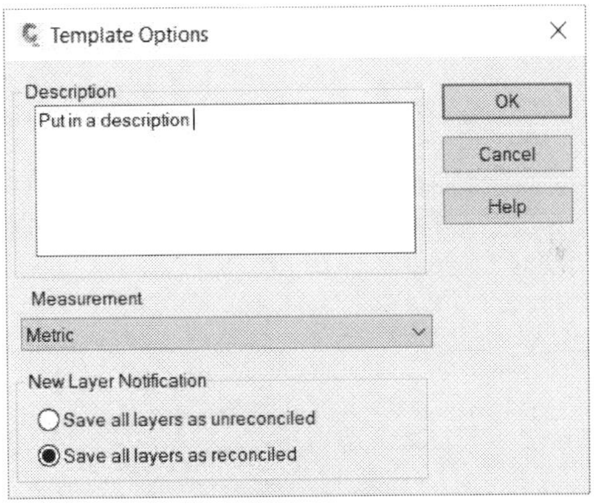

Figure 2–8

Once an Autodesk Civil 3D style has been created, it can be transferred between drawings and templates by selecting the style and dragging it to the required file. When dragging a style to a drawing, any associated style layers also transfer.

2.6 Survey Figures

Survey figures consist of linework generated by coding and placed in a file that is imported into the Survey Database. A figure represents linear features (edge-of-pavement, toe-of-slopes, etc.)

Therefore, a figure has many functions, as follows:

- A figure displays linework in a drawing.

- All preset figures in a drawing can be defined as breaklines for a surface definition with one step.

- All preset figures in a drawing can be defined as parcel lines.

- A figure can be drawn as a pipe run. For example, a surveyor notices that only one pipe comes through a manhole. The surveyor then invokes a figure command to draw a survey figure that denotes the location of a pipe run. The Elevation Editor in the Autodesk Civil 3D software enables you to lower each survey figure at each manhole to the distance of what was measured in the field, and what was written on the manhole field notes as the flow elevation at the invert of the pipe run. The pipe functionality can make this line represent various types of locations within the circumference of the cross-sectional pipe and convert the survey figure into an existing pipe run.

- Any figure can be targets for *Width* or *Offset Targets* in a Corridor.

- Any figure can be targets for *Slope* or *Elevation Targets* in a Corridor (e.g., limits of construction for a road rehab project might be to the face of walk, which exists in the drawing as a Survey Figure, hence a target).

- It is recommended that you set up a Figure Prefix database and figure styles before importing any survey data to obtain the required entities in a drawing. As point and label styles and the Description Key Set need to exist before importing points, figure styles and entries in the Figure Prefix database need to exist before importing survey data.

Drawing Settings

The Drawing Settings dialog box (shown in Figure 2–9) sets a universal layer for figures. You can access these settings by selecting the drawing name in the Toolspace>*Settings* tab, right-clicking, and selecting **Edit Drawing Settings**. When selecting the *Object Layer* tab and scrolling to the bottom of the list, the default layer names are displayed.

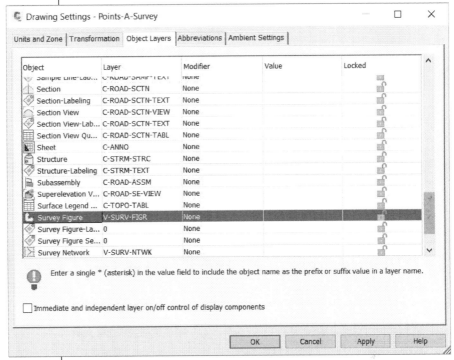

Figure 2–9

Your organization might have one or more default layers for each of the linework types. For example, edge-of-pavement, sidewalk, etc., each have their own layers in the drawing. To accomplish this, you need to define figure styles.

Figure Styles

Figure styles (found in the Toolspace>*Settings* tab) affect how the survey linework displays in a drawing. They should be part of your template file. These styles are not critical. However, to make figures work, you should define the layers they use in the drawing.

- Figure styles are tied to the Figure Prefix database.

- The Figure Prefix database assigns a figure style to a figure that is imported into a drawing.

- A figure style includes the layers for its linework and markers.

- A marker is a symbol placed on the figure's segment midpoints and end points. They call attention to the figure's geometry. Although a figure style includes marker definitions, they do not need to display.

Figures can be 3D and use the layers set in the *Display* tab in the Figure Style dialog box. The *Information* tab assigns a name to a style. The *Plan*, *Profile*, and *Section* tabs define how the marker displays in each of these views. The Figure Style dialog box is shown in Figure 2–10.

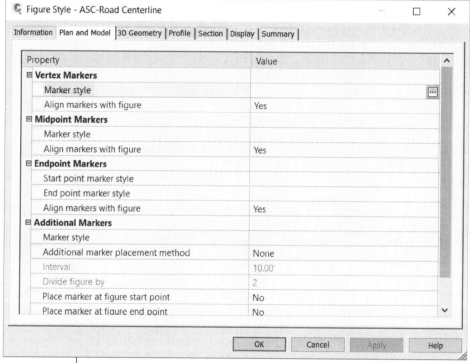

Figure 2–10

The *3D Geometry* tab defines a figure's vertical behavior. By default, the elevation of the point defines the figure. The *Display* tab defines which figure's components display and which layers they use for plan, profile, and section views, as shown in Figure 2–11.

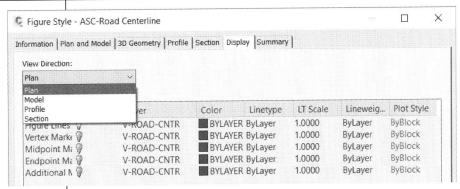

Figure 2–11

Figure Prefix Database

The Figure Prefix database, found in the Toolspace>*Survey* tab, does the following, as shown in Figure 2–12:

- Assigns the figure a style.

- Assigns the figure a layer. If you did not define any figure styles, you should at least assign a layer to correctly place the figure in the drawing.

- Defines whether the figure is a surface breakline. Toggling on the *Breakline* property enables you select all of the tagged survey figures and assign them to a surface without having to insert or select from a drawing.

- Defines whether the figure is a lot line (parcel segment). Toggling on the *Lot Line* property creates a parcel segment from the figure in the drawing and, if there is a closed polygon, assigns a parcel label and an entry in the designated site.

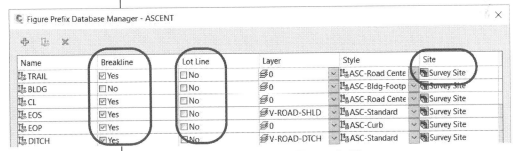

Figure 2–12

If the *Name* is **CL** (as shown in Figure 2–12), any figure starting with CL uses these settings. This is similar to using a Description Key Set, except that the entry in the Figure Prefix database does not need an asterisk (*). When inserting survey figures in the drawing, Survey checks the Figure Prefix database for style or layer values.

Practice 2a

Creating a Civil 3D Drawing Template

Practice Objectives

- Create a customized drawing template from an existing default template.
- Assign a coordinate system.
- Import Survey User Settings.
- Create a figure database for automatically stylizing linework on importing field book or ASCII files.

Task 1 - Create a drawing template.

1. In the ![icon] (Application Menu), start a new drawing file using the **Autodesk Civil 3D (Imperial) NCS.dwt** template that is included with the software, as shown in Figure 2–13.

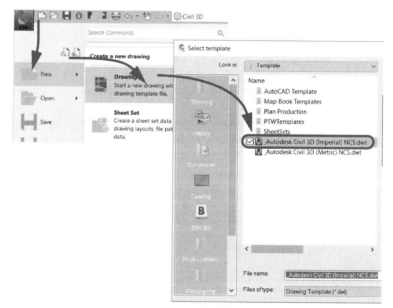

Figure 2–13

2. Click ![icon] (Application Menu) and select **Save As>Drawing Template** as shown in Figure 2–14.

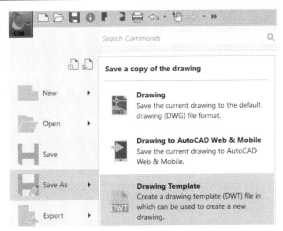

Figure 2–14

CA83-VIF designates the coordinate zone you use for this template.

3. Browse to the *C:\Civil 3D for Surveyors\Ascent-Config* folder and enter ***XXX-C3D (CA83-VIF) NCS.dwt*** as the template file name (substituting your initials for XXX) and then click **Save**.

4. In the *Template Options* dialog box, add an appropriate description for this newly created template, for example **Civil 3D Training template for Surveyors.**

5. Select the Toolspace>*Settings* tab, as shown in Figure 2–15.

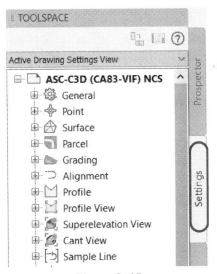

Figure 2–15

6. In the Toolspace>*Settings* tab, right-click on the drawing name (**XXX-C3D (CA83-VIF) NCS**, where XXX is your initials), and select **Edit Drawing Settings**.

7. In the Drawing Settings dialog box, select the *Units and Zone* tab, as shown in Figure 2–16.

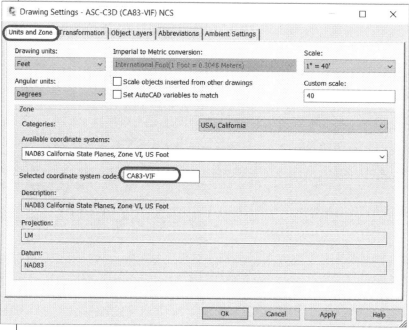

Figure 2–16

8. In the *Selected coordinate system code* field, enter **CA83-VIF**. This is the code for *NAD83 California State Planes, Zone VI, US Foot*.

These coordinates are in the vicinity of the CA83-VIF coordinate zone.

9. Note that the coordinates of the drawing are near **0,0**. In the command line, type **Zoom**, and press <Enter>. Enter **C** (for Center), and then press <Enter> again.

10. For the coordinates, type **6256700, 2036200**. At the ensuing *magnification or height* prompt, type 5300 and press <Enter>.

11. Start the **Single Line text** command (type in **DTEXT** at the command line or select in the ribbon>*Annotate* tab>*Multiline Text* drop-down list), then select the center of the display as the insertion point.

12. Set the *text height* to **150** and the *rotation angle* to **33**.

13. Type the following, pressing <Enter> after each line (when done typing the last line, press <Enter> twice to finish):

DRAWING SET TO CA83-VIF COORDINATE SYSTEM. GO TO DRAWING SETTINGS TO MODIFY IF NEED BE. DELETE THIS MESSAGE.

14. Save the drawing template.

Task 2 - Attach a styles template.

1. In the *Manage* tab>Styles panel, click (Reference).

2. In the Attach Referenced Template dialog box, click ✛ (Attach New Template).

To select both files, hold <Ctrl> when selecting the second file.

3. In the *C:\Civil 3D for Surveyors\Ascent-Config* folder, select **ASC-Base-Styles.dwg** and **ASC-Survey-Styles.dwg**, and then click **Open**.

4. In the Attach Referenced Template dialog box (shown in Figure 2–17), ensure that **ASC_Survey-Styles** is at the top of the list. If it is not, then press <Up Arrow> to move it.

Figure 2–17

5. Note all the alerts in the lower half of the dialog box. Click **Apply**, which clears all the alerts.

6. Click **OK**.

7. Save the drawing template.

Task 3 - Import survey user settings.

Importing survey user settings will have no effect on a drawing template. You import the survey user settings now to establish the path to where the Figure Prefix Database resides.

1. In the Toolspace, select the Survey tab. Click (Survey User Settings), as shown in Figure 2–18.

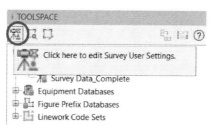

Figure 2–18

2. Click (Import User Settings), as shown in Figure 2–19

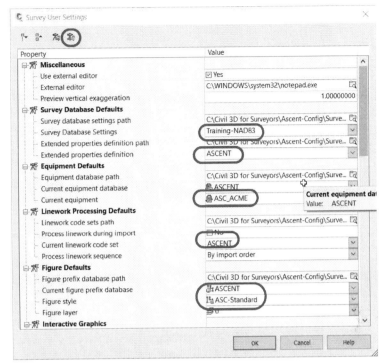

Figure 2–19

3. Browse to *C:\Civil 3D for Surveyors\Ascent-Config\Survey Settings* and select **ASCENT-Settings.usr_set**, then click **Open**.

4. Importing the user settings causes all branches to contract. You can expand each branch by clicking the **+** icon. A simple way of expanding all branches is to close the Survey User Settings window by clicking **OK** and reopening the file as you did in the first step of this practice.

5. Note how the paths have changed for the various entries.

6. Set the Survey User Settings drop-down lists as follows:

   - *Survey Database Setting*: **Training-NAD83**
   - *Extended properties definitions:* **Ascent**
   - *Current equipment database*: **Ascent**
   - *Current Equipment:* **ASC_ACME**
   - *Current linework code set*: **Ascent**
   - *Current figure prefix database*: **Ascent**
   - *Figure Style*: **ASC_Standard**

7. Click **OK** to exit the Survey User Settings.

8. Note that no changes were made in the template, so there is no need to save the drawing template. The changes were made to the *Survey User Settings.*

Task 4 - Create a Figure Prefix database.

1. Remain in the *Survey* tab of the Toolspace.

2. Right-click on **Figure Prefix Databases**, and select **New**. Set the *Name* to **XXX-Training** (substituting XXX with your initials).

3. Right-click on **XXX-Training** Figure Prefix database, and select **Make Current**.

4. Right-click on **XXX-Training** Figure Prefix database again, and select **Manage Figure Prefix Database**.

5. Click ✚ to create a new figure definition. The Autodesk Civil 3D software creates a default figure. Set the following, as shown in Figure 2–20:

   • Change the *Name* to **Trail**.
   • Set the *Breakline* to **Yes**.
   • Verify that *Lot Line* is set to **No**.
   • Set the *Layer* to **V-ROAD-CNTR**.
   • Set the *Style* to **ASC-Road Centerline**.

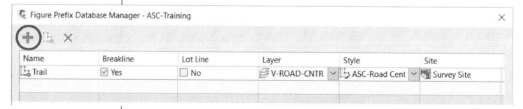

Figure 2–20

   • Any figure starting with **Trail** is now selectable for a surface breakline and uses the **Road Centerline** style. Unlike the Description Key Set, an asterisk (*) is not required to match Trail1, Trail2, etc.

   • The figure resides on the designated layer **V-ROAD-CNTR**.

6. Click to create a new figure definition and then set the following:

   - Change the *Name* to **Building**.
   - Verify that *Breakline* is set to **No**.
   - Verify that *Lot Line* is set to **No**.
   - Verify that *Layer* is set to **0**.
   - Set the *Style* to **ASC-Buildings**.
   - Click **OK** to exit the dialog box.

   Since no layer was assigned, the figure resides on Layer **0**, however the style resides on layer **V-BLDG-OTLN**.

7. Close the drawing template. There is no need to save the drawing template, as the changes are recorded in the Figure Prefix Database, which resides in the path designated in the *Survey User Settings*.

2.7 Points Overview

Within Civil 3D, there are three different types of points:

COGO is an abbreviation for Coordinated Geometry.

1. **COGO Points** reside in the drawing file and cannot be referenced into other drawings. There is little protection (other than locking the points); any Civil 3D user can add, manipulate, lock, or unlock COGO points. Therefore, they are mostly used as design points or stakeout points.

2. **Survey Points** reside in a protected survey database. Only users with proper permissions to the survey database folders can manipulate these points. They are inserted (or removed) from the drawings, thus can easily be shared among multiple drawings. They are used by the survey staff to create existing conditions and surfaces.

AutoCAD points are not covered in this guide. Consult other ASCENT AutoCAD guides or the AutoCAD Help for more information.

3. **AutoCAD Points** are regular AutoCAD objects with special properties for point display (**PDMODE** variable) and sizing behavior (**PDSIZE** variable). Beyond their standard AutoCAD use, they are not used much in Civil 3D.

Survey points are often used at the beginning of a project, while COGO points (for stakeout) are used at the end of a project. Surveyors collect data about existing site conditions (elevations, utilities, ownership, etc.) for the project. Their world is coordinates, which are represented by points. Each point has a unique number (or name) and a label containing additional information (usually the elevation of the coordinate and a short coded description).

There are no national standards for point descriptions in the surveying industry. Each organization or survey crew needs to establish its own conventions. There are no standards for symbols either. Each firm can have its own set of symbols. The symbols used in a submission set can be specified by the firm contracting the services.

Autodesk Civil 3D COGO/survey points are a single object with two elements: a point style and a point label style. A COGO/survey point definition is shown in Figure 2–21.

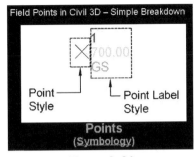

Figure 2–21

The following is important point information:

- A point style (no matter what it displays) is selectable with an AutoCAD **Node** object snap.

- Points can be displayed as an AutoCAD node, a custom marker, or a block.

A point label is not limited to the point's number, elevation, and description. A point label can contain lines, blocks, and other point properties. You can also set User-Defined point properties. For example, point labels might only display an elevation or description. This text can be manually overridden (as shown in Figure 2–22) or it can consist of intelligent variables that represent point characteristics (such as its convergence angle).

Figure 2–22

In U.S. state plane coordinate systems, the convergence angle is the difference between a geodetic azimuth and the projection of that azimuth onto a grid (grid azimuth) of a given point.

Point Marker Styles

A surveyor interacts with points daily. To easily use points in the Autodesk Civil 3D software, you need to have a basic understanding of their related styles.

The Autodesk Civil 3D software provides imperial and metric template files that contain several point styles: *Autodesk Civil 3D Imperial (NCS)* and *Autodesk Civil 3D Metric (NCS)*. These templates use the National CAD standards for their layers, and provide examples of styles that you can use in a project. To customize these styles, you need to modify and expand the list of point styles.

Customizing styles needs to be managed carefully. Consult with your CAD or BIM Manager as to the standards and procedures for such customization.

When installing the Autodesk Civil 3D software, the first thing you should do is to select one of these templates as your default template. Alternatively, your CAD or BIM Manager can develop styles to be used in your organization's drawing template file.

A point style defines a point's display, its 3D elevation, and its coordinate marker size. In the example shown in Figure 2–23, the point style is an X for a ground shot.

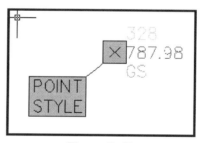

Figure 2–23

The Point Style dialog box has five tabs: *Information*, *Marker*, *3D Geometry*, *Display*, and *Summary*.

Information Tab

The *Information* tab names the style and sets the basic properties of the point style, as shown in Figure 2–24.

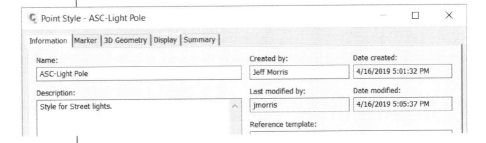

Figure 2–24

Marker Tab

The *Marker* tab supports three marker definition methods, as shown in Figure 2–25.

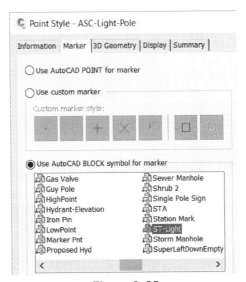

Figure 2–25

- **Use AutoCAD POINT [node] for marker:** All points in the drawing follow AutoCAD's **PDMODE** and **PDSIZE** system variables. You do not have independent control over points using this option. This option is seldom used.

- **Use custom marker:** This option creates markers similar to an AutoCAD point (node). However, the marker is controlled by the Autodesk Civil 3D software, and each point style can display a different combination of marker styles. When using this option, select the components of the style from the list of Custom marker style shapes. A custom marker can have shapes from the left and right sides. The first comes from one of the five icons on the style's left side, and you can optionally add none, one, or both shapes from the right.

- **Use AutoCAD BLOCK symbol for marker:** This option defines the marker using a block (symbol). The blocks listed represent definitions in the drawing. When the cursor is in this area and you right-click, you can browse to a location containing drawings that you want to include as point markers.

Options for scaling the marker are located in the marker panel's top right corner. The most common option is **Use drawing scale** (as shown in Figure 2–26), which takes the marker size (0.1000") and multiplies it by the current drawing's annotation scale, resulting in the final marker size. When the annotation scale changes, the Autodesk Civil 3D software automatically resizes the markers and their labels to be the appropriate size for the scale.

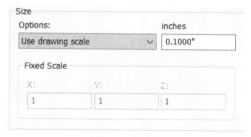

Figure 2–26

The other options are described as follows:

Use fixed scale	Specifies user-defined X, Y, and Z scale values.
Use size in absolute units	Specifies a user-defined size.
Use size relative to screen	Specifies a user-defined percentage of the screen.

3D Geometry Tab

The *3D Geometry* tab sets the point's elevation. The default option is **Use Point Elevation** (as shown in Figure 2–27), which displays the point at its actual elevation value.

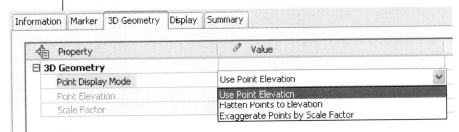

Figure 2–27

The other options are described as follows:

Flatten Points to Elevation	Specifies the elevation to which the point is projected (flattened). The Point Elevation cell highlights if this option is selected and is 0 elevation by default. When using an AutoCAD object snap to select a marker using this option, the resulting entity's elevation is the default elevation of 0. If selecting by point number or point object, the resulting entity is the point's actual elevation.
Exaggerate Points by Scale Factor	Exaggerates the point's elevation by a specified scale factor. When selecting this option, the Scale Factor cell highlights.

Display Tab

The *Display* tab assigns the marker and label layers, and sets their visibility and properties. Setting the property to **ByLayer** uses the layer's properties. Alternatively, you can override the layer properties by setting a specific color, linetype, or lineweight.

A style's View Direction value affects how the point and label components display in the plan, model, profile, and section views, as shown in Figure 2–28.

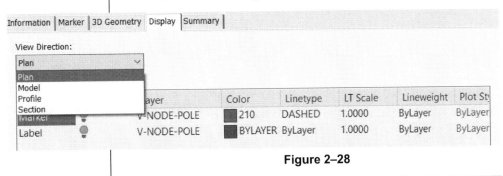

Figure 2–28

Summary Tab

The *Summary* tab is a report of all of the style's settings. Controlling a leader arrow from a label in the dragged state, points to the boundary of the marker (yes) or the center of the marker (no). It is also changed under **Marker>Leader**, and stops at marker. You can also edit style variables in this tab.

Point Label Styles

The Autodesk Civil 3D point label style annotates point properties beyond the typical point number, elevation and description. A typical point label style is shown in Figure 2–29.

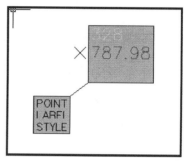

Figure 2–29

All Autodesk Civil 3D label style dialog boxes are the same. The basic behaviors for a label are in the settings in the Edit Label Style Defaults dialog box. The values in this dialog box define the label layer, text style, orientation, plan readability, size, dragged state behaviors, etc.

In the Toolspace>*Settings* tab, the drawing name and object collections control these values for the entire drawing (at the drawing name level) or for the selected collection (*Surface, Alignment, Point*, etc.) To open the Edit Label Style Defaults dialog box, select the drawing name or a heading, right-click, and select **Edit Label Style Defaults**, as shown in Figure 2–30.

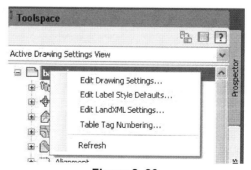

Figure 2–30

The Label Style Composer dialog box contains five tabs, each defining specific label behaviors: *Information*, *General*, *Layout*, *Dragged State*, and *Summary*.

Information Tab

The *Information* tab names the style and sets the basic properties of the label style, as shown in Figure 2–31.

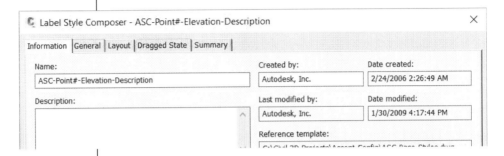

Figure 2–31

General Tab

The *General* tab contains three properties, as shown in Figure 2–32:

- *Label:* The text style and layer.

- *Behavior:* The orientation.

- *Plan Readability:* The amount of view rotation permitted before the text is flipped to read from the bottom or right side of the sheet.

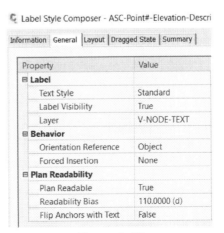

Figure 2–32

The *Label* property sets the *Text Style*, *Label Visibility*, and *Layer*. Select the *Value* cell next to the *Text Style* and *Layer* to open browsers and change their values. Selecting the *Label Visibility* cell displays a drop-down list containing the options **true** and **false**.

The *Behavior* property sets two variables that control the label's location. The *Orientation Reference* variable contains the three label orientation options.

Object	Rotates labels relative to the object's zero direction. The object's zero direction is based on its start to end vector. If the vector changes at the label's anchor point, the orientation updates automatically. This is the default setting.
View	Forces labels to realign relative to a screen-view orientation in both model and layout views. This method assumes that the zero angle is horizontal, regardless of the UCS or Dview twist. If the view changes, the label orientation updates as well. This is the recommended setting.
World Coordinate System	Labels read left to right using the WCS X-axis. Changing the view or current UCS does not affect label rotation. The label always references the world coordinate system.

Under the *Behavior* property, the **Forced Insertion** variable has three optional values that specify the label's position relative to an object. This setting only applies when the *Orientation Reference* is set to **Object**, and the objects are lines, arcs, or spline segments.

None	Maintains label position as composed relative to the object.
Top	Adjusts label position to be above an object.
Bottom	Adjusts label position to be below an object.

- **Note**: If you select **Top** or **Bottom**, the value of *Plan Readable* should set to **True**.

The *Plan Readability* property has three variables that affect how text flips when rotating a drawing view. Under the *Plan Readability* property, the *Plan Readable* variable has two options:

True	Enables text to rotate to maintain left to right readability from the bottom or right side of the drawing.
False	Does not permit text to flip. The resulting text might be upside down or read from right to left.

The *Readability Bias* variable is the amount of rotation required to flip a label to become left to right readable. The angle is measured counter-clockwise from the WCS 0 (zero) direction.

The *Flip Anchors with Text* variable has two options:

True	If the text flips, the text anchor point also flips.
False	The label flips, but maintains the original anchor point. The behavior is similar to mirroring the original text.

Layout Tab

The *Layout* tab defines the label contents, as shown in Figure 2–33. A label component is an object property that it labels. Point properties include northing, easting, raw description, etc. If User Defined properties are in use, they are also available. A label might have one component with several properties, or several components (each containing an object property) and regular text.

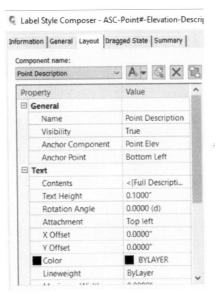

Figure 2–33

A point style label component can be text, lines, or blocks. Other object type label styles can include additional components, such as reference text, ticks, directional arrows, etc. To add a component, expand the drop-down list (shown in Figure 2–34) and select the component type.

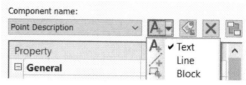

Figure 2–34

The remaining icons in the *Layout* tab are as follows:

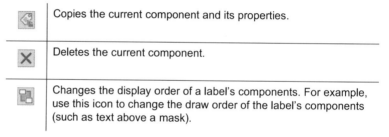	Copies the current component and its properties.
	Deletes the current component.
	Changes the display order of a label's components. For example, use this icon to change the draw order of the label's components (such as text above a mask).

Depending on the label component type, it might have any combination of three areas: **General**, **Text**, and **Border**.

- **General** defines how the label attaches to the object or other label components, its visibility, and its anchor point.

- If the label component is text, the **Text** property values affect how it displays its object property, as shown in Figure 2–35.

Figure 2–35

To set or modify a label's text value, select the cell next to *Contents* to display ⠶. Click ⠶ to open the Text Component Editor dialog box.

The Text Component Editor dialog box (shown in Figure 2–36) defines the properties that the label annotates. When creating a label component, double-click on the text in the right pane to highlight it. In the left pane, select the property that you want to add, set the property's format values, and then click ⇨ to add the new property to the label component.

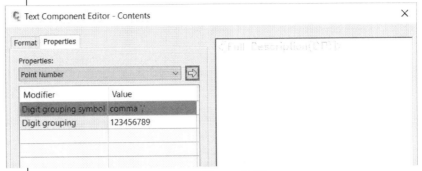

Figure 2–36

It is important to maintain the process order and to remember that the text on the right in brackets needs to be highlighted before you can revise its format values on the left, and then click ⇨ when you are ready to update it.

Dragged State Tab

The *Dragged State* tab has two properties: **Leader** and **Dragged State Components**. This tab defines how a label behaves when you are dragging a label from its original insertion point.

The *Leader* property defines whether a leader displays and what properties it displays. You can use the label's layer properties in the *General* tab (**ByLayer**) or override them by specifying a color, as shown in Figure 2–37.

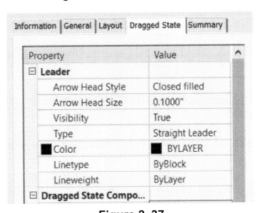

Figure 2–37

The **Dragged State Components** property defines the label component's display after it has been dragged from its original position. Select the cell next to *Display* to view the two display options, as shown in Figure 2–38.

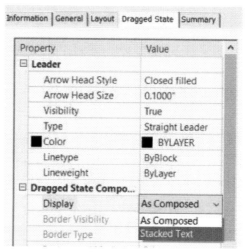

Figure 2–38

As Composed	The label maintains its original definition and orientation from the settings in the Layout panel. When you select **As Composed**, all of the other values become unavailable for editing.
Stacked Text	The label text becomes left justified and label components are stacked in the order listed in Layout's Component Name list. When you select **Stacked Text**, all of the blocks, lines, ticks, and direction arrows are removed. This is the recommended setting.

Summary Tab

The *Summary* tab lists the label component, general, and dragged state values for the label style. The label components are listed numerically in the order in which they were defined and report all of the current values.

Practice 2b

Point Marker and Label Styles

Practice Objective

- Create a point marker and label style to ensure that the correct symbol is assigned to specific points.

Task 1 - Add a block symbol.

1. Continue working on your drawing template file.

2. In the Toolspace>*Settings* tab, expand the *Point* collection until *Point Styles* displays. Expand the **Point Styles** collection.

Review the Point Styles list and note that there is no light pole style.

3. In the *Point Styles* list, select the **ASC-Guy pole** style, then right-click on it and select **Copy**.

4. In the *Information* tab, change the point style's name to **ASC-Light Pole.**

5. Select the *Marker* tab. Select the **Use AutoCAD BLOCK symbol for marker** option. In the block list, scroll across as required and select the AutoCAD block **ST-Light**, as shown in Figure 2–39.

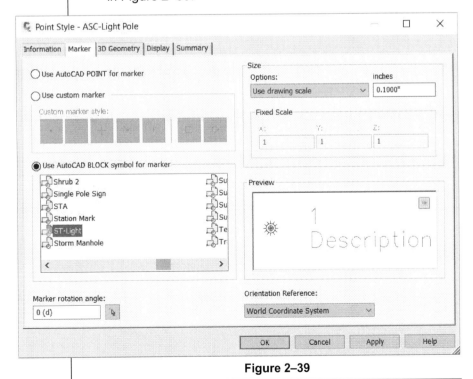

Figure 2–39

6. Select the *Display* tab and note that the layer settings are copied from the Guy Pole point style.

7. You can reassign the marker and label layer by selecting the layer name. Select the layer name to display the drawing layer list.

8. Click **New** in the top right corner of the Layer Selection dialog box. The Create Layer dialog box opens (as shown in Figure 2–40), enabling you to create new layers without having to use the Layer Manager.

9. Enter **V-NODE-POST** for the name and set the *Color* to **yellow**, as shown in Figure 2–40. Click **OK** to exit the Create Layer dialog box. Click **OK** to exit the Layer Selection dialog box.

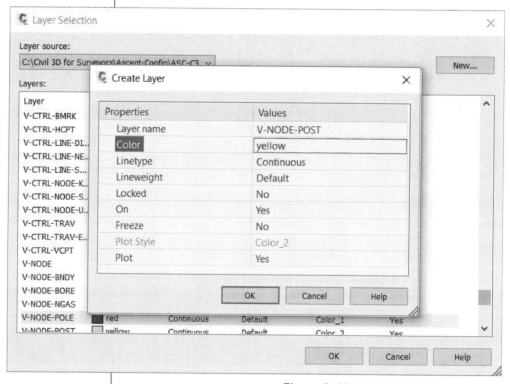

Figure 2–40

10. Click **OK** to create the point style.

11. Review the *Point Styles* list and note that **ASC-Light Pole** is now a point style, as shown in Figure 2–41. Also note that all of the other Point Styles have a paper clip icon, indicating that they are referenced from the *ASC-Survey-Styles.dwg* or the *ASC-Base-Styles.dwg*, while the style you just created is not referenced and does not have the icon.

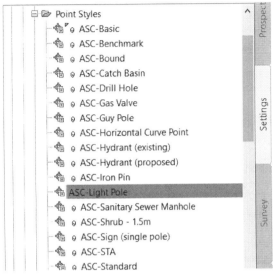

Figure 2–41

12. Save the drawing.

Task 2 - Create a point label style's components.

---

1. Continue working with the drawing template.

2. In the Toolspace>*Settings* tab, expand the **Point** collection until the *Point Label Styles* list displays.

3. In the list, select **ASC-Point#-Elevation-Description**, then right-click on it and select **Copy**.

4. In the *Information* tab, change the name to **ASC-Point#-Description-N-E**.

5. Select the *Layout* tab and set the following (as shown in Figure 2–42):

- *Component name:* **Point Number**
- *Anchor Component:* **<Feature>**
- *Anchor Point:* **Top Right**.
- *Attachment:* **Bottom left**.

These settings attach the bottom left of the label to the top right of the point object.

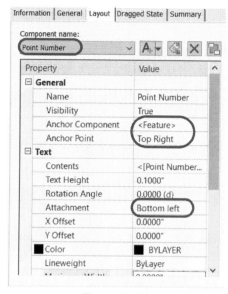

Figure 2–42

Since the elevation label is not required, you can delete it.

6. In the Component name drop-down list, select **Point Elev** and click ![X], as shown in Figure 2–43. At the *Do you want to delete it?* prompt, click **Yes**.

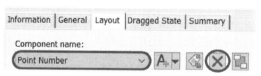

Figure 2–43

7. In the Component name drop-down list, select **Point Description**, and then set the following, as shown in Figure 2–44:
   - *Anchor Component*: **Point Number**
   - *Anchor Point*: **Bottom Left**
   - *Attachment*: **Top Left**

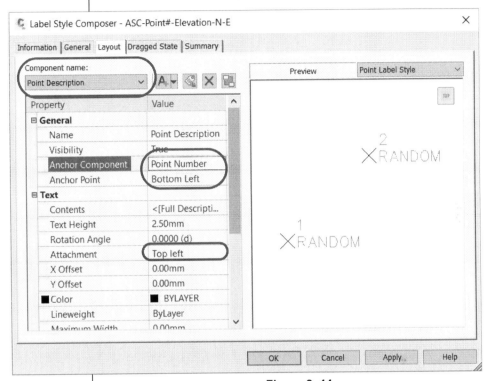

Figure 2–44

8. You will now add a new text component to display the Northing and Easting. Expand the **Create Text Component** button (shown in Figure 2–45) and select **Text** to create a text component.

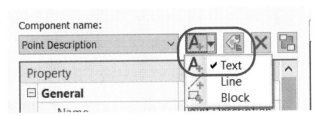

Figure 2–45

9. Change the default *Name* **text.1** to **Coordinates**, and then set the following:

   - *Anchor Component:* **Point Description**.
   - *Anchor Point:* **Bottom Left**.
   - *Attachment:* **Top Left**.

10. Next, change the contents from the default label set by the Autodesk Civil 3D software to display the coordinates. Click ⋯ in the *Contents* cell, next to *Label Text*, as shown in Figure 2–46.

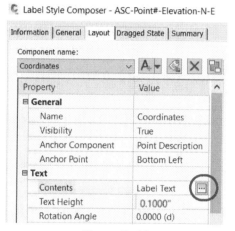

Figure 2–46

11. In the Text Component Editor dialog box, double-click on the text in the right side panel to highlight it, and then type **N:**.

12. In the Properties drop-down list, select **Northing**. Change the *Precision* to **0.001** and click ⮕ (as shown in Figure 2–47) to add the code to display the northing.

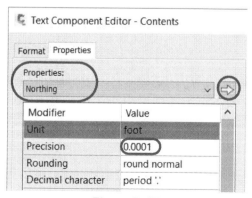

Figure 2–47

13. Click at the end of the code. Press **<Enter>** to insert a new line followed by **E:**. Then select **Easting** in the Properties drop-down list and add it to post the code in the right side panel. The following should be displayed:

    N:<[Northing(Uft|P3|RN|AP|GC|UN|Sn|OF)]>

    E:<[Easting(Uft|P4|RN|AP|GC|UN|Sn|OF)]>

14. In the easting, the value is displayed to the 4th decimal, *P4*. Change it so that it matches the northing.

15. Select all of the code for the easting. Change the *Precision* to **0.001** and click ⬆ to revise the easting code.

16. Select the *Format* tab and ensure that *Justification* is set to **Left**.

17. Click **OK** to accept the changes in the Text Component Editor dialog box, and click **OK** again to accept the changes in the Label Style Composer.

18. Save the drawing template.

2.8 Description Key Sets

Description Keys categorize points by their field descriptions (raw description). If a point matches a Description Key entry, the point is assigned a point and label style, and a full description (a translation of the raw description). Description Key Sets can also scale and rotate points. The **Description Key Sets** collection is shown in Figure 2–48.

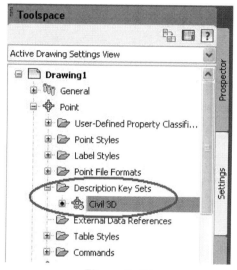

Figure 2–48

The Description Key's first five columns are the commonly used entries, as shown in Figure 2–49.

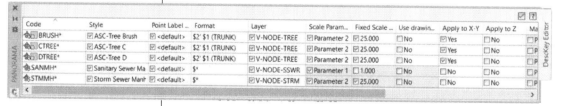

Code	Style	Point Label ...	Format	Layer	Scale Param...	Fixed Scale ...	Use drawin...	Apply to X-Y	Apply to Z	Ma
BRUSH*	☑ ASC-Tree Brush	☑ <default>	$2' $1 (TRUNK)	☑ V-NODE-TREE	☑ Parameter 2	☑ 25.000	☐ No	☑ Yes	☐ No	☐ P
CTREE*	☑ ASC-Tree C	☑ <default>	$2' $1 (TRUNK)	☑ V-NODE-TREE	☑ Parameter 2	☑ 25.000	☐ No	☑ Yes	☐ No	☐ P
DTREE*	☑ ASC-Tree D	☑ <default>	$2' $1 (TRUNK)	☑ V-NODE-TREE	☑ Parameter 2	☑ 25.000	☐ No	☑ Yes	☐ No	☐ P
SANMH*	☑ Sanitary Sewer Ma	☑ <default>	$*	☑ V-NODE-SSWR	☑ Parameter 1	☐ 1.000	☐ No	☐ No	☐ No	☐ P
STMMH*	☑ Storm Sewer Manh	☑ <default>	$*	☑ V-NODE-STRM	☑ Parameter 2	☑ 25.000	☐ No	☐ No	☐ No	☐ P

Figure 2–49

- To create a new Description Key row, select an existing code, right-click, and select **New**.

- To edit a Description Key code, double-click in the cell.

Code, Point, and Label Style

Description code is a significant part of data collection. Code assigned to a raw description triggers action by the Description Key Set. Each entry in the set represents all of the possible descriptions that a field crew would use while surveying a job. When a raw description matches a code entry, the Key Set assigns all of the row's values to the matching point (including point style and label style), translates the raw description, and possibly assigns a layer. Codes are case-sensitive and must match the field collector's entered raw description.

A code might contain wildcards to match raw descriptions that contain numbering or additional material beyond the point's description. For example, MH* would match MH1, MH2, etc. and UP* would match UP 2245 14.4Kv ACME. Common wild keys are described as follows:

# (pound)	Matches any single numeric digit. • Example: T# matches T1 through T9
@ (at)	Matches any alphabetic character. • Example: 1@ matches 1A through 1Z
. (period)	Matches any non-alphanumeric character. • Example: T. matches T- or T+
* (asterisk)	Matches any string of characters. • Example: T* matches TREE, TR-Aspen, Topo, or Trench
? (question mark)	Matches any single character. • Example: ?BC matches TBC or 3BC

Matching a Key Set entry for the code assigns a Point Style at the point's coordinates. If the *Point Style* is set to **Default**, the *Settings* tab's Point feature *Point Style* is used (set in the Edit Feature Settings dialog box), as shown in Figure 2–50.

Matching a Key Set entry also assigns a point label style to annotate important point values. This is usually a number, elevation, and description. If the *Point Label Style* is set to **Default**, the *Settings* tab's Point feature *Point Label Style* is used (set in the Edit Feature Settings dialog box), as shown in Figure 2–50.

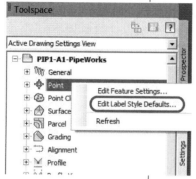 

Figure 2–50

Format

The *Format* column translates the raw description (what the surveyor typed) into a full description (what you want it to read). When including spaces in a raw description, the Autodesk Civil 3D software assigns parameter numbers to each description element.

Parameters are represented by a $ sign, followed by a number. For example, the description *PINE 6* has two elements: PINE and 6, with PINE as parameter 0 ($0) and 6 as parameter 1 ($1).

When the *Format* column contains $*, it indicates that the software should use the raw description as the full description. The *Format* column can reorder the parameters and add characters to create a full description. For example, the raw description *PINE 6* can be translated to 6' PINE by entering **$1' $0**.

A complex raw description is as follows:

CTREE PINE 3.4

For the raw description to match the Description Key Set entry, the entry **CTREE** must have an asterisk (*) after CTREE (as shown in Figure 2–51). The raw description elements and their parameters are CTREE ($0), PINE ($1), and 3.4 ($2). The *Format* column entry of **$2' $1 (TRUNK)** creates a full description of **3.4' PINE (TRUNK)**

CTREE is used to differentiate between deciduous (DTREE) and coniferous (CTREE) trees. This way different point styles can be assigned.

(TRUNK) designates that the value corresponds to the trunk diameter, as opposed to the drip line of the tree.

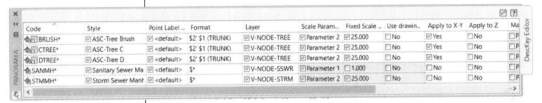

Figure 2–51

If a point does not match any Description Key Set entry, it receives the default styles assigned by the **_All Points** group.

The *Layer* column assigns a layer to the matching point. If the Point Style already has a marker and label layer, this entry should be toggled off. The Description Key Set also contains the *Scale* and *Rotate Parameter* columns. In the example shown in Figure 2–51, the **3** for the trunk diameter can also be a tree symbol scaling factor when applied to the symbol's X-Y.

Practice 2c

Creating a Description Key Set

Practice Objective

- Assign point symbols, labels, layers, etc., on importing by setting up Description Key Sets.

In this practice, you will learn to create a new Description Key Set entry and apply it to an existing point. In addition, you will update the Description Key Set to use parameters.

Task 1 - Create a new Description Key Set entry.

1. Continue working with the drawing template from the previous practice.

2. In the Toolspace>*Settings* tab, expand the **Point** collection until the **Description Key Sets** collection and its list display.

3. Right-click on **Description Key Sets** and select **New**. Enter **XXX-Training** as the name (substituting your initials for XXX), and then click **OK** to accept and close the dialog box.

4. Select **XXX-Training**, then right-click, and select **Edit Keys**.

5. Right-click in any *Code* cell and select **New**, as shown in Figure 2–52.

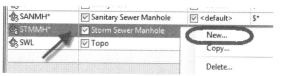

Figure 2–52

6. Double-click in the *Code* cell in the newly created row and type **HYD**, as shown in Figure 2–53.

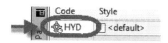

Figure 2–53

There are different point styles for existing and proposed hydrants. The insertion point of proposed hydrants is the center of the hydrant symbol.

7. In the *Style* cell, toggle on the Point Style and select the **Style** cell to open the Point Style dialog box, as shown in Figure 2–54. In the drop-down list, select **ASC-Hydrant (existing)** and click **OK** to assign the style to the code.

Figure 2–54

8. Make the following changes to the **HYD** description key, as shown in Figure 2–55:

- *Point Label Style*: **ASC-Description Only**
- *Format*: **$*** (This means the label will be the same as the one entered by the surveyor.)
- *Layer*: Uncheck checkbox
- *Use drawing scale*: **Yes**
- *Scale Parameter*: Uncheck checkbox

9. Right-click in any *Code* cell and select **New**.

10. Double-click in the *Code* cell in the newly created row and type **CTREE*** (ensuring that you include the asterisk).

11. In the *Style* cell, toggle on the Point Style and select the **Style** cell to open the Point Style dialog box. Select **ASC-TREE C** in the drop-down list and click **OK** to assign the style to the code, also as shown in Figure 2–55

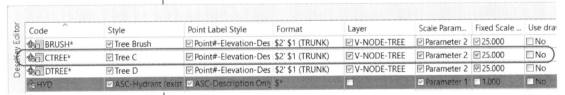

Figure 2–55

12. If need be, set the Point Label to *<default>*.

13. Set the *Format* to **$2' $1 (TRUNK)**.

14. For *Fixed Scale*, click in the checkbox to enable it, then type **25** for the scale value. This will scale the point style by 25.

15. For *Layer*, click in the checkbox to enable it, then select **V-NODE-TREE**.

16. For *Apply to X-Y*, click in the checkbox to enable it. This enables the *Scale Parameter* drop-down list in the next step.

*If the Scale Parameter list is not functional, ensure that you have **Apply to X-Y** checked.*

17. For *Scale Parameter*, click in the checkbox to enable it, then select **Parameter 2** from the drop-down list. This will scale the point style by the value in Parameter 2 ($2), and then by 25.

18. Select the *CTREE* code, then right-click on it and select **Copy**.

19. Rename the copied code to *DTREE* and select **ASC-Tree D** as the Point Style. Everything else remains the same.

20. Select the *DTREE* code you created, then right-click on it and select **Copy**

21. Rename the copied code to *BRUSH* and select **ASC-Tree Brush** as the Point Style. Everything else remains the same.

22. Click the green checkmark in the top right corner to close the Panorama.

23. Save the drawing template.

Task 2 - Set the default template for Autodesk Civil 3D.

Now that most of the settings have been established for the customized drawing template, you will set it as the default template when starting a new drawing from the *Start* Tab or from the *Quick Access Toolbar*>**QNew** command, shown in Figure 2–56.

Figure 2–56

1. Start the **Options** command using one of four ways:
   - Right-click on the command line.
   - Right-click in the drawing window.
   - Type **Options** in the command line.
   - In the Application drop-down menu, click **Options**.

2. In the *Options* dialog box, in the *Files* tab, go to **Template Settings>Default Template File Name for QNEW** and click **Browse**, as shown in Figure 2–57.

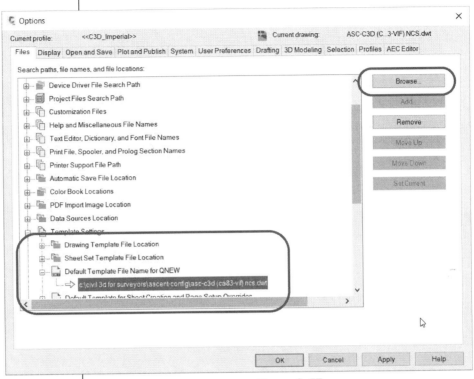

Figure 2–57

3. Browse to the *C:\Civil 3D for Surveyors\Ascent-Config* folder and select your template.

4. Click **Open** to select the file, then click **OK** to exit the *Options* dialog box.

5. Close the drawing template. If prompted, save the file.

2.9 The Survey Database

The Survey forking folder is the location for all of the Survey Databases and can be local or on the network. The preferred location is a network folder, in which you place the local Survey Databases. The Survey User Settings dialog box sets the defaults for all new Survey Databases. It is recommended to set them before starting Survey.

How To: Set the Working Folder for the Survey Database

1. In the *Survey* tab, select **Survey Databases**.
2. Right-click and select **Set working folder**, as shown in Figure 2–58.

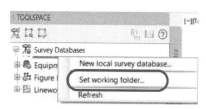

Figure 2–58

Survey Database

Survey Database folders cannot be deleted in the Autodesk Civil 3D Survey software. If you want to delete the working folder, it must be done through the Windows File Explorer.

A Survey Database is a subfolder in the working folder, as shown on the right in Figure 2–59. The Survey Working Folder contains the survey settings and the observation database. The database contains the survey's networks, figures, and survey points.

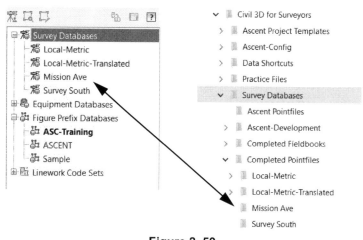

Figure 2–59

Each local Survey Database references files to perform some of its tasks.

- The Equipment database is an *.EDB file. The Equipment settings file contains values to estimate errors for the least squares adjustment process.

- The Figure Prefix database is an *. FDB file. The Figure Prefix database lists definitions for Survey figures (figure style and layers). The default location for these files is *C:\ProgramData\Autodesk\C3D 2021\enu\Survey.*

Survey has four nodes: **Import Events**, **Networks**, **Figures**, and **Survey Points**. **Import Events** is where files are imported into the survey's networks. The files can be a coordinate, field book, LandXML file, and points from a drawing. When importing a file, depending on its contents, the import results in figures and points. Information in the file also populates portions of survey's Network. When importing a coordinate or field book file containing only coordinates, the Figures and Survey Points nodes are used. When processing a file with observations, turned angles, zenith angles, slope distances, and setups, you use the network and its nodes.

> **Hint: Survey Database Migration to 2020 or 2021**
>
> The Survey Database format has changed as of the Autodesk Civil 3D 2020 software release. If you have existing Survey Databases that were created in an earlier format, they are marked and must be migrated, Right-click on the Survey Database and select **Migrate**. Select a new location for the updated Survey Database, as shown in Figure 2–60.
>
>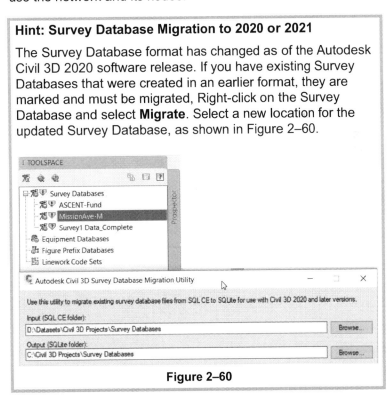
>
> **Figure 2–60**

How To: Migrate a Survey Database

When the Survey Database has a yellow alert icon, it must be migrated.

1. Right-click on the Survey Database and select **Migrate**, as shown in Figure 2–61

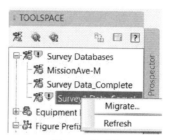

Figure 2–61

The Input and Output folders can be the same. However, it is recommended that you select a different folder to keep the original survey databases for archival purposes.

2. Click **Browse** to select the folder of the existing survey databases (Input), and the destination folder for where you want the migrated survey databases to reside (Output), as shown in Figure 2–62.

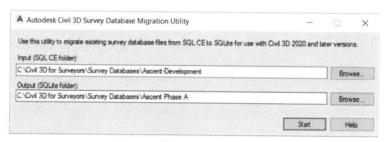

Figure 2–62

3. When the process is complete, a status window displays the results, as shown in Figure 2–63. Unsuccessful migrations are due to being too old (e.g., from AutoCAD Civil 3D 2012) or the databases have already been upgraded to the new version.

Figure 2–63

Survey Equipment Database

The Survey Equipment Database is used to define different Total Stations and their specific settings. However, these settings are not considered when importing data, because the actual equipment has already made the necessary adjustments when it generated the output files. The equipment database and its settings are only used when performing a traverse analysis in the Autodesk Civil 3D software, such as a least squares adjustment.

Within each Survey Equipment Database entry resides definitions specific to the values associated with a surveying instrument, such as the standard deviations associated with the measuring capabilities.

How To: Create an Equipment Database

1. In the *Home* tab>Palettes panel, click  (Survey Toolspace) to display the *Survey* tab, as shown in Figure 2–64.

Figure 2–64

2. In the Toolspace, select the *Survey* tab.
3. Right-click on **Equipment Database** and select **New**, as shown in Figure 2–65. Enter an equipment database name, then click **OK** to accept and close the dialog box.

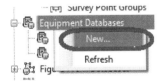

Figure 2–65

4. To open the Equipment Properties dialog box, select the equipment database, right-click, and select **Manage Equipment database**.
5. Review the settings. When done, click **OK** to close the dialog box.

6. By default, the Autodesk Civil 3D software saves the equipment database files in the *C:\ProgramData\Autodesk\ C3D 2021\enu\Survey* folder, as shown in Figure 2–66.

   • To change the path to a network drive, click 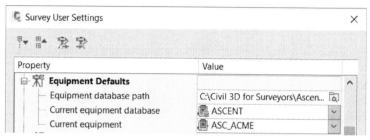 (Survey User Setting), scroll down to *Equipment Defaults*, and browse for a new path.

Figure 2–66

7. Review the settings. When done, click **OK** to close the dialog box.

How To: Create a Survey Database Using the Import Survey Data Command

1. In the *Home* tab>Create Ground Data panel, click 💬 (Import Survey Data).
2. In the Import Survey Data dialog box, click **Create New Survey Database**. Enter a name and click **OK**.
3. In the Import Survey Data dialog box, select the new survey database and click **Edit Survey Database Settings**.
4. In the dialog box, under *Units*, for the *Coordinate Zone*, click ⋯ and select a coordinate system, as shown in Figure 2–67. Click **OK**.

Note that the survey can be done in any coordinate system, even if it does not match the project coordinate system. The Autodesk Civil 3D software converts the coordinates and units in the drawing.

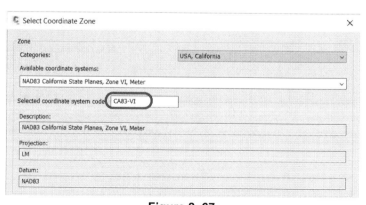

Figure 2–67

5. Set the *Direction*, *Temperature*, *Pressure*, and other settings, as shown in Figure 2–68. When done, click **OK** to close the dialog box.

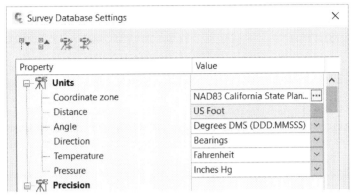

Figure 2–68

6. In the Import Survey Data dialog box, click **Next**.
7. Select the Data source type and browse for the file. Then click **Next**.
   - If the Data source type is set to **Point File**, specify the file format.
   - If the Data source type is set to **Points From Drawing**, click **Select points in current drawing**. Then, draw a selection window around the appropriate points and press <Enter>.
8. If a control network is required, click **Create New Network**. Then click **Next**.
   - If a control network in not required, just click **Next**.
9. Set the appropriate *Import Options* and click **Finish**.

How To: Create a Survey Database Without Importing Data at the Same Time

1. In the *Home* tab>Palettes panel, click 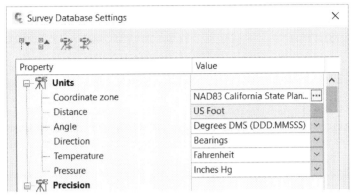 (Survey Toolspace) to display the *Survey* tab.
2. In the Toolspace, select the *Survey* tab.
3. Right-click on **Survey Databases** and select **New local survey database**.
4. Enter a name for the new database and click **OK**.

Open a Survey Database for Editing

Only one Survey Database can be opened at a time. When opened for editing, it prepares the survey for reading and writing. There are options to set the path or location for the Survey Database project files, as well as all of the settings.

- When you create a new Survey Database, a Windows folder is created with the same name.

- If you close a drawing with a survey open, the Survey Database closes automatically. You must start a new drawing or open en existing drawing, and then open the required Survey Database.

How To: Open a Survey Database

Double-clicking on the name of the survey database opens it as read-only.

1. Expand the **Survey Database** branch.
2. Select the survey database that you want to open, right-click and select **Open for edit** or **Open for read-only**, depending on your requirements, as shown in Figure 2–69.

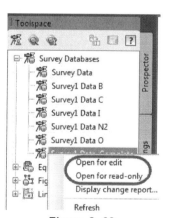

Figure 2–69

Practice 2d

Create a Survey Database

Practice Objectives

- Create three entries for the equipment database.
- Create two survey databases in preparation for importing survey data, one for metric data and one for imperial data.

Task 1 - Create an equipment database.

1. Start a new drawing. The Autodesk Civil 3D software will invoke your default drawing template. Since you will not be adding anything to the drawing, it does not matter which template you use.

2. If the Survey Toolspace is not displayed, in the *Home* tab> Palettes panel, click 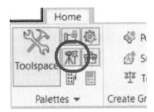 (Survey Toolspace), as shown in Figure 2–70.

Figure 2–70

3. In the Toolspace, select the *Survey* tab.

4. To create an equipment database, right-click on **Equipment Database** and select **New**, as shown in Figure 2–71.

   - For the equipment database name, type **XXX-Equip** (substituting your initials for XXX), as shown in Figure 2–72.
   - Click **OK** to accept and close the dialog box.

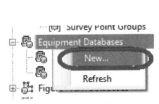

Figure 2–71

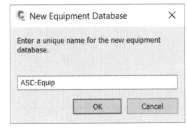

Figure 2–72

5. To open the Equipment Properties dialog box, select **XXX-Equip**, right-click, and select **Manage Equipment database**.

6. For the name, enter **XXX-ACME-M** (substituting your initials for XXX).

7. Ensure the unit for *Distance* is set to **Meter**, as shown in Figure 2–73.

8. Review the other settings.

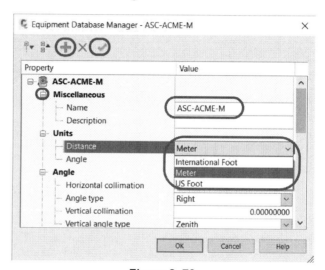

Figure 2–73

9. Click the ⊟ (minus sign) next to the **XXX-ACME-M** to collapse the branch.

10. Click the green plus (✚) to add a new set of equipment.

11. For the name, enter **XXX-ACME-USF** (substituting your initials for XXX).

12. Ensure the unit for *Distance* is set to **US Foot**.

13. Repeat Steps 10 to 12. For the name, enter **XXX-ACME-IF** (substituting your initials for XXX).

14. Ensure the unit for *Distance* is set to **International Foot**.

15. Collapse all three branches, then select **XXX-ACME-USF** and click the green checkmark (✓) to make it current.

16. When done, click **OK** to close the dialog box.

Task 2 - Create the Metric Survey Database.

1. In the *Survey* tab, right-click on **Survey Databases**, and select **Set working folder**, as shown in Figure 2–74.

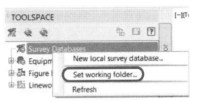

Figure 2–74

2. Browse to and select the *C:\Civil 3D for Surveyors\Survey Databases\Ascent-Development* folder. Click **Select Folder**.

3. In the Toolspace>*Survey* tab, right-click on **Survey Databases** and select **New local survey database**.

4. Set the *Name* to **Ascent Data-M** and click **OK**.

5. Right-click on the **Ascent Data-M** database and select **Edit Survey Database Settings**.

6. In the dialog box, under *Units*, for the *Coordinate Zone*, click

   ⬛ and select **NAD83 California State Planes, Zone VI, Meter**, as shown in Figure 2–75, and click **OK**.

Note that although some of the survey was done in CA83-VI and your drawings are in CA83-VIF, you can import the survey data to any coordinate system or units and the Autodesk Civil 3D software converts the coordinates and units in the drawing.

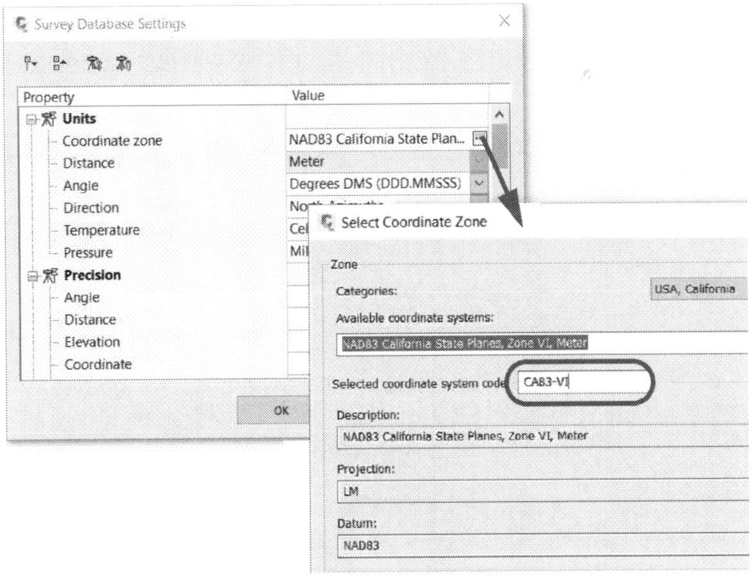

Figure 2–75

7. Set the following, as shown in Figure 2–76:
   - *Direction*: **North Azimuths**
   - *Temperature:* **Celsius**
   - *Pressure:* **Millimeters Hg**

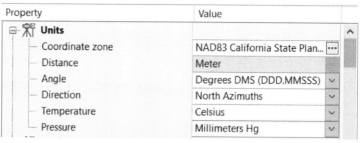

Property	Value
⊟ 🛱 **Units**	
Coordinate zone	NAD83 California State Plan... ⋯
Distance	Meter
Angle	Degrees DMS (DDD.MMSSS) ⌄
Direction	North Azimuths ⌄
Temperature	Celsius ⌄
Pressure	Millimeters Hg ⌄

Figure 2–76

8. When done, click **OK** to close the dialog box.

Task 3 - Create the Imperial Survey Database.

1. In the Toolspace>*Survey* tab, right-click on **Survey Databases** and select **New local survey database**.

2. Set the *Name* to **Ascent Data-USF** and click **OK**.

3. Right-click on the **Ascent Data-USF** database and select **Edit Survey Database Settings**.

4. In the dialog box, under *Units*, for the *Coordinate zone*, click ⬚ and select **NAD83 California State Planes, Zone VI, US Foot**, as shown in Figure 2–77, and click **OK**.

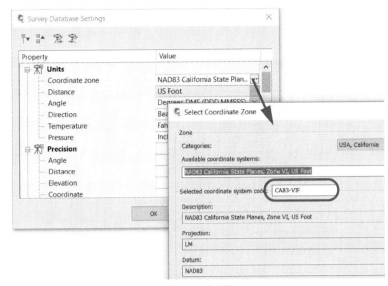

Figure 2–77

5. Verify that the following are set, as shown in Figure 2–78:
   - *Direction*: **Bearings**
   - *Temperature:* **Fahrenheit**
   - *Pressure:* **Inches Hg**

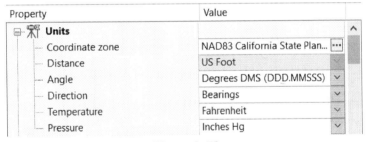

Figure 2–78

6. When done, click **OK** to close the dialog box.

7. Close the drawing. Note that no changes were made in the drawing, so there is no need to save it. The changes were made to the *Survey User Settings*.

Chapter Review Questions

1. What is the biggest difference between using a field book file and point file with connective codes for importing survey data? (Select all that apply.)

   a. There is no difference and they can be used interchangeably.

   b. When using a field book file, in the field, the connective code is added as a note which is separate from the point description. When using a point file with connective codes, the connective codes are entered in the same line as the point description.

   c. A field book file must be post processed where as a point file with connective codes can be directly imported.

   d. A point file with connective codes contains all of the data that was used during the survey field pickup by a total station (e.g., setups, back-sites, instrument height, prism height, turned angles, side shots, etc.)

2. What is the Figure Prefix Database used for? (Select all that apply.)

   a. To assign a layer to a figure.

   b. To add symbols to the drawing according to the point description.

   c. To determine whether a figure become a break line.

   d. To determine whether a figure becomes a lot line.

3. Which tab in the Point Label Style Composer dialog box controls the appearance of a point label when the point label grip is selected in the drawing and moved away from the point itself?

   a. *General* tab

   b. *Layout* tab

   c. *Dragged State* tab

   d. *Summary* tab

4. The survey database coordinate system must match the drawing coordinate system.

   a. True

   b. False

5. What is the purpose of the Equipment database?

   a. To ensure the imported survey data is adjusted correctly according to the Equipment database.

   b. To enable you to adjust imported survey data manually.

   c. It is used when performing a least squares adjustment of the survey data.

   d. It is used when performing using the Crandall Rule for adjustments to the survey data.

Command Summary

Button	Command	Location
	Bearing Distance	• **Toolbar:** Transparent Commands • **Command Prompt:** 'bd
	Coordinate Geometry Editor	• **Command Prompt:** CogoEditor
	Create Curve from End of Object	• **Ribbon:** *Home* tab>Draw panel • **Command Prompt:** CurveFromEndOfObject
	Create Reverse or Compound Curve	• **Ribbon:** *Home* tab>Draw panel • **Command Prompt:** ReverseOrCompound
	Survey Toolspace	• **Ribbon**: *Home* tab>Palettes panel
	Survey User Settings	• **Toolspace**: *Survey* tab

Entering Linework

Every good survey begins with research of the property to be developed before ever stepping foot on the property. Evidence plays a key role in determining where the true boundary lies. This evidence can be found in deeds, contracts, maps, wills, and other legal documents. In this chapter, you will learn how to prepare the model for importing survey data by creating a figure database and figure styles. Next, you will learn how to successfully create a new survey database for storing survey data and to create linework from a legal description of a property.

Accuracy is one of the most important factors of a land survey. Inaccuracies can eventually lead to legal issues. For that reason, it is important to reduce closure errors in a traverse. In this chapter, you will learn how to create a traverse and analyze and adjust it to find closure errors.

Learning Objectives in This Chapter

- List the steps in a typical survey workflow that are going to be used to create linework from coordinate files.
- Display the Survey Toolspace and content that is listed under each of its trees.
- Draw parcels from a legal description.
- Create a traverse by entering data manually.
- Find the error of closure by running a traverse adjustment.

3.1 Survey Workflow Overview

The three distinctive phases of a survey workflow are as follows:

- Phase 1: Prepare for survey data
- Phase 2: Obtain and create survey data
- Phase 3: Adjust, analyze, and output survey data

These phases are shown in Figure 3–1. This chapter focuses on Phase 2 and Phase 3

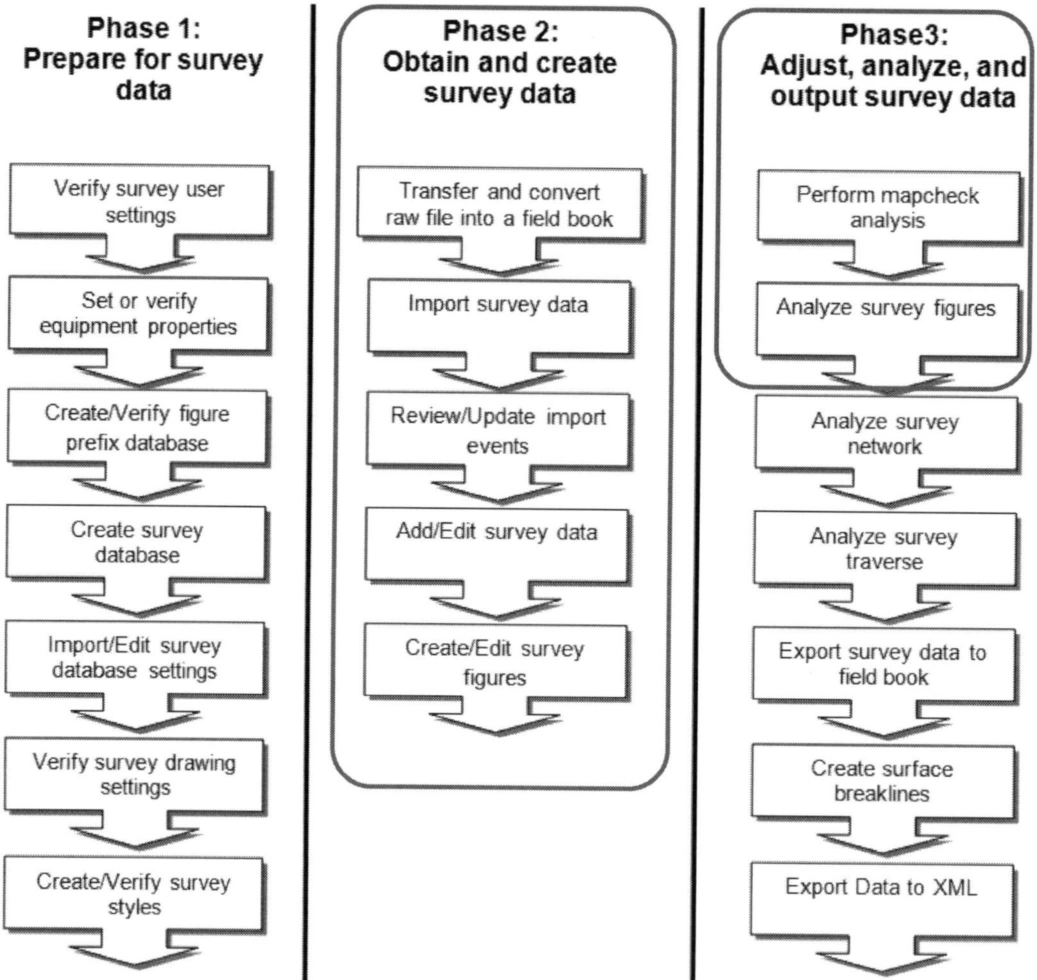

Phase 1:
Prepare for survey data

- Verify survey user settings
- Set or verify equipment properties
- Create/Verify figure prefix database
- Create survey database
- Import/Edit survey database settings
- Verify survey drawing settings
- Create/Verify survey styles

Phase 2:
Obtain and create survey data

- Transfer and convert raw file into a field book
- Import survey data
- Review/Update import events
- Add/Edit survey data
- Create/Edit survey figures

Phase3:
Adjust, analyze, and output survey data

- Perform mapcheck analysis
- Analyze survey figures
- Analyze survey network
- Analyze survey traverse
- Export survey data to field book
- Create surface breaklines
- Export Data to XML

Figure 3–1

3.2 Lines and Curves

Often, the first thing that has to be created is the legal description of the property being developed. Designers need to enter into the computer, in the form of lines and curves, what they are given in a text description. The Autodesk Civil 3D software makes this task easy with the many options under the **Lines** and **Curves** commands in the *Home* tab>Draw panel. Expanding the lines or curves commands displays several new options that are not found in the AutoCAD® software, as shown in Figure 3–2.

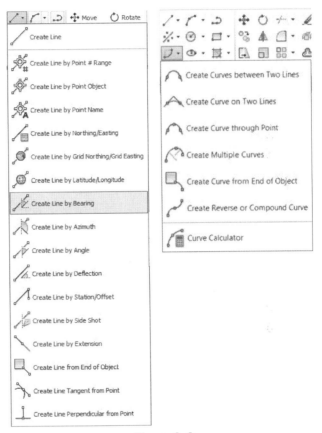

Figure 3–2

A second option is to use transparent commands. These are similar to Object Snaps because they can only be accessed while in another drawing command (when the AutoCAD or Autodesk Civil 3D software is searching for a point). Once the required command has been started, you can click the **Transparent** tool or type an apostrophe letter combination in the Command Line for the required **Transparent** command.

These commands are available in the ribbon in the *Transparent* tab, shown in Figure 3–3. The commands are extremely helpful when you need to stay within a specific right-of-way and you have the legal description of that right-of-way.

Figure 3–3

These Transparent commands are also available in a toolbar, shown in Figure 3–4.

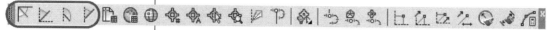

Figure 3–4

They are also available through the right-click menu when the AutoCAD or Autodesk Civil 3D software is searching for a point, as shown in Figure 3–5.

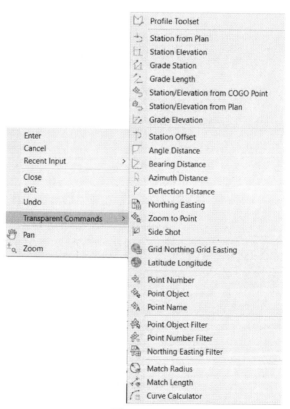

Figure 3–5

The benefit to using these to draw parcels over the **Lines** and **Curves** options (shown previously in Figure 3–2) is that a **Polyline** command can be used to create one entity rather than many individual lines that would need to be joined later.

Transparent Commands

Icon	Command Line	Description
	'AD	Angle Distance: Specifies a point location at an angle and distance from a known point and direction.
	'BD	Bearing Distance: Specifies a point location at a bearing and distance from a known point (or the last point occupied).
	'ZD	Azimuth Distance: Specifies a point location at an azimuth and distance from a known point (or the last point occupied).
	'DD	Deflection Distance: Specifies a point location at an angle and distance from a known point and previous direction.
	'NE	Northing Easting: Specifies a point location using northing and easting coordinates.
	'GN	Grid Northing Grid Easting: Specifies a point location using a grid northing and grid easting. (Note: You must have the drawing zone, coordinate system, and transformations set for grids.)
	'LL	Latitude Longitude: Specifies a point location using latitude and longitude. (Note: You must have the drawing zone, coordinate system, and transformations set.)
	'PN	Point Number: Specifies a point location using a point number found in the drawing or active project.
	'PA	Point Name: Specifies a point location using a point name found in the drawing or active project.
	'PO	Point Object: Specifies a point location by picking any part of an existing COGO point in the drawing.
	'ZTP	Zoom to Point: Zooms to a point in the drawing or active project by specifying the point number or name.
	'SS	Side Shot: Specifies a point location at an angle and distance from a known point and direction (uses the last two entered points to set the reference line).

	'SO	Station Offset: Specifies a point location at a station and an offset from an alignment in the current drawing.
	.g	Point Object Filter: Specifies a point location by picking any part of an existing COGO point in the drawing.
	'STAE	Profile Station from Plan: Specifies a profile view point location by specifying an alignment station in plan and an elevation.
	'SSE	Profile Station and Elevation from Plan: Specifies a profile view point location by specifying a surface, an alignment station, and a point in plan view.
	'SPE	Profile Station and Elevation from COGO Point: Specifies a profile view point location by specifying a COGO point and an alignment station in plan view.
	'PSE	Profile Station Elevation: Specifies a profile view point location by specifying a station and an elevation.
	'PGS	Profile Grade Station: Specifies a profile view point location using grade and station values from a known point.
	'PGE	Profile Grade Elevation: Specifies a profile view point location using grade and elevation values from a known point.
	'PGL	Profile Grade Length: Specifies a profile view point location using grade and length values from a known point (or the last point occupied).
	'MR	Match Radius: Specifies a radius equal to that of an existing object.
	'ML	Match Length: Specifies a length equal to that of an existing object.
	'CCALC	Curve Calculator: Calculates curve parameters based on input.

Practice 3a

Input the Project Boundary

Practice Objective

- Draw the property boundary to the model using Transparent commands.

In this practice, you will use the legal description below to draw a parcel. Later you will create a traverse from the linework.

From the **POINT OF BEGINNING**; thence, S 00° 26' 42.2" W for a distance of 922.4138 feet to a point on a line. Thence, S 00° 24' 20.8" W for a distance of 508.3493 feet to a point on a line. Thence, S 66° 03' 35.8" W for a distance of 92.1845 feet to the beginning of a curve.

Said curve turning to the right through 42° 35' 49.2", having a radius of 627.1788 feet, and whose long chord bears S 87° 21' 30.4" W for a distance of 455.6165 feet to the beginning of another curve.

Said curve turning to the left through an angle of 19° 13' 40.4", having a radius of 154.4828 feet, and whose long chord bears N 80° 57' 25.2" W for a distance of 51.6000 feet.

Thence, S 89° 25' 44.6" W for a distance of 724.9442 feet to a point on a line. Thence, N 00° 11' 09.9" E for a distance of 1904.2647 feet to a point on a line. Thence, S 61° 50' 15.3" E for a distance of 135.9034 feet to a point on a line. Thence, S 64° 05' 35.8" E for a distance of 77.8201 feet to a point on a line. Thence, S 78° 09' 29.2" E for a distance of 63.8821 feet to a point on a line. Thence, S 66° 23' 19.5" E for a distance of 379.2248 feet to a point on a line. Thence, S 66° 17' 17.4" E for a distance of 278.5122 feet to a point on a line. Thence S 84° 58' 37.7" E a distance of 466.8116 feet to the **POINT OF BEGINNING.**

1. Open **Boundary-A1.dwg** from the *C:\Civil 3D for Surveyors\Working\Survey* folder. For convenience, the boundary outline has already been drawn on a locked, faded layer (C-PROP-TEMP), which is frozen. You will redraw the boundary on layer 0 with the aid of the following instructions. If you get lost or need assurance, you can thaw the C-PROP-TEMP layer to check yourself.

2. In effect, you will be tracing over the green perimeter in the drawing, using the legal information provided, as shown in Figure 3–6.

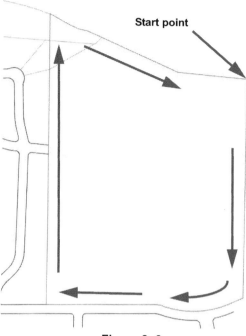

Figure 3–6

3. Start the **Line** command. For the starting point, type **6257490.0191,2037127.1292**, and press <Enter>.

4. In the Transparent toolbar, click (Bearing Distance).

The legal description at the beginning of the practice is used to find the bearings and distances to type.

5. For the first line, do the following:
   - Type **3** for the southwest quadrant and press <Enter>.
   - Type **0.26422** for the bearing and press <Enter>.
   - Type **922.4138** for the distance and press <Enter>.

6. Stay in the **Line** command with the **Bearing Distance Transparent** command running for the next few lines.
   - For the next two line segments, use the following values:

Quadrant	Bearing	Distance
3	0.24208	508.3493
3	66.03358	92.1845

7. Press <Esc> twice to end the command.

8. In the *Home* tab>Draw panel, click (Create Curve from End of Object). Then do the following:
   - Select the last line that was drawn using the **Bearing Distance** command.
   - Select **Radius** from the command options.
   - Set the *radius* to **627.1788**.
   - Select **Chord** from the command options.
   - Set the *chord length* to **455.6165**.

9. In the *Home* tab>Draw panel, click (Create Reverse or Compound Curve) and do the following:
   - Select the last curve drawn.
   - Select **Reverse** from the command options.
   - Set the *radius* to **154.4828**.
   - Select **Chord** from the command options.
   - Set the *chord length* to **51.6**.

10. Start the **Line** command. For the starting point, pick the endpoint of the last arc drawn. Then do the following:

    - In the Transparent toolbar, click (Bearing Distance).
    - For the remaining line segments, use the following values:

Quadrant	Bearing	Distance
3	89.25446	724.9442
1	0.11099	1904.2647
2	61.50153	135.9034
2	64.05358	77.8201
2	78.09292	63.8821
2	66.23195	379.2248
2	66.17174	278.5122

11. Press <Esc> once to exit the **Bearing Distance** command. Hold <Ctrl> as you right-click and select **Endpoint**, select the starting point of the parcel to close on the point of beginning.

This prevents closure errors from occurring later.

12. Start the **Polyline Edit** command by typing **PE** and pressing <Enter>. In the model, select one of the lines or curves you just created and at the prompt *Do you want to turn it into one?,* press <Enter> for **Yes** to turn it into a polyline.

13. Select the **Join** option and then select all of the lines and curves you just created. Press <Enter> to create one closed polyline. Press <Esc> to end the command.

14. Save the drawing.

3.3 Online Maps Service

If a drawing template is already set up with a coordinate zone, the Geolocation tab displays when using that template.

Once a coordinate zone is assigned to a drawing, a new *Geolocation* tab is available in the ribbon, as shown in Figure 3–7.

Figure 3–7

This service is only available if you have an Autodesk account and you are signed in. To sign in, go to the upper right area of the Autodesk Civil 3D software, as shown in Figure 3–8.

Figure 3–8

The online maps are geolocated, meaning that they have coordinates that define their precise location on the Earth. Since the Autodesk Civil 3D drawing is set up with a coordinate zone, drawing's precise location is also defined. The Online Map Service can access maps in various styles and dynamically reference them into your drawing. These maps have the following characteristics:

- The map is temporary (though there are options that enable you to capture a map).

- The map displays behind all other objects in the drawing, so that you do not need to change display orders.

- The map covers a large area, expanding to the extents of the coordinate zone assigned to the drawing.

- Since the map is temporary, you cannot plot the map.

The first time you access the online maps, you are greeted with a splash screen outlining the service details and a link to the **Terms of Service**. In order to use this service, you need to accept these terms. First, select **Remember my choice**, then click **Yes**, as shown in Figure 3–9.

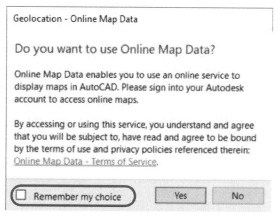

Figure 3–9

- **Hint:** If you have captured an online map (next topic), you do not need to use Online Map Data. Therefore, you can select **Remember my choice** and answer **No** to the above question.

- If you need to see this message again, restore the splash screen in the Options dialog box>*Systems* tab by changing the **Hidden Messages** setting.

Map Styles

In the *Online Map* panel>Map drop-down list, there are four choices for map styles, as shown in Figure 3–10.

Figure 3–10

- **Map Aerial**: Displays the map as a satellite image.

- **Map Road**: Displays the map as a vector image, similar to road maps.

- **Map Hybrid:** Displays the Map as a satellite image with the vector data draped over.

- **Map Off:** Displays no map.

If the maps are displayed in multiple viewports, then each viewport can use a different map style.

Capture Online Maps

Online maps are only temporary by default, which means that they do not remain with the drawing when it is reopened, and cannot plot. In order to plot them or save them with the drawing, the maps need to be captured.

To capture an map, there are two choices, as shown in Figure 3–11:

The captured online map is placed on the current layer. Prior to capturing the map, make the layer you want to place the map on current.

- **Capture Area:** Used in Modelspace, where you define a rectangle for the area of capture.

- **Capture Viewport:** A selected viewport in a layout. The viewport must be active in Modelspace mode through the viewport. Even if the viewport is an irregular shape, the captured area is rectangular to the extents of the viewport shape.

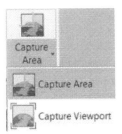

Figure 3–11

Once an area of an online map is captured, it remains in the drawing, and can be toggled off through its layer. By clicking the boundary of the captured map, a context sensitive ribbon is displayed as shown in Figure 3–12.

Figure 3–12

You can control the following:

- Change the Map style (Aerial / Road Hybrid / Off)

- Change the resolution of the map. The options are *Coarse, Optimal, Fine* and *Very Fine.*

- Control the brightness, contrast, or fade amount.

- Reload (update) the map.

You need to be logged in to your Autodesk account to make any of the above changes to the captured map.

Once the Map is captured, a copyright notice is added to the captured map, as shown in Figure 3–13

Figure 3–13

3.4 Traverse Editor

Before the areas of a piece of land can be computed, it is required to have a closed traverse. The Traverse Editor (shown in Figure 3–14) assists in entering, editing, and outputting 2D traverse data. In addition, it can be used to enter a legal description of a property in table format making it easier to find and fix errors in data entry. Traverse data can be created in the following ways:

- From existing COGO data.

- By loading it from a polyline.

- By manually entering known data.

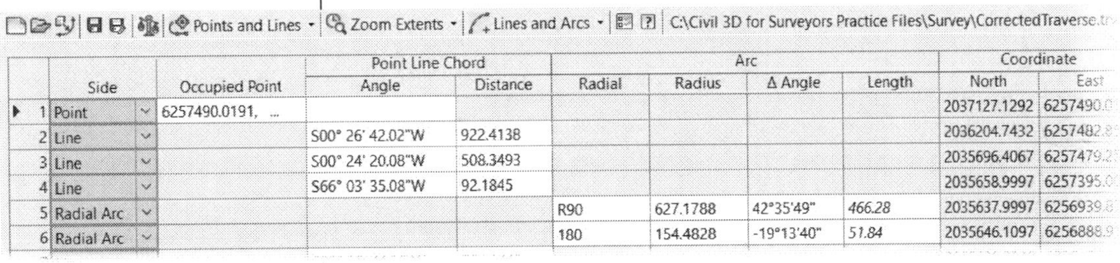

| | Side | Occupied Point | Point Line Chord | | Arc | | | | Coordinate | |
			Angle	Distance	Radial	Radius	Δ Angle	Length	North	East
1	Point	6257490.0191, ...							2037127.1292	6257490.0
2	Line		S00° 26' 42.02"W	922.4138					2036204.7432	6257482.8
3	Line		S00° 24' 20.08"W	508.3493					2035696.4067	6257479.2
4	Line		S66° 03' 35.08"W	92.1845					2035658.9997	6257395.0
5	Radial Arc				R90	627.1788	42°35'49"	466.28	2035637.9997	6256939.8
6	Radial Arc				180	154.4828	-19°13'40"	51.84	2035646.1097	6256888.9

Toolbar: Points and Lines ▾ | Zoom Extents ▾ | Lines and Arcs ▾ | C:\Civil 3D for Surveyors Practice Files\Survey\CorrectedTraverse.tr

Figure 3–14

Manually Entering COGO Data

Traverse data can be entered using a variety of formats and mathematical equations. The key when defining a traverse is to start by defining a point of beginning. Then, the sides of the traverse are defined. When entering data, keep the following guidelines in mind:

- The first Side type must be a point to represent the POB (point of beginning).

- The tab key is used to navigate between cells.

- Any data in red is considered invalid.

- Entered data is not affected if the traverse is adjusted, scaled, or rotated.

- Units of measure different from the project can be entered by typing ' (feet) or **m** (meters). Once entered, the software converts the measurement to the project units.

Data Entry

Each vertex in a traverse can be manually entered or selected from the model. The following data types can be entered using the formats listed for each.

Side	The side field determines which fields become available for entering data. For example: If the Line option is selected, the Radius and Delta Angle fields become gray which indicates they cannot be modified. Five side types are available as follows: • Point • Line • Chord Arc • Radial Arc • Side Shot
Point	Creates only a COGO point in the drawing. The point of beginning or point of closure can be entered using (X,Y) to set the Latitude/Longitude values. When typing the values, use any of the following formats: • DDMMSS.ss • DD MM SS.ss • DD.MMSSss
Line	The direction of a line or curve from the last point can be set using the quadrant number and then the angle or by typing the bearing just as it is listed in the legal description. • Quadrant..Angle (1..45 = N 45 E) • N DD MM SS.ss E
Chord Arc	Chord arcs require an angle and distance to be entered at a minimum. You can also type the radius, delta angle, or length. Entered data displays in regular font. Calculated values (radius, delta angle, or length) are shown in italics. Multiple cells can be: • Angle/Direction • Distance • Radius • Delta Angle • Length

Radial Arc	Radial arcs require a radial direction and a radius to be entered at a minimum. You can also type the delta angle or length. Entered data displays in regular font. Calculated values (delta angle or length) are shown in italics. Multiple cells can be: • Radial Direction • Radius • Delta Angle • Length *If an arc is tangent to the last line, you can type L90 or R90 (left 90 degrees or right 90 degrees).
Unknown Value	Up to two values per traverse might be unknown. The Traverse Editor calculates the values based on other known values. Known values display in the Traverse Editor as regular text while calculated values display as italicized text. • Enter **U** in the cell.
Mathematical equations	A variety of mathematical equations can be entered to calculate a traverse parameter value. This enables you to calculate relative values based on known information. The following are valid operators: • + • - • / • * • ( )

Traverse Editor Options

- When entering new traverse data, you have the choice of producing lines, COGO points, or both in the drawing, as shown in Figure 3–15.

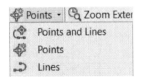

Figure 3–15

- You can control which zoom level the traverse information is displayed at in the drawing. Civil 3D can keep the extents of the whole traverse on the screen, zoom to the traverse element of the selected row of the Traverse Editor, or not change its zoom level, as shown in Figure 3–16.

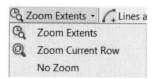

Figure 3–16

- You can choose to display only the traverse linear elements in the table or lines and arcs, as shown in Figure 3–17.

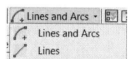

Figure 3–17

- Within the options ( ), you can choose how to handle conflicting points by overwriting the COGO point or creating a new one. You can also choose when to erase the traverse graphics that have been inserted into the drawing, as shown in Figure 3–18.

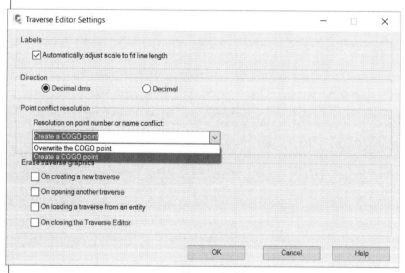

Figure 3–18

How To: Create a Traverse by Entering Data Manually

1. In the **Home** tab>Create Ground Data panel, expand **Traverse** and select 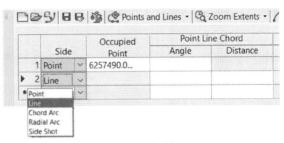 (Traverse Editor).

2. To clear any existing data in the Traverse Editor, click (New).

Alternatively, you can click (Select a point) and select an existing point in the model.

3. In the first row, enter the **(X,Y)** value for the *Point of Beginning*.

4. In the Side type drop-down list, select the required option (as shown in Figure 3–19), and complete the required cells to the right of it.

Figure 3–19

5. Repeat Step 4 until all segments of the traverse are entered.

6. To draw the traverse in the model, in the Traverse Editor palette, expand the Draw drop-down list and select which items you want in the model (Points and Lines, Points, or Lines), as shown in Figure 3–20. Review what is drawn in the model.

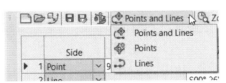

Figure 3–20

7. Right-click on any row and select **Insert Row After** (as shown in Figure 3–21) to add any missing segments.

You can also delete a row or move a row up or down using the same right-click menu.

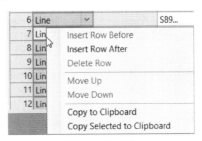

Figure 3–21

3.5 Traverse Adjustment

No survey is perfect; traverses will never close precisely. Minute errors in positioning, vertical adjustments, backsight readings, etc. will compound over the entire traverse, making closure of a traverse highly unlikely. Put another way, once one has circumnavigated around the perimeter of a lot or parcel collecting survey data (both horizontal and vertical), the last shot back to the start point will invariably be incorrect.

When a traverse file is created in the Civil 3D COGO Traverse Editor, the traverse file can be brought into the Civil 3D Traverse Adjustment to study the overall errors and closure discrepancies based on a variety of adjustment methods. There are other methods of adjusting the traverse that are explored later in this guide: the next chapter deals with field books and the appendix delves deeper into least squares adjustments.

Adjusting a COGO Traverse

The Civil 3D Traverse Adjustment window displays the following information for the traverse and adjustment options, as shown in Figure 3–22:

1. The traverse file name and location.
2. The traverse start point, end point, and point of closure.
3. A summary of closure based on the chosen closure methods.
4. Each component of the traverse, along with adjustments required based on the closure methods.
5. The chosen adjustment method.
6. Settings to pick the chosen adjustment methods.
7. Report of adjustment generation.
8. Apply chosen adjustment to the traverse file.
9. Exit the Traverse Adjustment window.

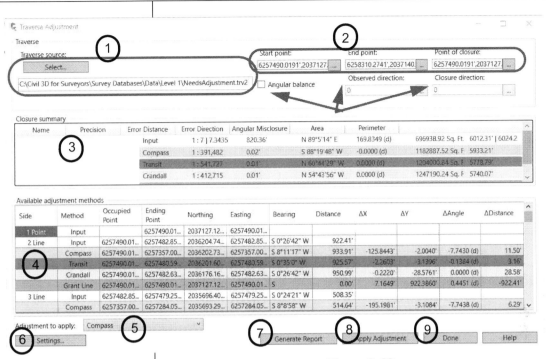

Figure 3–22

How To: Adjust COGO Traverses

1. Open the traverse file by clicking the **Select** button (top left corner).
2. If need be, you can adjust only part of the traverse by selecting the *Start point* and/or *End point* of the partial traverse.
3. By default, the *Point of closure* is the start point of the traverse, but it can be manually overridden.
4. By selecting the *Angular balance* checkbox, you enable the balance calculations for angles to be distributed across the angles in the traverse. If this is enabled and it is an open traverse, then you must also specify the directions for *Observations* and *Closure*. When this is selected, the *Closure summary* (and reports) and the *Available adjustment methods* display the Angular Adjustments in the chosen colors (see below).
5. Select which adjustment method to use when applying the adjustment to the traverse.
6. Customize the Civil 3D Traverse Adjustment window by clicking the **Settings** button.

7. Generate a report of the closure, for either your chosen adjustment method (from Step 5) or all methods, as shown in Figure 3–23.

Figure 3–23

8. The report can be in either HTML or PDF format. A sample is shown in Figure 3–24

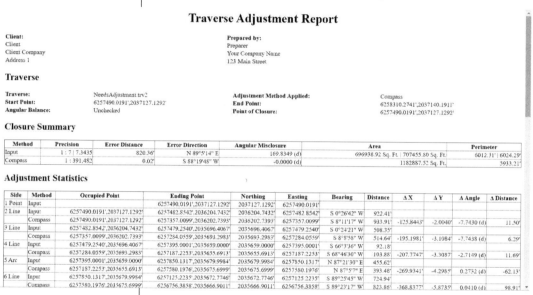

Figure 3–24

9. When exiting the Civil 3D Traverse Adjustment window (by clicking the **Done** button), you are prompted to save the adjusted traverse file. It is recommended you save it as a new file with an appropriate name branding it as being adjusted.

Customizing the Traverse Adjustment Display

By clicking the **Settings** button (Step 6), the COGO Adjustment Setting window opens, as shown in Figure 3–25.

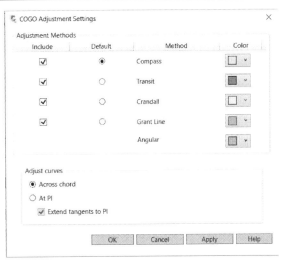

Figure 3–25

The Field Book chapter explains the adjustment methods in greater detail.

You can choose:

1. Which methods of adjustment to display and what color the methods are highlighted with. This includes:
    *   Compass
    *   Transit
    *   Crandall
    *   Grant Line (for open traverses only)
    *   Angular (can be toggled in the Traverse Adjustment window)

2. What type of curve adjustment method to use. Curves cannot be adjusted; therefore, lines are added to approximate the curve.

*   The lines can be added across the chord of the curve, as shown in Figure 3–26.

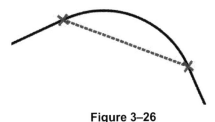

Figure 3–26

- Or the lines can be either added or extended to the Point of Intersection (PI) of the curve, as shown in Figure 3–27.

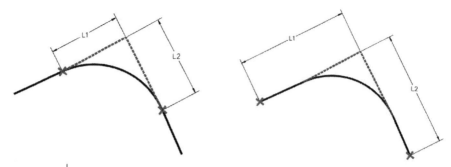

Figure 3–27

- If lines are added, they originate from the end point of the incoming chord and the start of the outgoing chord.
- If lines are extended, they originate from the start point of the incoming chord and the end point of the outgoing chord.

Practice 3b | Traverse Editor and Adjustment

Practice Objectives

- Reference an online map.
- Capture an area of the online map.
- Add the property boundary to the model by typing in the legal description into the Coordinate Geometry Editor.
- Key entry traverse information in the Traverse Editor.
- Adjust the entered traverse in the Traverse Adjustment window.

In this practice, you will reference an online map and capture it, then create a polyline from the previous legal description of a property boundary, as shown in Figure 3–28. This time, however, you will be using Traverse Editor tools, rather than drawing a polyline with transparent commands.

After realizing you missed a line of text in the legal description, you make edits to the boundary and import the polyline from the Traverse Editor into the drawing. You will then adjust the closure of the traverse with the Traverse Adjustment window.

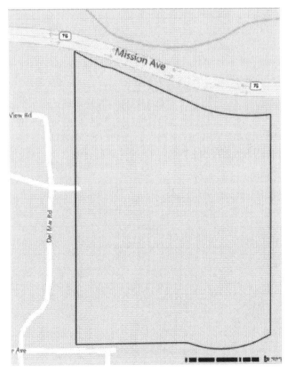

Figure 3–28

Task 1 - Reference a map from the Online Map Service.

1. Open **Boundary-A2.dwg** from the *C:\Civil 3D for Surveyors\Working\Survey* folder.

*If the Terms of Service splash screen displays, click **Yes**.*

2. If are not already signed in, sign into your Autodesk account, which can be accessed through the icon in the upper right corner of the Autodesk Civil 3D interface, as shown in Figure 3–29.

Figure 3–29

3. In the *Online Map* panel, expand the **Map** drop-down list and select **Map Road** as the map style, as shown in Figure 3–30.

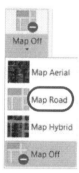

Figure 3–30

4. Note that the map is not limited to your drawing area. As you zoom out, the image resamples itself. As you zoom in, more detail becomes available.

When an online map is captured, it is placed on the current layer. Therefore ensure that the correct layer is current prior to capturing a map.

5. Make a new layer called **V-SITE-IMGE** and make it current.

6. In the *Online Map* panel, expand the **Capture** drop-down list and select *Capture Area,* as shown in Figure 3–31.

Figure 3–31

7. Pick two points representing the corners of a rectangular area, similar to the area shown previously in Figure 3–28.

8. Note that a copyright notice is added to the captured map in the lower left corner of the captured area.

9. Save the drawing.

Task 2 - Manually enter a traverse boundary.

1. In the *Home* tab>Create Ground Data panel, expand **Traverse** and select  (Traverse Editor).

2. To clear any existing data in the Traverse Editor, click (New).

3. For the first point, type **6257490.0191,2037127.1292**.

4. In the Side drop-down list, select **Line**, as shown in Figure 3–32.

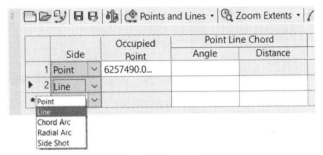

Figure 3–32

5. Set the following, taking care to use the spaces between the numbers and letters exactly as shown. Note that you can jump to the next cell by pressing <Tab>, and that <Up Arrow> and <Down Arrow> changes rows.

   • *Angle/Direction*: **S 00 26 42.2 W**
   • *Distance*: **922.4138**

6. Use the following table to set the remaining segments:

	Point, Line, Chord		Arc		
Side Type	Angle/Direction	Distance	Radial	Radius	Delta Angle
Line	S 00 24 20.8 W	508.3493			
Line	S 66 03 35.8 W	92.1845			
Radial Arc			L90	627.1788	42 35 49
Line	S 89 25 44.6 W	724.9442			
Line	N 00 11 9.9 E	1904.2647			
Line	S 61 50 15.3 E	135.9034			
Line	S 64 05 35.8 W	77.8201			
Line	S 78 09 29.2 E	63.8821			
Line	S 66 23 19.5 E	379.2248			
Line	S 66 17 17.4 E	278.5122			
Chord Arc	S 76 22 12 E	135.0030		1117.0	
Radial Arc			L90	1130.4720	-17

7. In the Traverse Editor palette, click (Save Traverse to File As).

8. Browse to the *C:\Civil 3D for Surveyors\Working\ Survey\Data Files\Level 1* folder and type **BOUNDARY** for the traverse file. Click **Save**.

9. Close the Traverse Editor.

Task 3 - Make corrections to the traverse.

After you have run the report or drawn the traverse in the model, you might realize that you inadvertently missed a segment and put in the wrong angle or direction for another segment. In this task, you will add the missing segment and make any other corrections.

1. In the *Home* tab > Create Ground Data panel, click

   (Traverse Editor).

2. In the Zoom drop-down list, select **Zoom Current Row** to zoom to the traverse element of the selected row of the Traverse Editor, as shown in Figure 3–33.

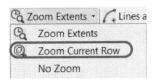

Figure 3–33

If you did not save the file, select **NeedsCorrections.trv2** *from the C:\Civil 3D for Surveyors\Survey Databases\Data\Level 1 folder.*

3. In the Traverse Editor, click 📂 (Load Traverse from File). Select the file you saved in the last task.

4. Note that the curve in line 5 is going in the wrong direction and that line 9 has a mistyped bearing. Correct it by doing the following:

   • In the *Radial* field of line 5, type R90 to change the direction of the curve from Left to Right, without changing the direction of the tangent.

   • In the *Angle/Direction* field of line 9, change the *Bearing* to **S 64 05 35.8 E** (change the **W** at the end to **E**).

5. Also note that the reverse curve is missing after line 5. To correct it, add a segment after line 5 by doing the following:

   • Right-click on line 6 and select **Insert Row Before**.

   • Change the *Side type* of the new line 6 to **Radial Arc**.

   • Set the *Radial* to **180**.

   • Set the *Radius* to **154.4828**.

   • Set the *Delta Angle* to **19 13 40**.

   • Note that the arc is going the wrong direction but has the correct length.

   • Copy the *length* value by highlighting it and pressing <Ctrl>+<C> on the keyboard.

   • In the *Delta Angle* field, type - (negative) in front of the angle value. Unfortunately, this causes the arc to lengthen.

   • Put the cursor in the Length field, press <Ctrl>+<V> to paste the correct length value.

   • Note the corrected linework in the model. If the negative disappears from the *Delta Angle* field, reinsert it.

6. Select row 14 and note that the arc is not tangent to the incoming line. To correct this, set the *Angle* to a negative value by putting a minus sign in front of the value (-06°55'45").

7. Note that even with these corrections, the traverse does not close properly. This means it needs to be adjusted. You could go directly to the Traverse Adjustment window by clicking the (Load Balance Tools) icon in the upper left corner. However, we will go the long way around in the next task.

8. In the Traverse Editor palette, click (Save Traverse As to File). Browse to *C:\Civil 3D for Surveyors\Survey Databases\ Data\Level 1* and save the file as **BOUNDARY-Corrected**.

9. Close the Traverse Editor palette by going to the side bar and clicking the **X** that appears, then save the drawing.

Task 4 - Adjust the traverse in the Traverse Adjustment window.

---

1. In the *Home* tab>Create Ground Data panel, click (Traverse Adjustment).

2. Click the **Select** button and browse to the folder and file name you saved in the previous task, or open *C:\Civil 3D for Surveyors\Survey Databases\Data\Level 1\ NeedsAdjustment.trv2*.

3. Click the **Settings** button and uncheck the Transit method so it does not show in the Traverse Adjustment window, as shown in Figure 3–34.

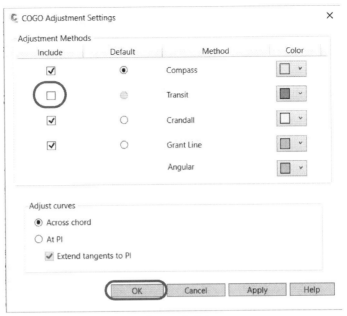

Figure 3–34

4. Click **OK** to return to the Traverse Adjustment window.

5. Ensure that **Compass** is selected in the Adjustment to apply drop-down list, as shown in Figure 3–35.

6. Click the **Generate Report** button and select **Current Adjustment to Apply**, as shown in Figure 3–35.

Figure 3–35

7. Ensure the *Save as type* is set to **HTML**, browse to *C:\Civil 3D for Surveyors\Survey Databases\Data\Level 1*, and enter the *File Name* as **Boundary-Adjusted-Compass**.

8. Click the **Apply Adjustment** button, browse to *C:\Civil 3D for Surveyors\Survey Databases\Data\Level 1*, and enter the *File Name* as **Boundary-Adjusted-Compass**.

9. Click **OK** to close the Apply Adjustment alert box.

10. Click the **Done** button to close the Traverse Adjustment window.

11. Note that the curves have changed to straight segments. Adjusting traverses will do that.

12. Save and close the drawing.

Task 5 - Add a boundary to the Survey Database.

1. Open **Boundary-A3.dwg** from the *C:\Civil 3D for Surveyors\Working\Survey* folder.

2. If needed, in the *Survey* tab, right-click on **Survey Databases**, then select **Set working folder** and select the *C:\Civil 3D for Surveyors\Survey Databases\ Ascent-Development* folder.

3. Right-click on the **Ascent Data-USF** database and select **Open for Edit**.

4. Right-click on **Figures** and select **Create figure from object**, as shown in Figure 3–36.

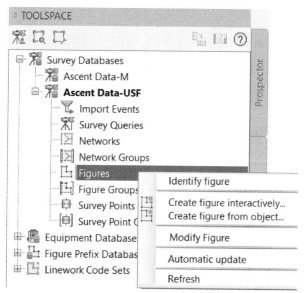

Figure 3–36

5. When prompted, select the red polyline representing the boundary traverse.

6. In the Create Figure From Object window, for the *Name*, type
   Boundary, and then select ASCENT for the *Current figure
   prefix database*. Do NOT associate survey points to vertices,
   as shown in Figure 3–37.

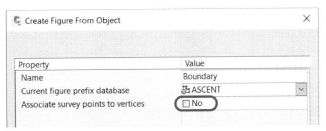

Figure 3–37

7. Note that no changes were made in the drawing, so there is
   no need to save it. The changes were made to the *Survey
   Database.*

Chapter Review Questions

1. What is required to use the Online Map Service? (Select all that apply.)

   a. An Autodesk account

   b. The Map workspace needs to be active

   c. Agreeing to the Terms of Service

   d. An Internet connection

2. Can online maps be plotted?

   a. Yes

   b. No

   c. Only if captured

3. Are Transparent commands available through the right-click menu?

   a. Yes

   b. No

4. What is the best way to find and fix errors when inputting a property boundary from a legal description?

   a. When an error is made, it is always required to undo the linework and start over at the beginning of the legal description.

   b. Use Transparent command tools.

   c. Use expanded line or curve tools.

   d. Use the Traverse Editor.

Command Summary

Button	Command	Location
	Bearing Distance	• **Toolbar:** Transparent Commands • **Command Prompt:** 'bd
	Coordinate Geometry Editor	• **Command Prompt:** CogoEditor
	Create Curve from End of Object	• **Ribbon:** *Home* tab>Draw panel • **Command Prompt:** CurveFromEndOfObject
	Create Reverse or Compound Curve	• **Ribbon:** *Home* tab>Draw panel • **Command Prompt:** ReverseOrCompound
	Survey Toolspace	• **Ribbon:** *Home* tab>Palettes panel
	Survey User Settings	• **Toolspace:** *Survey* tab
	Traverse Adjustment	• **Ribbon:** *Home* tab>Create Ground Data panel • **Command Prompt:** TraverseAdjustment
	Traverse Editor	• **Ribbon:** *Home* tab>Create Ground Data panel • **Command Prompt:** TraverseEditor

Field Book Files

Field book files are unique ASCII files with special coding that connects linework automatically. They are different from point files with connective codes and must be treated differently both in the field and when processing the files. In this chapter, you will learn how to import and work with field book files.

Learning Objectives in This Chapter

- Establish horizontal and vertical control for the project by creating a survey network.
- Import a field book file and process linework to automatically display the collected field data in the drawing.
- Modify figures in a survey database to correct errors or add additional linework to the database.
- Adjust observed point coordinates in a traverse survey without adjusting control points.
- Create and edit a traverse to speed up debugging problem surveys.
- Perform traverse adjustments on multiple field book files.
- Filter a survey database to isolate only the points or figures required for the tasks being completed in the current drawing to reduce file sizes.
- Create network groups.

4.1 Survey Networks

A survey network is a collection of all of the known control points, instrument setups, and directions. They are usually represented by a series of interconnected lines indicating where the instrument was set up and where the side shots were taken. A local Survey Database has one or more networks. You can import one or more field books or point files into a network when the Survey spans more than one field book or point file. For example, networks are usually a day of field work. The larger the area of interest, the greater the number of networks required. At least one network is required when importing field book files to create linework and points.

Before importing a Survey, you create a named network. You can also do so during the importation process. To create a new network, select Survey's network heading, right-click, select **New**, and type the network's name. After creating a named network, Survey creates five nodes below its name: Control Points, Non-Control Points, Directions, Setups, and Traverses, as shown in Figure 4–1.

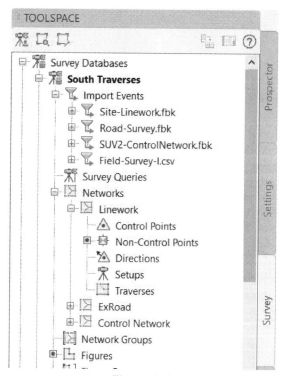

Figure 4–1

You can import one or several field books or LandXML files into the same network. By default, each import supplements the previous import. When you re-import a file, Survey automatically deletes the information from the original file import and recalculates the observations from the re-imported file.

Importing multiple files with the correct settings creates a single network whose data is a combination of the imported files. This enables you to create traverses, or perform a least squares analysis from data that spans more than one file.

When importing a file, Survey sequentially processes each line, creating setups and processing the setup's observations. When processing the setup's observations, Survey stores them in the observation database and calculates a point's preliminary coordinates from the observation values.

When toggling on interactive graphics, Survey displays the setups, draws figure linework, and populates the Control Points, Non-Control Points, Directions, and Setups.

When completing the import, Survey populates all or some of the nodes under the *Networks* heading.

Control points are NE or NEZ entries in a field book. Directions are azimuth entries between points used in the stationing process. Survey points are initially calculated coordinates from the file's setups and observations. Any NE SS entries become non-control points. These points have coordinates, but are not control points (not used in a setup or as stationing points). You can promote them to control points by using them as part of a traverse or referencing them as part of a setup.

Non-control points can also be the result of importing a point coordinate file instead of an observation-based file.

4.2 Importing a Field Book

To import a field book, you use the Survey's **Import Events** collection. **Import Events** provides access to an import wizard, which takes you through the steps of creating a survey database, and network, and importing a file. To open the Import wizard, in the *Home* tab>Create Ground Data panel, click 💬 (Import survey data).

The Specify Database page (shown in Figure 4–2) sets the survey, creates a new survey, and edits a survey's settings.

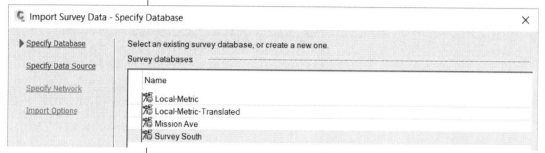

Figure 4–2

Select a survey and then click **Next**. The Specify Data Source page (shown in Figure 4–3) defines the file import type, the file's path, and its format (if it is a point file).

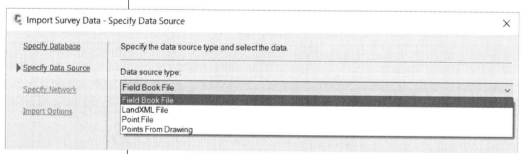

Figure 4–3

Click **Next**. The Specify Network page (shown in Figure 4–4) enables you to change the network or create a new survey network.

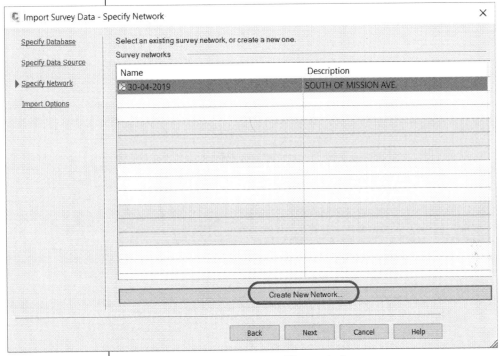

Figure 4–4

To set up a new network, click **Create New Network**. Give the network a meaningful name and use the description if more clarity is required, as shown in Figure 4–5

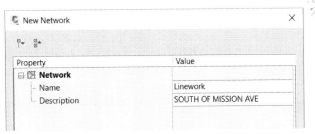

Figure 4–5

Click **Next**. The Import Options page (shown in Figure 4–6) sets the values for the import. These settings affect what the import does and which support files it uses.

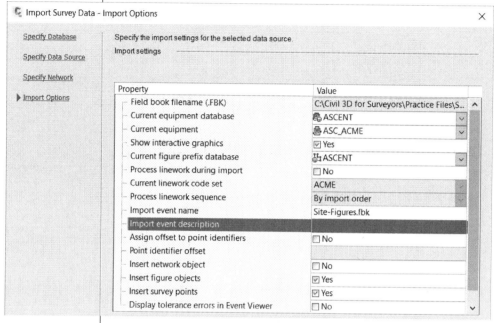

Figure 4–6

If the field book has figure coding from a conversion, you do not need to toggle on the *Process linework during import* property. This is for files with **Linework Code Set** commands and not CONT or END lines.

Inserting figures requires entries to be in the Figure Prefix database and figure styles to be in the drawing. This is required to point figure and linework to the correct layers in the drawing and to specify whether the figure is also a breakline in a surface.

When inserting points, it is required to have a Description Key Set defined to assign point, point label styles, and layers, and to translate raw descriptions to full descriptions.

Practice 4a

Importing a Field Book

Practice Objective

- Import a field book file and process linework to automatically display the collected field data in the drawing.

Task 1 - Import a field book and create a network.

1. Open **FB-A-Survey.dwg** from the *C:\Civil 3D for Surveyors\ Working\Survey* folder.

2. If you are greeted with a splash screen about using Online Map Data, select **Remember my choice** and click **No**, as shown in Figure 4–7. (Since you have captured an online map in a previous chapter, you do not need to use Online Map Data.)

Figure 4–7

*The captured online map resides on the **V-SITE-IMGE** layer, which can be toggled off if required.*

3. In the *Survey* tab, right-click on **Survey Databases** and select **Set working folder**, as shown in Figure 4–8.
   - Browse and select the *C:\Civil 3D for Surveyors\Survey Databases\Ascent Fieldbooks* folder.
   - Click **Select Folder**.

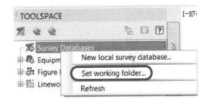

Figure 4–8

4. In the Toolspace>*Survey* tab, right-click on **Survey Databases** and select **New local survey database**.

5. Set the *Name* to **Survey South** and click **OK**.

6. Right-click on the **SurveySouth** database and select **Edit Survey Database Settings**.

7. In the dialog box, ensure that under *Units*, the *Coordinate zone* is set to **NAD83 California State Planes, Zone VI, US Foot**.

   - If not, click 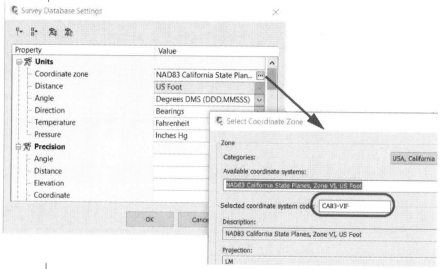 (Browse) and select **NAD83 California State Planes, Zone VI, US Foot**, as shown in Figure 4–9. Click **OK**.

Figure 4–9

8. Click **OK** to close the dialog box.

9. In the *Home* tab>Create Ground Data drop-down panel, click (Import Survey Data).

10. In the Import Survey Data dialog box - Specify Database page, select **SurveySouth**. Click **Next**.

11. Set the *Data source type* to **Field Book File** and click 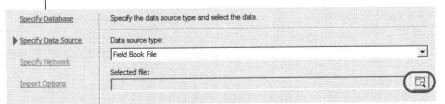, as shown in Figure 4–10.

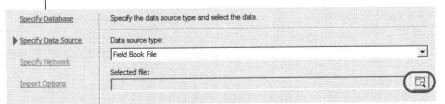

Figure 4–10

12. For the *Field book filename (.FBK)*, browse to the *C:\Civil 3D for Surveyors\Survey Databases\Data\Level 1* folder and open **Site-Linework.fbk**. Click **Next**.

13. In the Import Survey Data dialog box, click **Create New Network**.

14. In the New Network dialog box, set *Network Name* to **Linework**, and *Description* to **SOUTH OF MISSION AVE**, as shown in Figure 4–11.

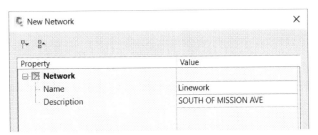

Figure 4–11

15. Click **OK** to create the network, and then click **Next**.

Process linework during import only applies to point files, not field books.

16. In the Import Survey Data dialog box, set the following values, as shown in Figure 4–12:
    - *Show interactive graphics:* **Yes**
    - *Process linework during import:* **No**
    - *Assign offset to point identifiers:* **No**
    - *Insert network object:* **Yes**
    - *Insert figure objects:* **Yes**
    - *Insert survey points:* **Yes**

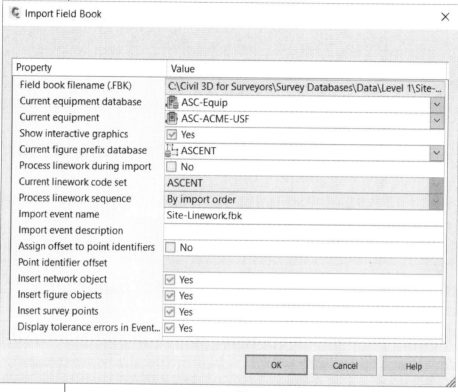

Figure 4–12

17. Click **Finish** to accept the changes. The field book is processed and the survey points and figures are inserted.

18. There is no need to save the drawing. Any changes are stored in the **Survey South** survey database, and the graphical information in the drawing can be easily inserted from the survey database at any time.

With **Show interactive graphics** selected, the drawing pans around as each point is inserted into the drawing and the figures are connected.

Task 2 - Create a new network.

In this task, you will create a new network and import the field book file into it.

1. Continue working with the drawing from the previous task.

2. In the **Survey Databases**>**Survey South** survey database collection, select **Networks**, right-click, and select **New**, as shown in Figure 4–13.

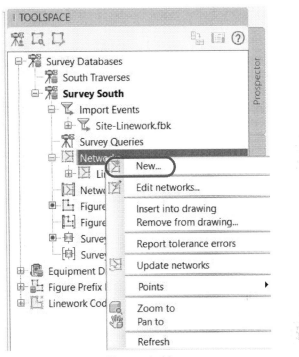

Figure 4–13

3. Set the *Name* to **ExRoad** and the *Description* to **Mission Ave**. Click **OK**.

4. To import the field book for the Mission Avenue survey, select the network **ExRoad**, right-click, expand *Import* and select **Import Field Book**.

5. For the *Field book filename (.FBK)*, browse to the *C:\Civil 3D for Surveyors\Survey Databases\Data\Level 1* folder, select **Road-Survey.fbk**, and open it.

6. In the Import Field Book dialog box, set the following values:
   - *Show interactive graphics*: **Yes**
   - *Process linework during import*: **No**
   - *Assign offset to point identifiers*: **No**
   - *Insert network object*: **Yes**
   - *Insert figure objects:* **Yes**
   - *Insert survey points*: **Yes**

7. Click **OK** to accept the changes.

With *Show interactive graphics* selected, the drawing pans around as each point is inserted into the drawing and the figures are connected.

8. The survey points are imported first, then the figures are created. Note that the figures have different names and styles, as can be seen in the tooltip shown in Figure 4–14.

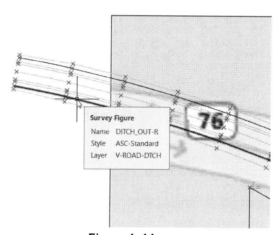

Figure 4–14

9. Note that the new figures are listed in the survey database, as shown in Figure 4–15

Figure 4–15

10. There is no need to save the drawing. Any changes are stored in the **Survey South** survey database, and the graphical information in the drawing can be easily inserted from the survey database at any time.

4.3 Traverse Basics

A traverse is a systematic method of collecting field observations. It is used to accurately locate a parcel's boundary, but there are also other uses for the traverse methodology. You can observe two types of traverses: Open and Closed.

Open Traverse

An Open traverse begins at a control point (with known coordinates) and ends at a location relative to the starting point. The only available observations are forward and back to the points along the survey path. There are no other measurements with which to check the survey's errors.

Closed Traverse

A Closed traverse is the most common type of traverse. It starts at a known location and ends at the starting location. The initial backsight is an azimuth or a second known point. Traditionally, this point is not a point in the traverse.

Closed Connected Traverse

The Closed Connected traverse is a variation of the Closed traverse as shown in Figure 4–16. It starts at a known points and ends at known points that are not the beginning points. The ending points have known coordinates, which are not affected when the traverse is modified. The traverse report notes the location error of the points and adjusts the survey's observations to that the traverse ends at the known coordinates of these points. The error is in the observations from the known starting points to the first last known point.

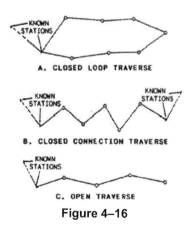

Figure 4–16

One problem with the traditional traverse is that its data is limited to observations made between the current, last, and next stations. No observations are made to other traverse points across the loop or to external points that are viewable from other traverse points (e.g., antennas, water towers, etc.). These observations would help to define a better calculated shape because they add another dimension to the traverse data. The least squares adjustment at the Network level is the only method that analyzes a survey containing traverse and redundant cross or external observations.

All Network traverses use traditional adjustment methods and only use forward and backsight measurements. The traditional traverse adjustment methods are: **Compass**, **Crandall**, **Transit**, and **Least Squares**.

- The **Compass** rule assumes that the coordinate error is distributed in proportion to the traverse leg's distance and that both the angle and distance values contribute to the survey error. The largest error occurs along the longest distances.

- The **Transit** rule assumes that the coordinate error is distributed in proportion to the amount of coordinate change between points and that the surveyor's error is due to distance rather than angle. The greater the amount of coordinate change, the more errors there are in the observations.

- **Crandall's** rule distributes the error throughout the traverse and makes adjustments to the distances in the traverse.

- Traverse **Least Squares** adjusts the point coordinates based on the traverse's foresight and backsight observations.

Traverse Data in a Field Book

Depending on the field crew and the survey task, a traverse can be easy to identify or have portions in non-sequential setups (stations). Some field crews execute the traverse first and then return to the stations to collect additional data. These new observations are known as sideshots. Some field crews execute the traverse and sideshots at the same time. They have to research the observations from each station to validate and edit any possible errors. A large error is easily detected, while small errors are harder to locate.

4.4 Defining a Traverse

A traverse is often part of the initial survey. In some surveys, the traverse is interspersed throughout the observations. In others, the traverse is the survey. A field book may contain topography and a traverse. The survey stations also represent the traverse stationing. When defining a traverse, you need to enter its definition, as shown in Figure 4–17. Since you call out the initial station, you do not include it in the traverse stations list. If you include the initial station, you cannot adjust the traverse.

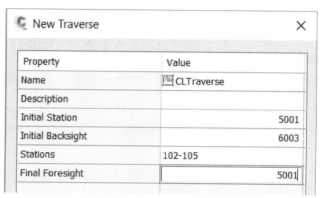

Property	Value
Name	CLTraverse
Description	
Initial Station	5001
Initial Backsight	6003
Stations	102-105
Final Foresight	5001

Figure 4–17

When reviewing each station's observations, you should look for observations to the previous station and to the next occupied station. If these observations are missing, you are at the end of the traverse. If you are near the end or at a point around the perimeter of the site, the traverse data set is probably broken.

Traverse Editor

The Traverse Editor's primary function is to enable you to manually enter a traverse. It understands the data requirements for the traverse and prompts you for the correct values as you enter the data.

The Traverse Editor can also be used to debug problem traverses. It displays where a traverse breaks and enables you to edit or add data.

Least Squares Traverse

Using least squares on a traverse implies that it contains redundant observation data. Although the traverse data might include observations across and outside the traverse's course, these observations are ignored and only foresight and backsight data are analyzed. To analyze a traverse with outside or across observations, you must use network-based least squares, not traverse-based least squares.

Adjustment Reports

Traditional traverse data and adjustment techniques produce an approximate point along the course of the traverse. Because the analysis does not contain any across or outside data, you might not end up in the correct place when walking from one side of the traverse loop to the other.

When a traverse adjustment is processed, it displays four Notepad reports. Each one contains specific adjustment results.

- The **Raw Closure.trv** report lists the traverse quality and any possible traverse problem locations.

- The **Balance Angle.trv** report lists the original raw coordinates from the traverse observations on the left. The application of an angle correction to each observation's angle is displayed on the right. The accumulated error is displayed on the far right and a new traverse precision from correcting an angular error is displayed at the bottom. The report lists the improved precision and might also display a value that passes when the initial traverse fails.

- The **Traverse Name.lso** report is similar to the **Balance Angle.trv** report, except that it uses the angular correction and the selected rule to do the final traverse adjustment.

- The **Vertical Adjustment.trv** report lists the amount of vertical adjustment that is done using the selected adjustment method. The report displays when you select a vertical adjustment method.

Practice 4b

Creating a Network Traverse

Practice Objective

- Perform traverse adjustments on multiple field book files.

In this practice, you will import a number of different field book files and perform traverse adjustments.

Task 1 - Import the control network.

1. Continue working with the drawing from the previous practice or open **FB-B-Survey.dwg** from the *C:\Civil 3D for Surveyors\Working\Survey* folder.

2. Continue working in the **Survey South** survey database. If required, right-click on the **Survey South** survey database to open it for editing.

*If **Survey South** is not listed under Survey Databases, change your working folder to C:\Civil 3D for Surveyors\ Survey Databases\ Ascent Fieldbooks.*

3. In the Toolspace>*Survey* tab, in the **Survey South** database, right-click on **Networks**, and then select **New**.

4. In the New Network dialog box, set the *Name* to **Control Network**. Click **OK**.

5. Right-click on **Control Network** and select **Import>Import field book**.

6. Select the field book file **ControlNetwork.fbk** from the *C:\Civil 3D for Surveyors\Survey Databases\ Data\Level 2* folder and click **Open**.

You might need to zoom extents to see the results.

7. In the Import Field Book dialog box, ensure that **Assign offset to point identifier** is not selected. All other checkboxes should be selected as shown in Figure 4–18. Click **OK**.

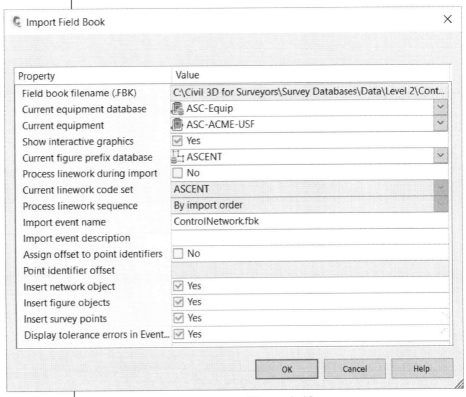

Figure 4–18

Task 2 - Import the traverse.

In this task, you will import a Closed Loop field book file into the Closed Loop network. For the proper definition of the new traverse, another survey database, **South Traverses**, needs to be opened. This survey database contains the control points required to create the new traverses.

The control points were generated with a least squares survey, as detailed in Appendix A1.

1. If need be, right-click on the **South Traverses** survey database to open it for editing.

2. In the **Survey Databases**>**South Traverses** survey
database collection, select **Networks**, right-click, and select
New, as shown in Figure 4–19.

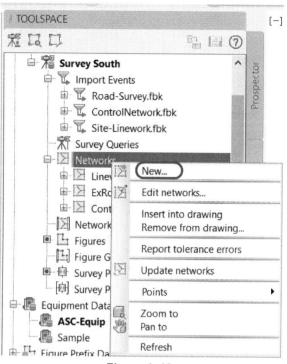

Figure 4–19

3. Set the *Name* to **Closed Loop** and the *Description* to **Closed
Loop Traverse**. Click **OK.**

4. Import the field book file by right-clicking on **Closed Loop**
(shown in Figure 4–20) and selecting **Import>Import field
book**.

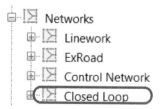

Figure 4–20

5. Select **ClosedLoop.fbk** from the *C:\Civil 3D for Surveyors\
Survey Databases\Data\Level 2* folder and click **Open**.

6. In the Import Field Book dialog box, set **Assign offset to
point identifier** and **Process Linework during import** to
No. All of the other checkboxes should be selected.

7. Click **OK.**

8. There is no need to save the drawing. Any changes are stored in the **South Traverses** survey database, and the graphical information in the drawing can be easily inserted from the survey database at any time.

Task 3 - Define a traverse.

---

1. A traverse needs at least one control point. You need to define a control point in the ClosedLoop network.

2. Expand the ClosedLoop Network branch and right-click on **Control Points** and select **New**, as shown in Figure 4–21.

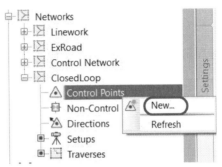

Figure 4–21

3. In the New Control Point window, enter the point number **5001**. When you do this, the remainder of the dialog box fills in with 5001's coordinates, as shown in Figure 4–22.

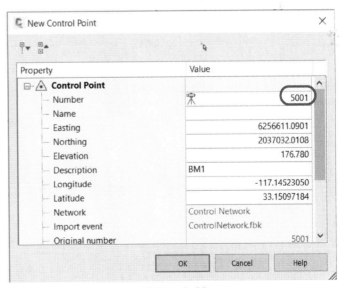

Figure 4–22

4. Click **OK** to exit the New Control Point window.

5. With this update, the ClosedLoop network is outdated, as indicated by the alert symbol next to it (as shown in Figure 4–23).

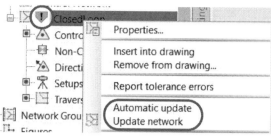

Figure 4–23

6. Right-click on the **ClosedLoop** network and select **Update network**, as shown above in Figure 4–23.

7. Now the figures are out of date for the same reason. Right-click on **Figures** and select **Automatic update.**

8. In the **South Traverses** survey database, in the **Networks** collection, expand the **Closed Loop** collection. Right-click on the **Traverses** branch and select **New**, as shown in Figure 4–24.

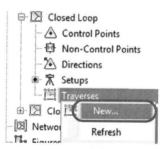

Figure 4–24

9. In the New Traverse dialog box, set the following, as shown in Figure 4–25:

- *Name:* **CLTraverse**
- *Description:* **Closed Loop Traverse**
- *Initial Station:* **5001**
- *Initial Backsight:* **6003**
- *Stations:* **102-105**
- *Final Foresight:* **5001**

Notice how, after you enter the Initial Station of 5001, Civil 3D fills in the rest of the fields to anticipate the traverse.

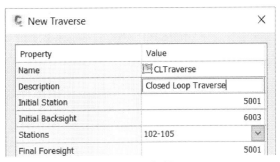

Figure 4–25

10. Click **OK** when done.

Task 4 - Review the traverse and station observation.

1. In the *Networks* collection, expand the **Closed Loop** collection.

2. In the **Traverses** branch, right-click on **CLTraverse**, as shown in Figure 4–26. Select **Edit Traverse**.

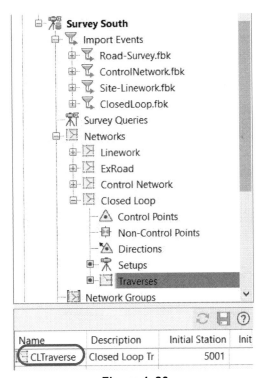

Figure 4–26

3. In the Traverse Editor panorama, review the Traverse, as shown in Figure 4–27. Click ✖ to close the panorama.

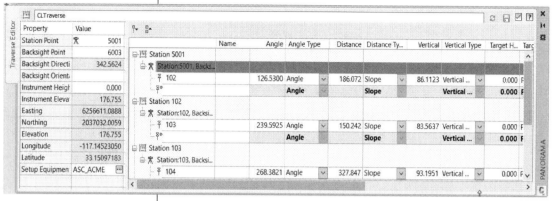

Figure 4–27

4. In the **South Traverses** survey, in the **Networks** collection, expand the **Closed Loop** collection and select **Setups**.

5. Right-click on **Station Point 103** (as shown in Figure 4–28) and select **Edit Observation**.

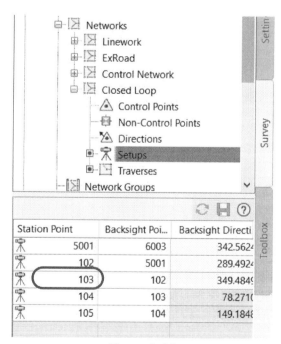

Figure 4–28

6. In the Observation Editor panorama, review the Observation, as shown in Figure 4–29. Note that in the graphics view, the Autodesk Civil 3D software will zoom to the selected setup point. Click ✖ to close the panorama.

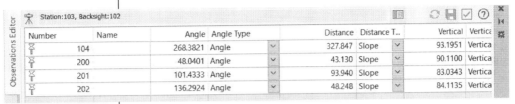

Figure 4–29

7. There is no need to save the drawing. Any changes are stored in the **South Traverses** survey database, and the graphical information in the drawing can be easily inserted from the survey database at any time.

Task 5 - Adjust a traverse.

1. In the **South Traverses** survey, in the **Networks** collection, expand the **Closed Loop** collection and select **Traverses**.

2. In the panorama window at the bottom, right-click on **CLTraverse** and select **Traverse Analysis**.

3. In the Traverse Analysis dialog box, ensure the following is set and adjust as needed, as shown in Figure 4–30:
   - Horizontal adjustment method: **Compass rule**
   - Vertical adjustment method: **Length weighted distribution**
   - Horizontal closure limit 1:X: **15000.00**
   - Vertical closure limit 1:X: **15000.00**
   - Update survey database: **No**

We are not updating the survey database yet until we see the reports.

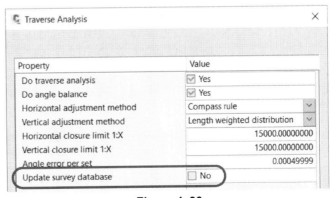

Figure 4–30

4. Click **OK** to review the adjustment values.

5. There is no need to save the drawing. Any changes are stored in the **South Traverses** survey database, and the graphical information in the drawing can be easily inserted from the survey database at any time.

Task 6 - Review the preliminary results.

1. In the previous task, the Traverse Analysis opened a number of reports in the default text editor. The reports are usually expanded and overlap each other, hiding one another. You may need to select each one and resize the notepad window, as shown in Figure 4–31.

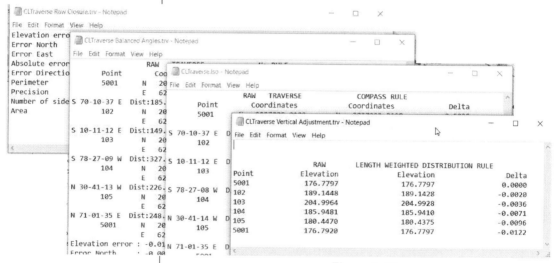

Figure 4–31

2. Select the file **CLTraverse Raw Closure.trv** and review its values. The traverse passes. Close the file.

3. Select the file **CLTraverse Balance Angles.trv** and review its values. Angle Balance slightly increased the traverse's values. Close the file.

4. Select the file **CLTraverse.Iso** and review its values. The file contains the results of balancing angles and the **Compass** rule adjustment. Close the file.

5. Select the file **CLTraverse Vertical Adjustment.trv** and review its values. The file lists the vertical changes in the adjustment. Close the file.

6. Use the **Crandall** and **Transit** adjustments to run a preliminary adjustment on the **Boundary** traverse again. Try using a different vertical adjustment as well to display any differences in the results.

7. Use the **Least Squares** method to create a preliminary adjustment on the **Boundary** traverse. Review the results.

Task 7 - Apply the survey adjustments.

1. In the **Networks** collection, expand the **Closed Loop** database and select **Traverses**.

2. Right-click on **CLTraverse** and select **Traverse Analysis** to apply the **Survey** adjustments to the traverse.

3. In the Traverse Analysis dialog box, ensure the following are set and adjust as needed, as shown in Figure 4–32:
   - *Horizontal adjustment method:* **Compass rule**
   - *Vertical adjustment method*: **Length weighted distribution**
   - *Horizontal closure limit 1:X*: **15000.00**
   - *Vertical closure limit 1:X*: **15000.00**
   - *Update survey database*: **Yes**

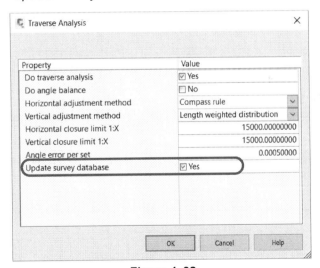

Figure 4–32

4. Click **OK** to apply the adjustment values to the traverse.

5. The Notepad reports open. Read and close each one.

6. Click **Save** to save the drawing.

4.5 Multiple Network Surveys

A survey might contain traverses that depend on control points from an initial site survey. For example, for a site with multiple phases, each succeeding survey builds on the previous survey's control points.

Survey Points

Each network in a survey contributes to an overall list of survey points. Any control point in the list is available to any network that needs to use the point for its control. For example, Network 1 is a boundary traverse. The survey's initial control point is added to the survey points list. The traverse's observed, occupied, and adjusted points become control points because of their adjustment. Their survey icons change from observed/occupied (a tripod symbol) to an adjusted control point (a control point triangle with a prism) as shown in Figure 4–33. The icon indicates that the point's origin was an observation, which was occupied and part of a traverse adjustment.

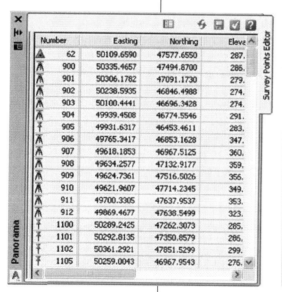 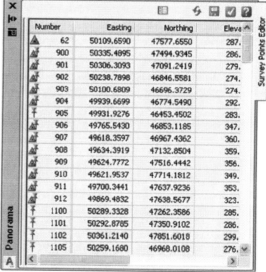

Figure 4–33

Once a point becomes a network control point, it also becomes a control point in the survey points list. The point is available to any other network in the survey as a control point.

Closed Connected Traverse

A closed connected traverse starts and ends with control points. Although it starts at a known location, the traverse observations do not arrive at the same coordinates as the ending point. This is because the field observations contain errors. With observations that have errors, the traverse has to be adjusted to make the observations arrive at the correct coordinates.

- When a survey's starting and ending points are control points, the traverse adjustment only adjusts the observed points and not the control points.

The Autodesk Civil 3D software does not change the control point coordinates when they are part of a traverse. The adjustment changes the survey's observation values so that the survey arrives at the control point coordinates. The adjustment result arrives at the control point coordinates after correcting the observation errors.

Field Book Edits

If a field book contains control point NEZ entries that are duplicates of existing control points, they must be removed from the field book. This prevents duplicate points and the redefining of existing control error messages when you are importing the field book.

The field crew might also use different point numbers for the closed loop control points. If this is done, you have to find these observation point numbers and change them to the actual control point numbers.

For example, you can facilitate this by having the field crew include the new and old point numbers in the point descriptions. They can enter the new point number and include the original control point number in the description as follows:

!NEZ 902 46846.5179 50238.6309 274.7200 ""PIN/C(s) TRAV""

!NEZ 903 46696.3614 50100.4920 274.8600 ""D.H.(S) TRAV""

!NEZ 934 47714.2556 49621.9667 349.8000 ""AKA910""

!NEZ 935 47637.9849 49700.3467 353.4600 ""AKA911""

...

AD VA 934 290.11250 142.093 83.07180 "AKA910/65"

STN 934 5.28

BS 933 0.00000

PRISM 5.33

AD VA 935 185.0222 109.427 88.0343 "AKA911"

To have the field book calculate the traverse closer, the coordinates entered in the field book need to be commented out. When importing the field book, the control point's coordinates in the Survey Points point list are used. The last five lines of the example require that the point number be changed to 911 and that the observation before and the stationing point number should change to 910. The field book import then uses the coordinates from the point numbers 910 and 911 in the Survey Point point list.

Network Groups

When multiple networks are created in a survey database, you can create **Network Groups** to better manage the individual networks, as shown in Figure 4–34.

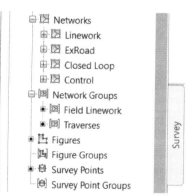

Figure 4–34

How To: Create Network Groups

1. Ensure that the survey database is opened for editing.
2. In the survey database collection, select **Network Groups** (shown in Figure 4–35), and then right-click and select **New**.

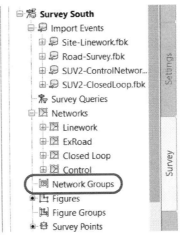

Figure 4–35

3. Give the Network Group a meaningful name and a description, as shown in Figure 4–36.

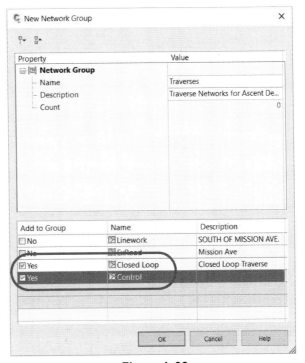

Figure 4–36

4. Select the networks you want to add to the group by selecting the checkboxes in the *Add to Group* column. Click **OK** to exit. Once networks are grouped together, you can right-click on a Network Group name to perform many options (shown in Figure 4–37), including:

- Modifying the properties of the network group
- Edit the individual network names and descriptions
- Insert or remove the networks from the current drawing.
- Zoom or pan to the network group in the current drawing.
- Edit the points within the network group.
- Update the networks in the group.

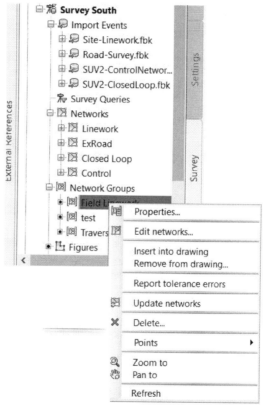

Figure 4–37

Practice 4c

Closed Connected Traverse

Practice Objective

- Import and adjust open, closed, and closed connected traverse surveys.

In this practice, you will import and adjust the three different types of traverse: **Open**, **Closed**, and **Closed connected traverse**.

Task 1 - Import the traverse.

In this task, you will import your Closed Connected field book file into the **Closed Connect** network.

1. Continue working with the drawing from the previous practice or open **FB-C-Survey.dwg** from the *C:\Civil 3D for Surveyors\Working\Survey* folder.

2. Continue with the previously opened database or open **South Traverses** survey database**.**

*If **South Traverses** is not listed under Survey Databases, change your working folder to C:\Civil 3D for Surveyors\ Survey Databases\ Ascent Fieldbooks.*

3. In the **Survey Databases**>**South Traverses** survey database collection, select **Networks**, right-click, and select **New**.

4. Set the *Name* to **Closed Connect** and the *Description* to **Closed Connected Traverse**. Click **OK**.

5. Right-click on **Closed Connect** and select **Import>Import field book**.

6. Select the field book file **ClosedConnected.fbk** from the *C:\Civil 3D for Surveyors\Survey Databases\Data\Level 2* folder and click **Open**.

You might need to zoom extents to see the results.

7. In the Import Field Book dialog box, if not already selected, set the **Assign offset to point identifier** to **No**. All of the other checkboxes should be selected. Click **OK**.

Task 2 - Create control points in the Control Network.

1. The Control Network imported in the previous task consists of observed and occupied points only, designated with the 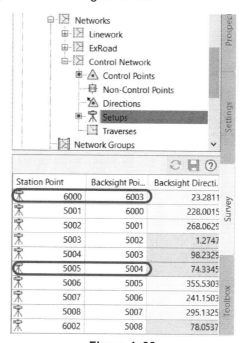 symbol, as shown in Figure 4–38.

Station Point	Backsight Poi...	Backsight Directi.
6000	6003	23.2811
5001	6000	228.0015
5002	5001	268.0629
5003	5002	1.2747
5004	5003	98.2329
5005	5004	74.3345
5006	5005	355.5303
5007	5006	241.1503
5008	5007	295.1325
6002	5008	78.0537

Figure 4–38

2. Points 5005 and 5007 are also part of the Closed Connect network just imported, as shown in Figure 4–39.

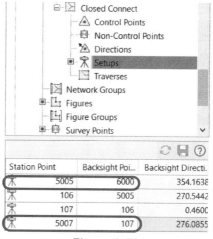

Station Point	Backsight Poi...	Backsight Directi.
5005	6000	354.1638
106	5005	270.5442
107	106	0.4600
5007	107	276.0855

Figure 4–39

3. In order to create and analyze a traverse in Closed Connect, these points need to be reduced to control points in the Control Network.

4. In the **South Traverses** survey, expand the **Networks**>**Control Network** collection. Right-click on **Traverse** and select **New** to create a new traverse.

5. In the New Traverse dialog box, set the following, as shown in Figure 4–40:
   - *Name:* **CN Traverse**
   - *Description*: **Control Network Traverse**
   - *Initial Station point number:* **6000**
   - *Initial Backsight:* **6003**
   - *Stations:* **5001-5008**
   - *Final Foresight*: **6002**

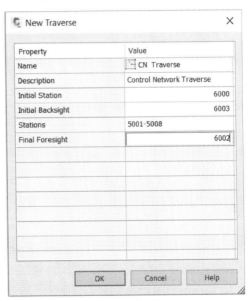

Figure 4–40

6. Click **OK**.

Task 3 - Apply the survey adjustments.

---

1. In the **South Traverses** survey, expand the **Networks**>**Control Network** collection and select **Traverses**. In the panorama window at the bottom, right-click on **CN Traverse** and select **Traverse Analysis** to apply the survey adjustments to the traverse.

---

2. In the Traverse Analysis dialog box, ensure the following is set and adjust as needed:

   - *Horizontal adjustment method:* **Compass rule**
   - *Vertical adjustment method*: **Length weighted distribution**
   - *Horizontal closure limit 1:X*: **15000.00**
   - *Vertical closure limit 1:X*: **15000.00**
   - *Update survey database*: **No**

3. Click **OK** to apply the adjustment values to the traverse.

4. A Warning box opens, indicating that the survey does not meet the user-specified limits, as shown in Figure 4–41. Click **OK** to continue.

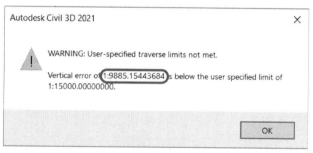

Figure 4–41

5. In the Notepad report list, select **CN Traverse Raw Closure.trv** to review its values. Other text reports display in the Notepad program. Read each report and close the Notepad program when done.

6. To adjust the traverse loop, right-click on **CC Traverse** again and select **Traverse Analysis** to apply the survey adjustments to the traverse.

The Vertical error is 1:9885, so you need to lower the limit to below that value.

7. In the Traverse Analysis dialog box, change the following, as shown in Figure 4–42:

   - *Horizontal closure limit 1:X*: **150000.00**
   - *Vertical closure limit 1:X*: **7500.00**
   - *Update survey database*: **Yes**

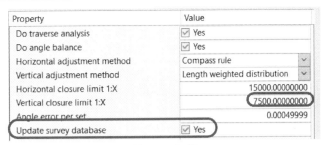

Figure 4–42

8. Click **OK** to apply the new adjustment values to the traverse.

9. With this update, the ClosedLoop network is outdated, as seen by the alert symbol next to it (as shown in Figure 4–43).

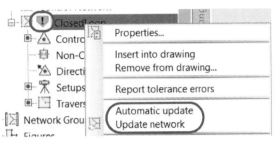

Figure 4–43

10. Right-click on the ClosedLoop network and select **Update network**, as shown above in Figure 4–43.

11. With this update, the Closed Connect network is outdated, as seen by the alert symbol next to it. As you did above, right-click on the **Closed Connect** network and select **Update network.**

12. Now there are control points in the Control Network, which allows a traverse to be defined and analyzed in the Closed Connect network, as shown in Figure 4–44.

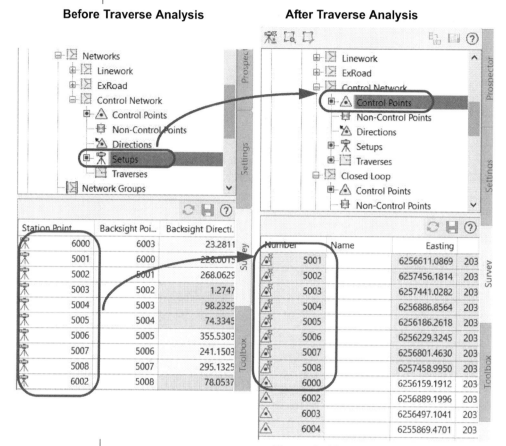

Figure 4–44

Task 4 - Define a traverse and apply the survey adjustments.

1. In the **South Traverses** survey, expand the **Networks**>**Closed Connect** collection. Right-click on **Traverse** and select **New** to create a new traverse.

Notice how, after you enter the Initial Station of 5005, Civil 3D cannot fill in the rest of the fields as there are multiple possible solutions.

2. In the New Traverse dialog box, set the following, as shown in Figure 4–45:
   - *Name:* **CC Traverse**
   - *Description*: **Closed Connected Traverse**
   - *Initial Station point number*: **5005**
   - *Initial Backsight*: **6000**
   - *Stations:* **106,107**
   - *Final Foresight*: **5007**

Property	Value
Name	CC Traverse
Description	Closed Connected Traverse
Initial Station	5005
Initial Backsight	6000
Stations	106,107
Final Foresight	5007

New Traverse ✕

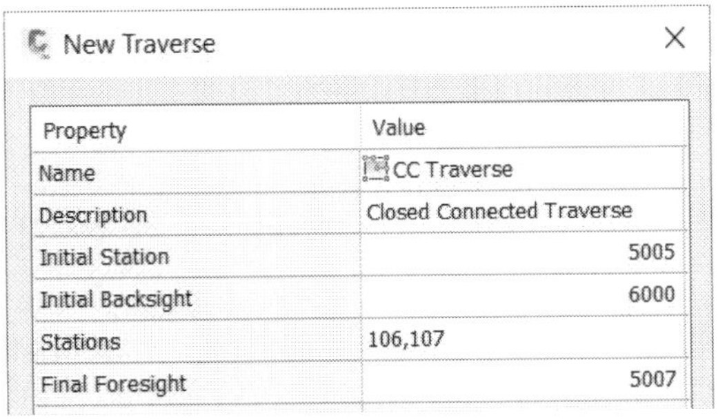

Figure 4–45

3. Click **OK**.

4. In the **South Traverses** survey, expand the **Networks**>**Closed Connect** collection and select **Traverses**. In the panorama window at the bottom, right-click on **CC Traverse** and select **Traverse Analysis** to apply the survey adjustments to the traverse.

5. In the Traverse Analysis dialog box, ensure the following is set and adjust as needed:
   - *Horizontal adjustment method:* **Compass rule**
   - *Vertical adjustment method*: **Length weighted distribution**
   - *Horizontal closure limit 1:X*: **15000.00**
   - *Vertical closure limit 1:X*: **7500.00**
   - *Update survey database*: **No**

6. Click **OK** to apply the adjustment values to the traverse.

7. A Warning box opens, indicating that the survey does not meet the user-specified limits, as shown in Figure 4–46. Click **OK** to continue.

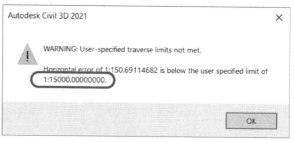

Figure 4–46

8. The text reports display in the Notepad program. Read each report and close the Notepad program when done.

9. To adjust the traverse loop, right-click on **CC Traverse** again and select **Traverse Analysis** to apply the survey adjustments to the traverse.

10. In the Traverse Analysis dialog box, change the following, as shown in Figure 4–47:

   - *Horizontal closure limit 1:X*: **150.00**
   - *Update survey database*: **Yes**

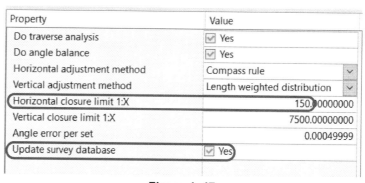

Property	Value
Do traverse analysis	☑ Yes
Do angle balance	☑ Yes
Horizontal adjustment method	Compass rule
Vertical adjustment method	Length weighted distribution
Horizontal closure limit 1:X	150.00000000
Vertical closure limit 1:X	7500.00000000
Angle error per set	0.00049999
Update survey database	☑ Yes

Figure 4–47

11. Click **OK** to apply the new adjustment values to the traverse.

12. In the Survey Toolspace, in the **South Traverses** branch, right-click on Figures and select *Update Figures*.

Task 5 - Make network groups.

1. In the survey database collection, select **Network Groups** (shown in Figure 4–48), and then right-click and select **New.**

Rather than lowering the closure limit, the proper procedure would be to add more observations to get a better closure. However, you will proceed with lowering the limit to get a successful adjustment.

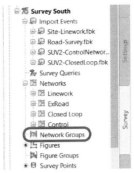

Figure 4–48

2. In the New Network Group dialog box, set the *Name* to **Traverses** and the *Description* to **Traverse Networks for Ascent Development**, as shown in Figure 4–49.

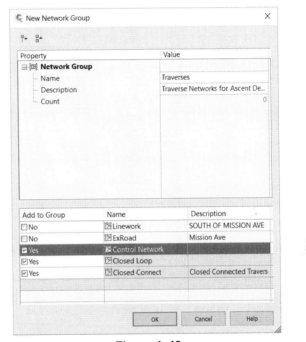

Figure 4–49

3. In the *Add to Group* column, select the checkboxes beside the *Closed Connect, Closed Loop* and *Control Network* to add them to the network group.

4. Click **OK**.

5. While any changes should be stored in the **South Traverses** survey database, ensure that any other changes are saved by clicking **Save**.

4.6 Working with Figures

Figures can represent many linear elements (such as surface breaklines, lot lines, pipe runs, targets for corridors, etc.). The layer on which these elements are located can be toggled off before the final deliverable plots.

A figure does not need to be inserted into a drawing to review its location. By selecting a figure from the Survey's figure list, it is previewed in the drawing, as shown in Figure 4–50.

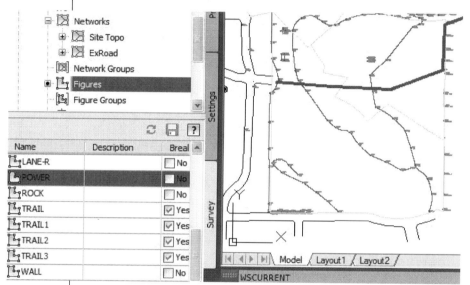

Figure 4–50

Right-click on a selected figure under the **Figures** collection to display a list of options (as shown in Figure 4–51), which enable you to remove the figure from the drawing, display its properties, insert the figure into the drawing, or insert its points into the drawing.

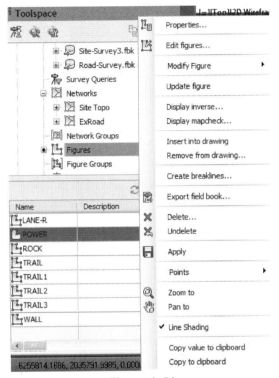

Figure 4–51

- You can access the Panorama's *Grading Elevation Editor* tab by selecting the figure in the drawing, right-clicking, and selecting **Elevation Edit**. Alternatively you can select the figure and click ![icon](Edit Elevations) in the *Figure* contextual tab>Modify panel. Then, click ![icon](Elevation Editor) in the *Figure* contextual tab>Edit Elevations panel.

The icons in the editor enable you to raise or lower its elevation for all or single vertices, as shown in Figure 4–52. You can also click in each cell and edit its elevation. The edits made in this Panorama transfer back to the survey when you select **Update Survey Data from Drawing** (select the figure and right-click to access this option).

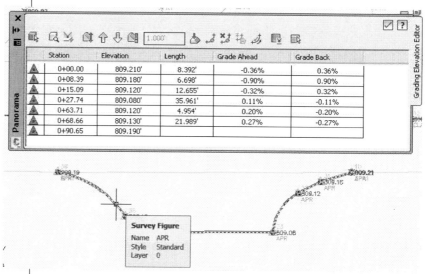

Figure 4–52

When a figure is selected in the drawing, the ribbon displays all of the tools that are applicable to the figure. If you select the **Edit Geometry** icon in the ribbon, you can also add or remove vertices, and offset figures to create new figures (e.g., top-face-curb from the gutter figure).

Practice 4d

Field Book Edits, Styles, and Figure Prefixes

Practice Objective

- Edit a field book file by drawing linework and then adding it to the survey.

In this practice, you will edit the field book and manually create a figure.

Task 1 - Edit the field book.

1. Continue working with the drawing from the previous practice or open **FB-C-Survey.dwg** from the *C:\Civil 3D for Surveyors\Working\Survey* folder.

*If **South Traverses** is not listed under Survey Databases, change your working folder to C:\Civil 3D for Surveyors\ Survey Databases\ Ascent Fieldbooks.*

2. Continue with the previously opened database, or open the **South Traverses** survey database.

3. In the *Survey* tab, select **Figures**. In the preview area at the bottom (shown in Figure 4–53), select **Building1**, right-click, and select **Zoom to**.

4. The survey crew in the field shot the building corners, but some minor work is still required to close the linework in the area shown in Figure 4–54.

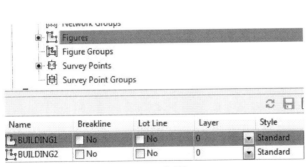

Figure 4–53

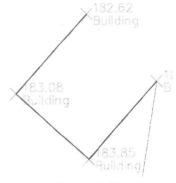

Figure 4–54

5. In the *Survey* tab, expand the **Networks** collection. Select **Linework**, right-click, and select **Edit Field Book**.

6. For the *Field book filename (.FBK)*, browse to the *C:\Civil 3D for Surveyors\Survey Databases\Data\Level 1* folder and select **Site-Linework.fbk**. This opens the field book file in a text editor.

7. Scroll down to the line containing point number **574**. Note that for Building1 and Building2, you have an *End* for the figure (as shown in Figure 4–55) instead of a *Close*. Change the *End* to **Close**, which will close the figure.

```
Begin Building1                          Begin Building1
NE SS 571 620894.4701 1906908.           NE SS 571 620894.4701 1906908.
NE SS 572 620888.7293 1906903.           NE SS 572 620888.7293 1906903.
NE SS 573 620883.9411 1906908.           NE SS 573 620883.9411 1906908.
NE SS 574 620889.5634 1906913.           NE SS 574 620889.5634 1906913.
End Building1  ◀━━━                       Close Building1
Begin Building2                          Begin Building2
NE SS 575 620834.9955 1906904.           NE SS 575 620834.9955 1906904.
NE SS 576 620820.588 1906904.7           NE SS 576 620820.588 1906904.
NE SS 577 620820.588 1906911.9           NE SS 577 620820.588 1906911.
NE SS 578 620834.9955 1906911.           NE SS 578 620834.9955 1906911.
End Building2  ◀━━━                       Close Building2

NE SS 579 620827.5755 1907112.           NE SS 579 620827.5755 1907112.
NE SS 580 620820.3717 1907112.           NE SS 580 620820.3717 1907112.
NE SS 581 620820.3717 1907105.           NE SS 581 620820.3717 1907105.
NE SS 582 620827.5755 1907105.           NE SS 582 620827.5755 1907105.
```

Figure 4–55

8. Exit Notepad and when prompted, save the edits.

Task 2 - Re-import the field book.

Now that the field book file has been revised in the previous task, you will need to update the drawing.

1. Under the **Import Events** collection, select **Site-Linework.fbk**, right-click, and select **Re-import**, as shown in Figure 4–56.

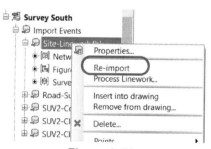

Figure 4–56

2. In the Re-import Field Book dialog box, click **OK** to reset the survey and re-import the network.

3. Select **Figures**. In the preview area at the bottom, double-click on **Building1** and then on **Building2**. As the Autodesk Civil 3D software zooms into each of these figures, note that each one is now closed.

Task 3 - Create a figure manually.

1. In the Toolspace>*Prospector* tab, expand the **Point Groups** collection and select the **_All Points** point group.

2. In the preview area at the bottom, scroll to point number **579**, as shown in Figure 4–57. Select it, hold <Shift>, and select point number **582**. While still holding <Shift>, right-click, and select **Zoom to**.

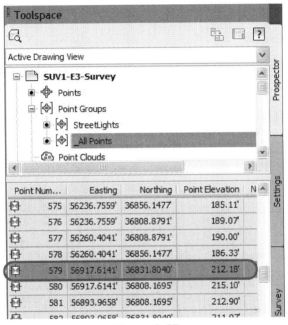

Figure 4–57

You can also use some of the Autodesk Civil 3D tools, such as the Transparent command tools.

3. Using the AutoCAD® **3D Polyline** command (type **3P** in the Command Line) and the **Node** object snap, draw a polyline connecting the nodes, as shown in Figure 4–58.

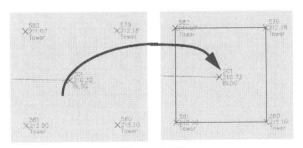

Figure 4–58

4. In the *Survey* tab, under the **Survey Databases>South Traverses** collections, select **Figures**, right-click, and select **Create figure from object**, as shown in Figure 4–59. In the drawing, select the polyline that you just drew.

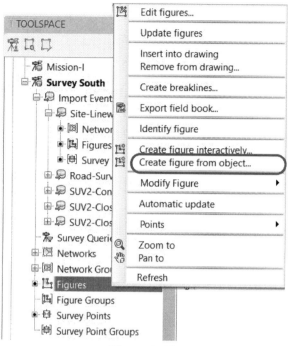

Figure 4–59

5. In the Create Figure From Object dialog box, set the *Name* to **Tower**, as shown in Figure 4–60. Click **OK** to create the new figure. Press <Enter> to exit the command.

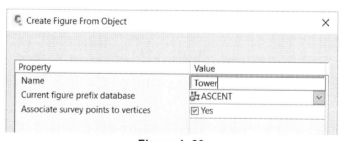

Figure 4–60

It is not required to insert a figure that you create into a drawing. Step 7 has been included to ensure that you know how to insert a figure for other purposes.

6. To update the drawing with the figure, select **Figures**, right-click, and select **Insert into drawing**, as shown in Figure 4–61.

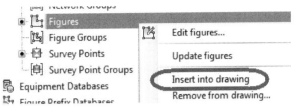

Figure 4–61

7. Next you will review the figure's properties. In the *Survey* tab, select **Figures**.

8. In the preview window, select the **Tower** figure, right-click, and select **Properties**.

9. Review the figure's properties, as shown in Figure 4–62. If required, change the *Style* to **ASC-Buildings**. When done, click **OK** to exit the dialog box.

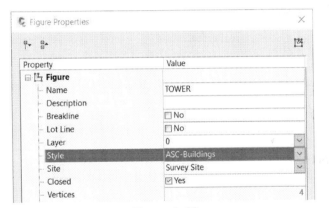

Figure 4–62

10. Save and close the drawing.

Chapter Review Questions

1. If you need to analyze the field data using the analysis tools available in the Survey Database, you must use a field book file rather than a text file.

   a. True

   b. False

2. How many field book files can you import into one network?

   a. One

   b. Two

   c. Ten

   d. Unlimited

3. When modifying a survey to close a figure created from a field book file, you:

   a. Right-click on the figure and select **Close**.

   b. Modify the point code in the field book file.

   c. Modify the field note proceeding the point in the field book file.

   d. You cannot make changes to figures once they are imported.

4. What is the biggest difference between using a field book file and point file with connective codes for importing survey data? (Select all that apply.)

   a. There is no difference and they can be used interchangeably.

   b. When using a field book file, in the field, the connective code is added as a note which is separate from the point description. When using a point file with connective codes, the connective codes are entered in the same line as the point description.

   c. A field book file must be post processed where as a point file with connective codes can be directly imported.

   d. A point file with connective codes contains all of the data that was used during the survey field pickup by a total station (e.g., setups, back-sites, instrument height, prism height, turned angles, side shots, etc.)

Command Summary

Button	Command	Location
	Create Points	• **Ribbon**: *Home* tab>Create Ground Data panel
	Import Points from File	• **Ribbon**: *Insert* tab>Import panel • **Toolbar**: Create Points • **Command Prompt**: ImportPoints
	Import Survey Data	• **Ribbon**: *Home* tab>Create Ground Data panel • **Command Prompt**: ImportSurveyData
	Survey Toolspace	• **Ribbon**: *Home* tab>Palettes panel
	Survey User Settings	• **Toolspace**: *Survey* tab
	Zoom To Points	• **Toolbar**: Transparent Commands • **Command Prompt**: 'ZTP

Points with Connective Codes

Importing points with line connectivity codes enables you to create figures from survey data. In this chapter, you will learn how to work with connective codes. You will import points and then modify linework as required. Finally, you will learn how to transpose a survey database so that points and figures fall in the correct locations.

Once the survey database is populated with point and linework data, you can perform and store queries in the survey database to manage the data. You can also create survey point groups to assist in managing the point data in the survey database.

Learning Objectives in This Chapter

- List some basic syntax coding rules used in the Autodesk® Civil 3D® software.
- Describe how survey figures are used in the Autodesk Civil 3D software.
- Edit the Linework Code Set to ensure coding used in the field survey will create linework upon import into the drawing.
- Move survey data from an assumed location to a known location using the translation wizard.
- Insert Import events into the current drawing.

5.1 Field Codes

During the survey pickup for each point, the surveyor assigns a field code that describes the point or line feature. This information is saved in the data collector and is output as an ASCII file. A line feature or connective code can be appended to a point description and indicates whether the feature line is a line segment or curve segment, and whether it is the beginning, continuation, or end of a segment.

Example

310,620918.3755,1907041.4409,53.0132, CL1 B

In this example, CL1 B is the field code in which:

- CL = An abbreviation that represents a center line.

- 1 = The center line number.

- B = The code in the linework code that is set to begin a figure.

Field codes are associated with both the Figure Prefix database and the description keys in the current drawing. If **CL** has been defined in the Figure Prefix Database (as shown in Figure 5–1), CL1 matches CL and is assigned the properties of the CL figure prefix, such as **Layer**, **Figure Style**, **Lotline** and **Breakline**.

Note that when you import the survey data, you can omit the Begin code if the feature name matches a figure prefix that is defined in the current figure prefix database. If the feature name does not match a figure prefix, you must specify a Begin code.

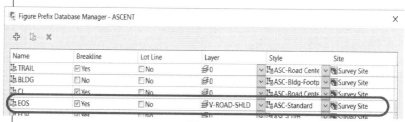

Figure 5–1

If the survey point with the description CL1 B is placed in a drawing that has a description key of CL* (as shown in Figure 5–2), CL1 B matches the description key CL* and is assigned the point properties defined in the CL* description key, such as **Layer**, **Point Style**, and **Point Label Style**.

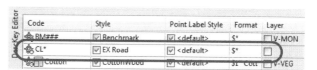

Figure 5–2

Linework Codes: Coding syntax

Some basic coding syntax rules are as follows:

CL1 B	It is recommended that you use <space> as the Field/Code delimiter property value (i.e., the <space> between the description CL1 and the B).
CL1 B/ Start of the centerline	A / <forward slash> is the recommended escape field code. It indicates that anything entered after the escape indicator is a comment.
CL1 B	Select **Yes** to specify that in CL1 B, CL1 matches the figure prefix of CL, and B is the Begin code. Select **No**, if you do not want the first instance of CL1 to automatically start a new figure named CL.

Linework Codes: Special Codes

CL1 B SW1 B B CL1 B SW1	**B** = Begin CL1 and SW1 are figure names. The letter B is the special code that is used to begin new figures named CL1 and SW1.
CL1 C SW1	**C** = Continue (Not used very much in practice) CL1 is a figure name. C continues the active figure named CL1. If the field code does not contain an explicit <Continue> code and the figure name in the field code matches an active figure, the figure is continued.
CL1 E SW1 B	**E** = End E is the End code. It continues an active figure with the name CL1 to this point and is then terminated (it is no longer an active). However, figure SW1 with the B code is starts at this point.
CL1 SW1 CLS	**CLS** = Close CLS is the Close code. A line segment is closed back to the starting vertex for the figure SW1. However, figure CL1 is still active and continues.
1,500,490,100.0 1,BC1 B H-4 V.1 H.5 H.75 V-.7 H2.25 V-.35	**H** = Horizontal offset H is the <Horizontal offset> code and -4 is the value for the first horizontal. **V** = Vertical Offset V is the <Vertical offset> code and .1 is the first vertical offset value, etc., for each of the remaining 3 offsets.
7,500,550,100.0 7,BC1 SO	**SO** = Stop offsets SO is the <Stop Offset> code. It terminates the offset for this figure.

Note that there are no spaces between RPN, CPN, or RECT, and the point number.

Linework Codes: Line Segment Codes

CL1 RPN CL1 RPN101	**RPN** = Recall point RPN is the Recall Point code. If a point is not supplied, it connects from the previous point to the current point and inserts a segment before the current point. If a point is supplied, as in the code CL1 RPN101, it connects from the current point to the indicated point.
CL1 B **CPN**101	**CPN** = Connect point A new figure CL1 is created at the current point, and a new figure with a single line segment is drawn to point 101 and called CL1.CPN101.
BLD1 RECT40	**RECT** = Rectangle A positive number indicates an offset to the right and a negative number indicates an offset to the left, which is relative to the direction of the line segment coming into the current point. If a number does not follow the Rectangle code, the code closes the figure by performing a perpendicular/ perpendicular line intersection between the previous segment coming into the current point and the first segment of the figure.
BLD1 RT X10.1 5 -12.2 -5 -12.2	**RT** = Right Turn Continues an active figure BLD1 to the current point, extends the current segment 10.1 units, and then draws perpendicular segments for each value
BLD1 X15.5	**X** = Extend BLD1 continues an active figure, X is the Extend code, and 15.5 is the value that the figure line segment is extended through the current point.

Linework Codes: Curve Segment Codes

CL1 BC	**BC** = Begin Curve BC indicates that the current point is the beginning of the curve segments.
CL1 EC	**EC** = End Curve EC indicates that the current point is the end of curve segments. You can have multiple figure points between the Begin and End curve segment codes.
CL1 CIR5.0	**CIR** = Circle CIR is the <Circle> code. It creates a new circular figure in which the current point is the radius point and 5.0 is the circle radius value.
CL1 OC	**OC** = Point On Curve OC is the Point On Curve code. The figure is continued and the point is evaluated as a point residing on a curve.

5.2 Survey Data - Figures

A Survey Figure is a line that is defined and coded during the field data pick up process. The name of the Survey Figure in the Autodesk Civil 3D software is defined based on the description code assigned to the point in the survey data file. When importing a points line coded connective file through the Survey Database, if the Linework Code Set "B" is appended to the description code, defining the beginning of a line, GUT B begins a Survey Figure and the Survey Figure is named GUT in the drawing.

The Figure Prefix Database Manager is set up in advance so that rows are tagged analogous to the Description Key Set and a Figure Style can be assigned to define the Figure. Survey Figures are an improvement in the advance of Survey technology in that they are not just AutoCAD lines connecting points; they contain all of the properties of intelligent survey data that can be used by other tools in the Autodesk Civil 3D software. These survey figures can be edited using the feature line tools to not only edit the data geographically but also perform design calculations to the vertical aspect of the survey line.

Both office and field personnel need to be consistent when using the set of standards that result from the preset naming conventions. The conventions can assign multiple figures as breaklines or as lot lines in a parcel. For example, all figures that are preset as breaklines, populate the Breaklines variable in the Surface.

When using figures, you might need to create a Survey Figure of a building measure with a tape. A surveyor only needs to pick up a few key reference points and either enter the turned measured distances into the survey data file or edit the survey figure in the Autodesk Civil 3D software to enter the turned measured distance. However, it must be noted that using this method assumes that the turned angles are 90 degrees.

Practice 5a

Importing Data - Figures

Practice Objective

- Import figures from survey data and create new figures interactively.

In this practice, you will import text files in which figures are defined. The surveyor has used a local coordinate system for the survey pickup and has worked in metric units. Therefore, you will start a new drawing from a different drawing template and a survey project database, both without an established coordinate zone.

The survey data you are importing was collected in metric units, but your project drawings are in imperial units. The Autodesk Civil 3D software handles the conversions automatically, without giving any notifications.

The template established for this practice is set up to use a particular established coordinate zone. You need to pick a different template with no established coordinate zone.

Task 1 - Start a new drawing and create a new survey database.

1. In the Start Tab, select the Templates drop-down list to start a new drawing file. Select **_Autodesk Civil 3D (Imperial) NCS.dwt** (which is provided with the software), as shown in Figure 5–3.

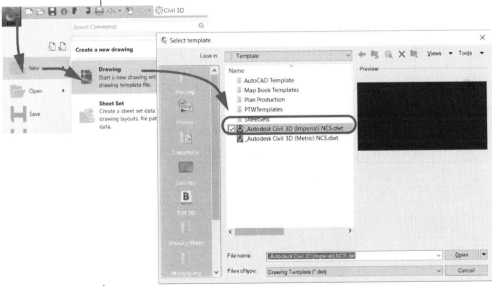

Figure 5–3

2. Click 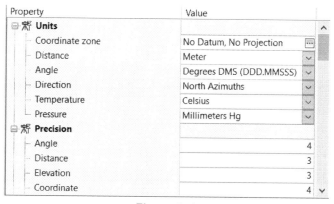 (Application Menu) and select **SaveAs**. Browse to *C:\Civil 3D for Surveyors\Working\Survey* and click **Save**. Name the new drawing **LineCodes-A-Survey.dwg**

3. In the *Survey* tab, right-click on **Survey Databases**, and select **Set working folder**.

   - Browse and select the *C:\Civil 3D for Surveyors\Survey Databases\Ascent Pointfiles* folder.
   - Click **Select Folder**.

4. In the Toolspace>*Survey* tab, right-click on **Survey Databases** and select **New local survey database**.

5. Set the *Name* to **Local-Metric** and click **OK**.

6. Right-click on the **Local-Metric** database and select **Edit Survey Database Settings**.

7. In the Select Coordinate Zone dialog box, set the following, as shown in Figure 5–4.

   - *Coordinate Zone:* **No Datum, No Projection**
     Hint: An easy way to select **No Datum, No Projection** is to type a period (**.**) into the *Selected coordinate system code* field, as shown in Figure 5–5.
   - *Direction*: **North Azimuths**
   - *Temperature:* **Celsius**
   - *Pressure:* **Millimeters Hg**

Property	Value
⊟ 🎥 **Units**	
Coordinate zone	No Datum, No Projection
Distance	Meter
Angle	Degrees DMS (DDD.MMSSS)
Direction	North Azimuths
Temperature	Celsius
Pressure	Millimeters Hg
⊟ 🎥 **Precision**	
Angle	4
Distance	3
Elevation	3
Coordinate	4

Figure 5–4

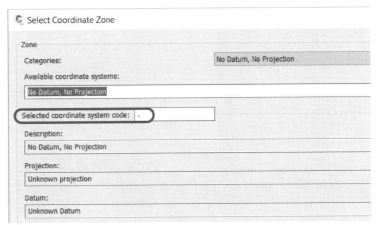

Figure 5–5

8. When done, click **OK** to close the dialog box.

9. In the Toolspace>*Prospector* tab, note that there are no sites in the drawing, as shown in Figure 5–6.

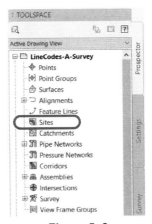

Figure 5–6

Task 2 - Set up a network and import a survey.

1. Expand the survey database collection and then right-click on **Networks**. Select **New**.

2. In the New Network dialog box, set the *Name* to **Figures-LineCodes**. Click **OK**.

3. Right-click on **Figures-LineCodes** and select
   Import>Import point file to import the ASCII file, as shown
   in Figure 5–7.

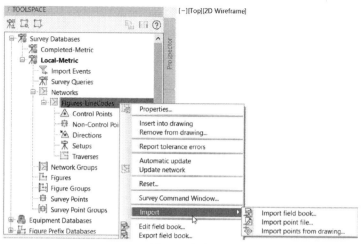

Figure 5–7

*You may have to set the
Files of type to **All
Files (*.*)** or **Text (*.txt)**.*

4. Select the field book file **Properties-Assumed.txt** from the
   C:\Civil 3D for Surveyors\Survey Databases\Data\Level 1
   folder, and then click **Open**.

5. In the Import Point File dialog box, *Point file format*
   drop-down list, select **PNEZD (comma delimited)**. Verify the
   following settings are selected, as shown in Figure 5–8.

   • *Current figure prefix database*: **ASCENT**
   • *Process linework during import*: **Yes**
   • *Current linework code set*: **ASCENT**
   • *Insert figure objects*: **Yes**
   • *Insert network object:* (Immaterial when importing point
     files)
   • *Insert survey points*: **Yes**

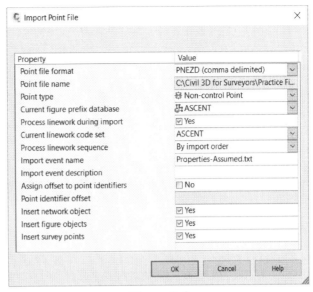

Figure 5–8

6. Click **OK**.

7. In the Status Bar, change the view scale to **1"=10'**, as shown in Figure 5–9.

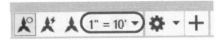

Figure 5–9

8. In the rare case where the linework does not display, in the **Local-Metric** survey database, right-click on the **Proposed-Assumed.txt** Import Event and select **Process Linework**, as shown in Figure 5–10.

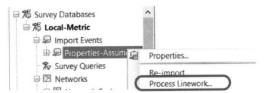

Figure 5–10

9. In the Toolspace>*Prospector* tab, note that there are now two
sites in the drawing, but no parcels, as shown in Figure 5–11.

*The sites were created
from matches within the
Figure prefix database.
Some figures are
assigned as Lots.*

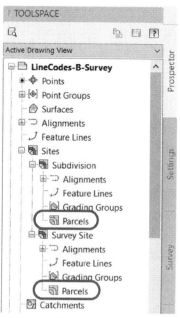

Figure 5–11

10. Save the drawing.

Task 3 - Review the survey data and create a survey figure.

In this task, you will review the survey data without making any
changes. To make it easier to view, you will change the
Annotative scale.

1. Continue working with the drawing from the previous task.

In reviewing your imported points file (shown in Figure 5–12),
note that there are a number of errors that need to be fixed.
The errors dealing with Line Code will be fixed in a later
section. Additionally, there are a number of solutions to fixing
the missing figure.

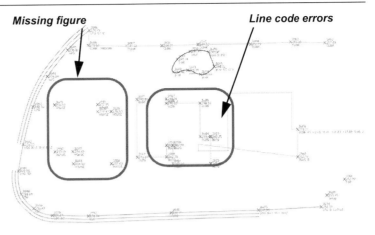

Figure 5–12

In addition to adding **B** and **CLS** line code connective to your survey data file, you can also change the survey data description from *House* to **BLDG**, as shown in Figure 5–13. As a BLDG is defined in the Figure prefix database, on re-import, a BLDG figure will be created.

```
28,5010.5005,9928.7677,72.4282,HOUSE
29,5026.5950,9928.7677,72.7032,HOUSE
30,5026.5950,9924.3764,72.3679,HOUSE

28,5010.5005,9928.7677,72.4282,BLDG  B
29,5026.5950,9928.7677,72.7032,BLDG
30,5026.5950,9924.3764,72.3679,BLDG
```

Figure 5–13

You can also create a new figure definition in the Figure prefix database, as shown in Figure 5–14.

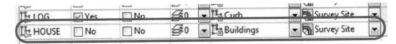

Figure 5–14

Alternatively, you can draw a figure manually, based on the survey points. For demonstration purposes, this practice uses this method.

2. In the Survey Toolspace, right-click on the **Figures** collection and select **Create figure interactively**, as shown in Figure 5–15.

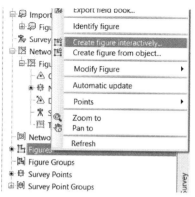

Figure 5–15

You can also use some of the Autodesk Civil 3D tools, such as the transparent command tools.

3. In the New figure dialog box, type **W. Building** for the figure name (as shown in Figure 5–16) and click **OK**.

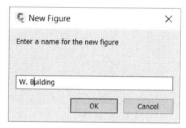

Figure 5–16

4. When prompted, select the point objects, select points **2028-2033**, **2047**, and **2048** in order, and then press <Enter>.

5. In the Figure Properties dialog box, set the following, as shown in Figure 5–17:
   - *Style*: **ASC-Buildings**
   - *Closed*: **Yes**

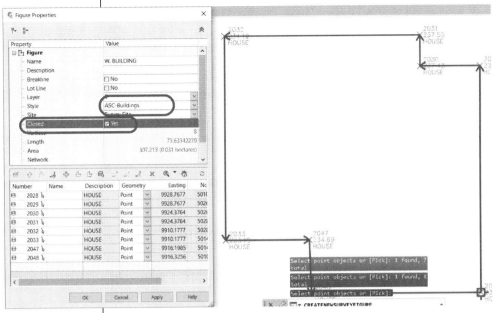

Figure 5–17

6. Click **OK**.

7. If the figure does not appear in the drawing, you can insert it by selecting it in the Survey Toolspace, in the **Figures** collection in the survey database. In the list of figures, right-click on **W. Building** and select **Insert into drawing**, as shown in Figure 5–18.

The figure might display as not closed. Reselect the figure in the survey figures panorama window, and select **Properties**. *This refreshes the screen and the figure displays as closed.*

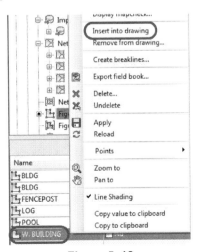

Figure 5–18

8. Save the drawing.

5.3 Figure Prefix Database

Amongst other functions, the Figure Prefix Database defines whether a figure is a lot line (parcel segment), as shown in Figure 5–19. Toggling on the *Lot Line* property creates a parcel segment from the figure in the drawing.

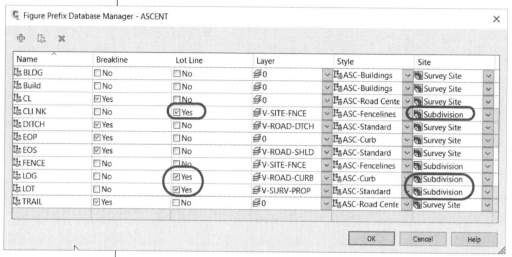

Figure 5–19

Therefore, when a figure with a prefix designated as a *Lot Line* is generated, the Autodesk Civil 3D software creates a site as specified in the Figure Prefix Database and then places the parcel segment on that site. When such figures (which are parcel segments) are closed or intersect to form an enclosure, a parcel is created in the site, and a parcel label displays.

Practice 5b

Importing Data - Figures, Parcels

Practice Objective

- Import figures from survey data which create parcel segments and parcels.

In this practice, you will import data from a text file with additional figures defined. The surveyor has used a local coordinate system for the survey pickup.

The survey data you are importing was collected in metric units, while your project drawings are in imperial units.

1. Continue working with the drawing from the previous practice, or open the file **LineCodes-B-Survey.dwg** from the *C:\Civil 3D for Surveyors\Working\Survey* folder.

*If **Local-Metric** is not listed under Survey Databases, change your working folder to C:\Civil 3D for Surveyors\ Survey Databases\ Ascent Pointfiles.*

2. If you are greeted with a splash screen about using Online Map Data, select **Remember my choice** and click **No**, as shown in Figure 5–20. (Since you have captured an online map in a previous chapter, you do not need to use Online Map Data.)

Figure 5–20

3. Continue working in the **Local-Metric** survey database. If required, right-click on the **Local-Metric** survey database to open it for editing.

4. Right-click on the **Local-Metric** survey database and select **Import>Import point file**, as shown in Figure 5–21.

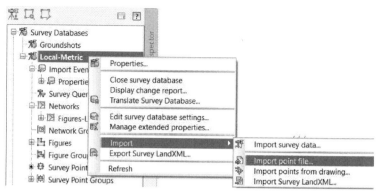

Figure 5–21

5. Select the text file **Local-lots.txt** from the *C:\Civil 3D for Surveyors\Survey Databases\Data\Level 1* folder and click **Open**.

6. In the Import Point File dialog box, in the *Point file format* drop-down list, select **PNEZD (comma delimited)**. Verify the following settings are selected as shown in Figure 5–22.

    *   *Current figure prefix database*: **ASCENT**
    *   *Process linework during import*: **Yes**
    *   *Current linework code set*: **ASCENT**
    *   *Insert network object:* (Immaterial when importing point files)
    *   *Insert figure objects*: **Yes**
    *   *Insert survey points*: **Yes**

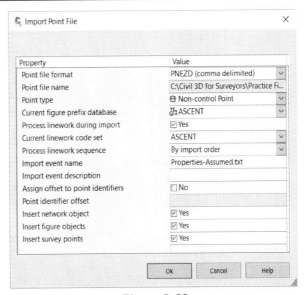

Figure 5–22

7. Click **OK**.

8. Note that parcels have been created from parcel lines that intersect and form an enclosure, as shown in Figure 5–23.

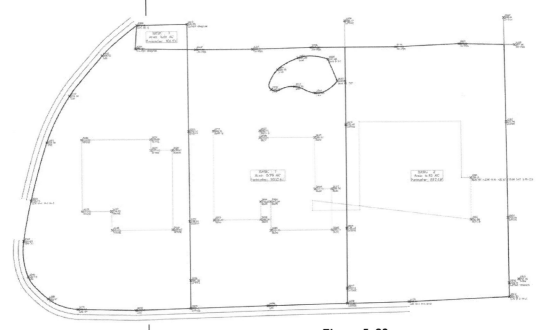

Figure 5–23

9. Note that these parcels are also listed in the Toolspace> *Prospector* tab, as shown in Figure 5–24.

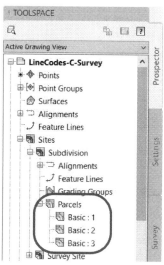

Figure 5–24

10. Note that three lots have been created, while the fourth lot has a small opening somewhere and therefore is not considered a parcel.

11. Save the drawing.

5.4 Survey Data - Line Code

Linework Code Set can be used to customize the language used to create the linework geometry. The Sample Linework Code Set shown in Figure 5–25 requires that the field crew enter the Figure commands in the Value cells to create a variety of geometry. You can modify this to use your Survey company's standard methodology to create automated linework as was done in legacy Civil/Survey software before the Autodesk Civil 3D software was available.

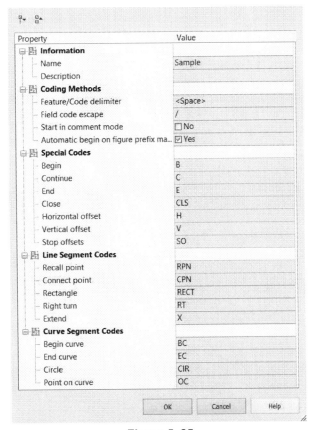

Property	Value
Information	
Name	Sample
Description	
Coding Methods	
Feature/Code delimiter	<Space>
Field code escape	/
Start in comment mode	☐ No
Automatic begin on figure prefix ma...	☑ Yes
Special Codes	
Begin	B
Continue	C
End	E
Close	CLS
Horizontal offset	H
Vertical offset	V
Stop offsets	SO
Line Segment Codes	
Recall point	RPN
Connect point	CPN
Rectangle	RECT
Right turn	RT
Extend	X
Curve Segment Codes	
Begin curve	BC
End curve	EC
Circle	CIR
Point on curve	OC

Figure 5–25

Select the **Automatic begin on figure prefix match** option to enable a Survey Figure to be created if a code in the point file matches a code in the Figure Prefix Database. The Survey Figure begins at the first instance at which the point codes match and continues until the matching point codes no longer occur. The Survey Figure then ends.

If a project contains multiple figures of the same name, it is important to use the **End Figure** command. You can also add an alpha or numeric suffix (depending on whether you are using alpha or numeric codes). For example, GUT B starts the figure GUT for the left side. Using the Zorro method for survey pickup, where an entire station cross-section from left to right is surveyed before proceeding to the next station, the right side of the street is usually entered as GUT1 B. If 59 is the numeric code for a gutter shot, then 59 B starts the figure 59 and the other side of the street is 59A B.

The Autodesk Civil 3D software enables you to use double coding methodology. For example, in GUT APR B a gutter shot is taken and an apron figure is started.

In earlier releases of the Autodesk Civil 3D software, a curve had to be completed before a different shot was taken. This caused problems in the field with large curves. You can now use the **Begin Curve** figure command when one shot is taken on the curve and ends with the **End Curve** command. Alternatively, if you shoot at least two incoming tangent shots and at least two outgoing tangent shots, only one **Point on Curve** command shot is required.

For example, if a survey crew conducts a field survey on an existing parking lot that contains many raised islands, a large number of figures with the same names might be created for the gutter shots. Large parking lots can contain many islands and multiple aprons for entering and exiting the site. You sometimes need to use the End figure command to keep track of the multiple sequencing suffixes. An example of this geometry is shown in Figure 5–26.

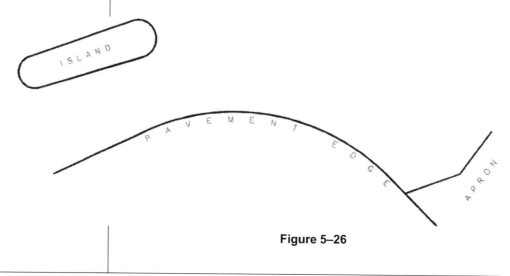

Figure 5–26

*This process replaces the **MCS** and **MCE** commands from previous releases of Civil 3D.*

For the island, you can use the **Begin Curve** command to start the figure and then use the **End Curve** and **Close** figure commands as shown in Figure 5–27. At least one point on the curve must be shot between the **Begin Curve** and **End Curve** commands. Shoot as many points as required between the commands, to create an accurate curve.

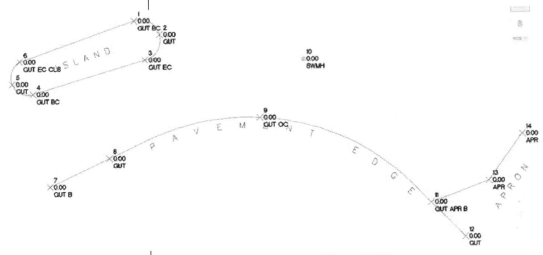

Figure 5–27

Use the **Begin** figure command to create the pavement edge. If you shoot at least two incoming tangents and two outgoing tangents, you only need to use one **Point on Curve (OC)** figure command.

In Figure 5–27, point #10 defines a SWMH manhole and was shot before the curve ended. There is double-coding for the gutter and apron shot. The P.C. and P.T. of the curve for the pavement edge was not required because the two shots that define the bearing for the incoming and outgoing tangents were taken.

In the Linework Code Set defining the custom figure commands, you can also create horizontal and vertical offsets from a Survey Figure. For example, the horizontal offset and vertical offset commands can be used if a segment of a length of an area within the project limits is defined by consistent cross-sectional geometry, such as an existing curb.

In defining an offset survey figure, as shown in Figure 5–28, point #7 starts the pavement edge and is then defined by GUT B H-.1 V.5 H-.5. The Autodesk Civil 3D software then creates another gutter figure that has a horizontal offset to the left of 0.1 units (H-.1) and a vertical offset of 0.5 units (V.5). This creates the top face of the curb. Another gutter figure is then created at 0.5 units to the left (H-.5). Since another vertical callout is not listed, the Autodesk Civil 3D software uses the same vertical offset of 0.5 units (V.5). This creates the top back of a 6" high curb that is 6" wide. This is a fast and accurate methods of creating breaklines for existing surfaces.

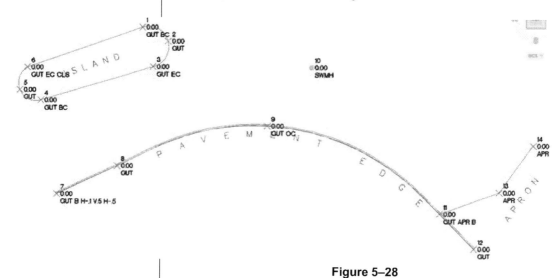

Figure 5–28

In the Toolspace, the two offset figures are named LOG.1 and LOG.2. They become a subset of the original LOG figure, as shown in Figure 5–29.

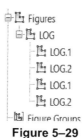

Figure 5–29

5.5 Adjusting Figures

Figures can import incorrectly due to a variety of issues, such as blown shots, missed shot, no curve information, etc. Rather than hunting down the error in the survey input file, you can edit the figure within the survey database after it is imported.

How To: Adjust a Figure

1. Select the figure that needs to be adjusted. Right-click and select **Edit Survey Figure Properties**, as shown in Figure 5–30.

   Note: You can also start this command in the contextual ribbon, but do not select **Figure Properties** from the right-click menu.

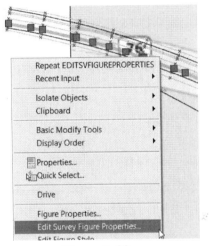

Figure 5–30

2. The *Figure Properties* dialog box displays.

   If the survey figure is vector based, it cannot be edited, and the detailed properties pane does not display in the lower half of the window, as shown on the left in Figure 5–31.

   When this occurs, the survey figure must be converted into a chain-based survey figure.

3. In the top-right corner of the Figure Properties dialog box, click 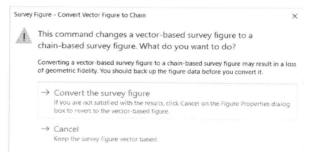 (Convert), as shown in Figure 5–31.

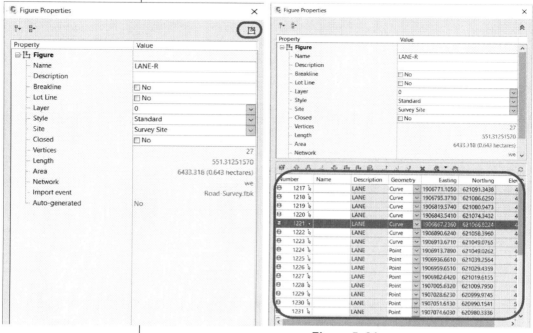

Figure 5–31

4. In the Survey Figure - Convert Vector Figure to Chain dialog box, select **Convert the Survey Figure**, as shown in Figure 5–32.

Figure 5–32

5. In the Figure Properties window, you can now insert or delete vertices, change the geometry, reverse the direction, or make other changes as required.

Practice 5c

Line Code

Practice Objective

- Correct errors in survey figures by editing the line code connotative file.

Task 1 - Review the survey data.

In this task, you review the errors that you will fix in the next task.

1. Continue working with the drawing from the previous practice or open **LineCodes-C-Survey.dwg** from the *C:\Civil 3D for Surveyors\Working\Survey* folder.

2. If you are greeted with a splash screen about using Online Map Data, select **Remember my choice** and click **No**, as shown in Figure 5–33. (Since you have captured an online map in a previous chapter, you do not need to use Online Map Data.)

Figure 5–33

*If **Local-Metric** is not listed under Survey Databases, change your working folder to C:\Civil 3D for Surveyors\ Survey Databases\ Ascent Pointfiles.*

3. Continue working in the **Local-Metric** survey database. If required, right-click on the **Local-Metric** survey database to open it for editing.

4. Review the imported points file and note the errors that need to be fixed, as shown in Figure 5–34.

- Close the building figure (A).
- Correct the linecode in the imported points file (B).
- Modify an offset line to display the back of the sidewalk (C).

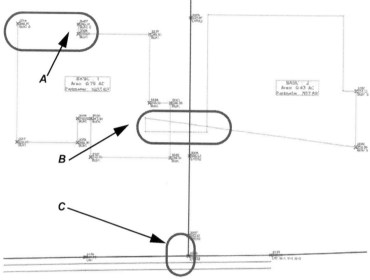

Figure 5–34

Labeling is covered in more detail later in this guide.

5. Select the figure shown in Figure 5–35. In the contextual ribbon, expand the **Add Label** menu and select **Single Segment**. Select the line segment shown in Figure 5–35 and note that the distance is 31.69 feet.

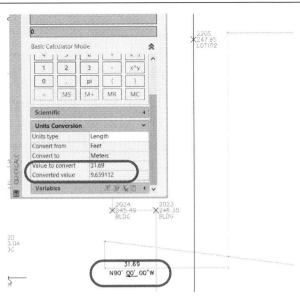

Figure 5–35

*<Ctrl>+<8> is a quick
way to launch the Quick
Calculator.*

6. Civil 3D's Quick Calculator tells us that 31.69' is the
    equivalent to 9.659m. As the metric survey database was
    inserted into the imperial drawing, it converted the units from
    meters to feet.

    *   **Note:** Civil 3D will give no notification when it converts
        measurements between units.

Task 2 - Fix the line code survey file.

In this task, you will fix the error in the line code file.

1. Right-click on the **Local-Metric** survey database and select **Properties**, as shown in Figure 5–36.

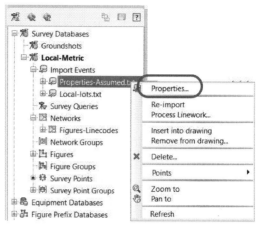

Figure 5–36

2. In the **Import Event Properties** window, by the *File* name, click 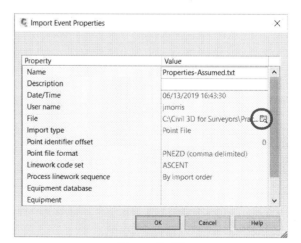 (Select) icon, as shown in Figure 5–37. The **Properties-Assumed.txt** imported text file opens in your default text editor.

Figure 5–37

3. Prior to making any changes, save the file as **Properties-Assumed.ori** in the *C:\Civil 3D for Surveyors\Survey Databases\Data\Level 1* folder (as an archived *original* file). Save the file again as **Properties-Assumed.txt**. Click **Yes** to overwrite the file.

4. At point 2027, after **E** in the description, type **CLS** as shown in Figure 5–38. This fixes error "A" by closing building error 1 from point **16** to point **27**.

```
2026,5028.9361,9946.7723,73.4284,BLDG
2027,5030.3992,9946.7723,73.4284,BLDG E CLS
2028,5010.5005,9928.7677,72.4282,HOUSE
```

Figure 5–38

5. In the line for point **2050**, after the west edge of the building, -17.85 in a south direction, change *9.66* to **-9.66**, as shown in Figure 5–39. This will fix the building error "B".

```
2049,5012.1099,9990.2467,76.9132,BLDG B
2050,5020.5961,9990.2467,77.1798,BLDG RT x0 -2.05 11.41 -21.23 -17.85 -9.66 2.05 CLS
```

Figure 5–39

6. To create a back of sidewalk offset line, you will add a horizontal and vertical offset. The sidewalk only runs from the BC of the curb return. At point **2035** (shown in Figure 5–40), modify the code for the horizontal and vertical offset of the LOG to swap the side of the offset that represents the sidewalk. Delete the minus (-) from the H codes so that it is **LOG H1 V-1 H2**.

7. At point **2041** (shown in Figure 5–40), remove **SO** to continue the offset. SO is the code for "Stop Offset" and by removing this code, the offsets continue.

8. At point **2042** (also shown in Figure 5–40), remove the horizontal and vertical offsets. These offsets are redundant because the curb cut has been eliminated (in the above step).

```
2034,4996.4421,9998.1000,76.9104,LOG B LOT103          2034,4996.4421,9998.1000,76.9104,LOG B LOT103
2035,4995.5734,9977.0976,75.5193,LOG H-1 V-1 H-2        2035,4995.5734,9977.0976,75.5193,LOG H1 V-1 H2
2036,4994.9943,9948.1286,73.5023,LOG                    2036,4994.9943,9948.1286,73.5023,LOG
2037,4994.2704,9921.0427,71.5496,LOG                    2037,4994.2704,9921.0427,71.5496,LOG
2038,4994.5600,9909.1654,70.6753,LOG BC                 2038,4994.5600,9909.1654,70.6753,LOG BC
2039,4996.7317,9903.0819,70.2459,LOG                    2039,4996.7317,9903.0819,70.2459,LOG
2040,5001.2199,9899.0263,70.0084,LOG                    2040,5001.2199,9899.0263,70.0084,LOG
2041,5008.4589,9898.1572,70.0576,LOG SO                 2041,5008.4589,9898.1572,70.0576,LOG
2042,5016.5667,9899.7505,70.3261,LOG H-1 V-1 H-2        2042,5016.5667,9899.7505,70.3261,LOG
```

Figure 5–40

9. Save the text file and exit the text editor program.

10. Close the Import Event Properties dialog box by clicking **OK**.

11. In the *Survey* tab, in the current survey database collection, expand **Import Events**, right-click on **Properties-Assumed.txt**, and select **Re-import**, as shown in Figure 5–41.

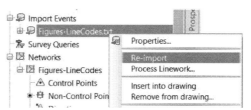

Figure 5–41

12. In the Re-import Points File dialog box, accept the defaults and click **OK**.

13. Now that the sidewalk has flipped, note that the parcel lines for the first lot intersect correctly, and a lot is created, as shown in Figure 5–42. However, also note that additional lots were inadvertently created for the sidewalk.

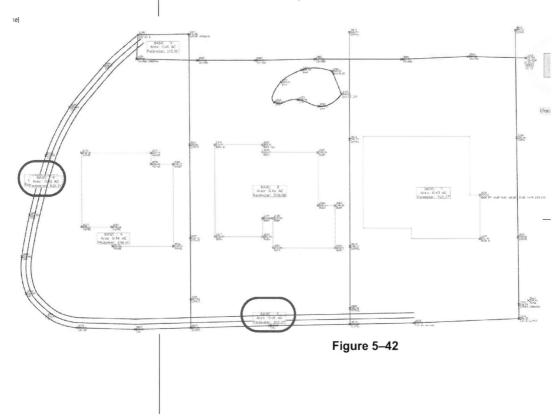

Figure 5–42

14. In the Transparent toolbar, click (Zoom to Point) and type **2001**. Zoom out to understand where this point is located in the drawing. Note that the point is a iron pipe found in the field. You will use this point to translate the survey database to a coordinate zone in the next practice.

15. Save the drawing.

5.6 Translating a Survey Database

Translating a survey database is used when you need to move all of the data in the survey database from an assumed location to a known location. This is done before the survey data is imported into the Autodesk Civil 3D software.

To translate a survey database you need to specify a base point, rotation angle, destination point, and elevation (optional). To use data that is based on local coordinates, you need to convert it to a known common coordinate system that is used by everyone in the project team. The team can include many departments in the same organization, as well as consultants from outside the organization, such as contractors or architects.

The Autodesk Civil 3D software enables you to convert the data using the Translation wizard (shown in Figure 5–43), which applies a **Move and Rotate** command to all of the objects in the survey database project.

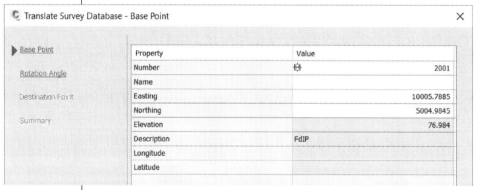

Figure 5–43

Practice 5d | Translating Survey Database

Practice Objectives

- Move survey data from an assumed location to a known location using the translation wizard.
- Study how errors can occur in linework code sets.

The surveyor has used a local coordinate system for the survey pickup. This survey was done using a local coordinate base, in metric. You will translate part of the database to the correct coordinates.

Task 1 - Translate survey data to a coordinate system.

1. In the *C:\Civil 3D for Surveyors\Working\Survey* folder, open **Boundary-B.dwg**.

2. If you are greeted with a splash screen about using Online Map Data, select **Remember my choice** and click **No**, as shown in Figure 5–44. (Since you have captured an online map in a previous chapter, you do not need to use Online Map Data.)

Figure 5–44

3. In the Toolspace>*Prospector* tab, note there are currently no sites in the drawing.

4. If the **Local-Metric** survey database is open, right-click on the **Local-Metric** survey database to close it.

5. In Windows Explorer, navigate to the survey database working folder (*C:\Civil 3D for Surveyors\Survey Databases\Ascent Pointfiles*). Make a copy of the **Local-Metric** folder and name the copy **Local-Metric-Translated**.

6. In the Autodesk Civil 3D software, in Survey Databases, ensure that **Local-Metric-Translated** is listed.

   - If it is not listed, right-click on **Survey Databases** and select **Refresh**. If it still is not listed, change the working folder to *C:\Civil 3D for Surveyors\Survey Databases\Ascent Pointfiles*.

7. Right-click on **Local-Metric-Translated** to open it for editing.

8. In the Toolspace>*Survey* tab, right-click on the **Local-Metric-Translated** and select **Translate survey database**.

Next > does not activate until you press <Enter>.

9. In the Translate Survey Database dialog box, set the *Number* to **2001** and press <Enter>. The values for *Northing*, *Easting*, *Elevation*, and *Description* are already populated with the base point that the surveyor used as the assumed coordinate base point, as shown in Figure 5–45. Click **Next>**.

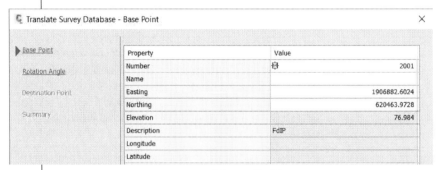

Figure 5–45

10. Set the *Rotation Angle* to **0**, as shown in Figure 5–46. Press <Enter>, and then click **Next>**.

Property	Value
Rotation Angle	0.0000

Figure 5–46

11. In the bottom left corner of the Translate Survey Database dialog box, click **Pick In Drawing**.

12. In Model Space, zoom to the property line in the south-west corner of the site and select the corner endpoint of the boundary line. This reference point has the correct coordinates, as shown in Figure 5–47. Click **Next>**.

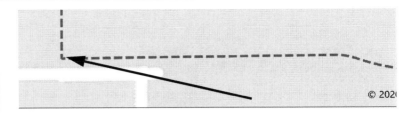

Figure 5–47

13. The Summary page opens, displaying the information shown in Figure 5–48. Review the results, then click **Finish**.

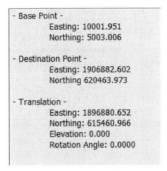

- Base Point -
    Easting: 10001.951
    Northing: 5003.006

- Destination Point -
    Easting: 1906882.602
    Northing 620463.973

- Translation -
    Easting: 1896880.652
    Northing: 615460.966
    Elevation: 0.000
    Rotation Angle: 0.0000

Figure 5–48

14. The survey data has now been converted to the correct coordinates, however, note that it has not been inserted into the drawing. To insert the survey data, expand **Import event**, right-click on **Property-Assumed.txt**, and select **Insert into drawing**, as shown in Figure 5–49.

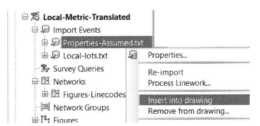

Figure 5–49

15. Change the annotation scale to **1"=10'**.
16. Repeat Step 14 for the **Local-Lots.txt** data. If you reverse the order, you will get errors.

- The errors which occur if you reverse the order are because the **Property-Assumed.txt** Import event contains points that **Local-Lots.txt** uses to connect to. If these points are not available, errors occur.

17. The corrected survey is shown in Figure 5–50.

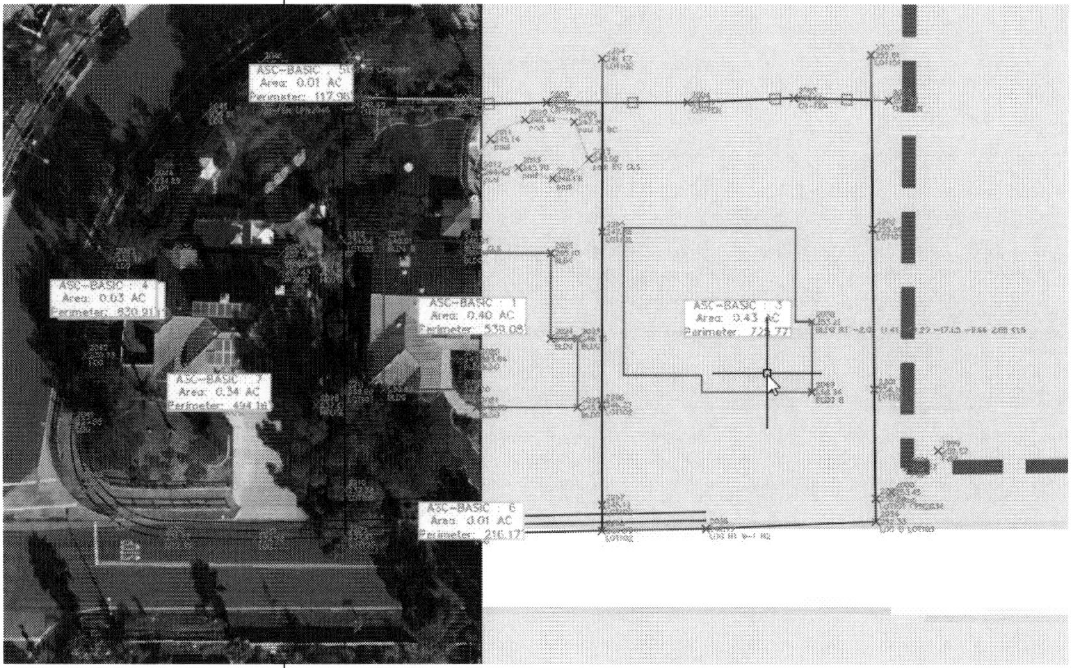

Figure 5–50

18. These parcels are also listed in the Toolspace>*Prospector* tab, as shown in Figure 5–51. The sites were created when the first **Property-Assumed.txt** was inserted into the drawing, while the lots were created when **Local-Lots.txt** was inserted.

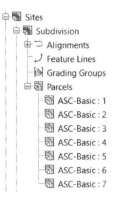

Figure 5–51

19. Save the drawing.

Task 2 - Insert survey data with wrong line coding.

1. Continue working with the drawing from the previous practice, or open **Boundary-C.dwg** from the *C:\Civil 3D for Surveyors\Working\Survey* folder.

2. Change the annotation scale to **1"=40'**.

3. In the *Survey* tab, right-click on **Survey Databases** and select **Set working folder**.
   - Browse and select the *C:\Civil 3D for Surveyors\Survey Databases\Ascent-Development* folder.

4. Click **Select Folder**.

5. In the *Home* tab>expanded Create Ground Data panel, click (Import Survey Data).

6. On the Specify Database page, click **Create New Survey Database**, as shown in Figure 5–52 (1).

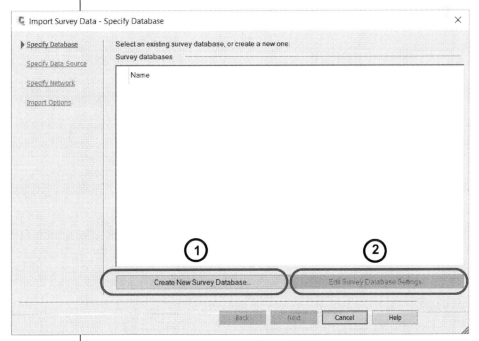

Figure 5–52

7. For the name, type **Mission Ave** and click **OK**.

8. Click **Edit Survey Database Settings**, as shown above in Figure 5–52 (2).

9. In the Survey Database Settings dialog box, for the *Coordinate zone*, click 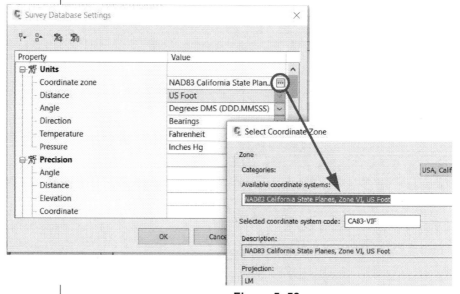 (Browse), as shown in Figure 5–53.

10. In the Select Coordinate Zone dialog box, verify that **NAD83 California State Planes, Zone VI, US Foot** is set, as shown in Figure 5–53. Click **OK** twice and then click **Next**.

Figure 5–53

11. On the Specify Data Sources page, do the following, as shown in Figure 5–54:

- Expand the Data source type drop-down list and select **Point File**.

- Click (Add file), browse to *C:\Civil 3D for Surveyors\Survey Databases\Data\Level 1*, and double-click on **Mission_Ave-I.csv** to open it.

- In the *Specify point file format* area, verify that **PNEZD (comma delimited)** is selected.

- Click **Next**.

You might need to set the Files of type to *.csv or *.* to see the .CSV files in the list.

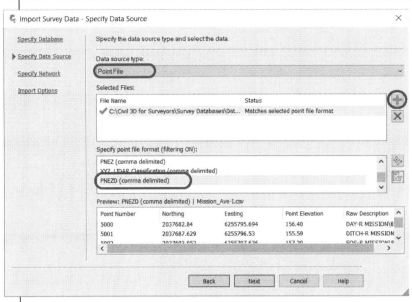

Figure 5–54

12. On the Survey Network page, click **Next**. Note that when importing point files, networks are optional.

13. On the Import Options page, set the following, as shown in Figure 5–55:

- *Process linework during import*: **Yes**
- *Insert figure objects*: **Yes**
- *Insert survey points*: **Yes**
- *Current linework code set*: **ASCENT**

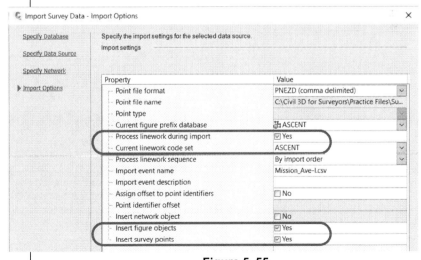

Figure 5–55

14. Click **Finish** and then save the drawing.

15. At the beginning of Mission Ave., note that some of the linework is missing, as shown in Figure 5–56.

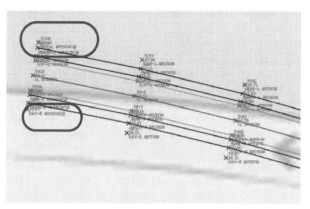

Figure 5–56

16. Examine the .CSV pointfile and the ACME Linework Code Sets, and note that the problem is that the *Feature/Code Delimiter* is set to a slash (\), as shown in Figure 5–57.

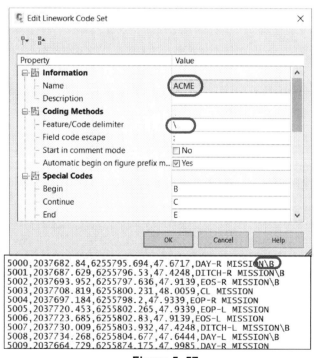

Figure 5–57

17. To correct this, right-click on the **Mission_Ave-I.csv** Import Event and select **Process Linework**. Change the *Current linework code set* to **ACME**, as shown in Figure 5–58.

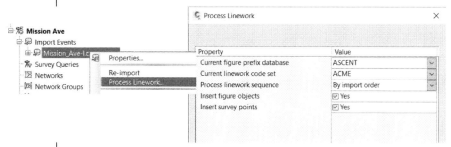

Figure 5–58

18. Click **OK**.

19. Note that the error is corrected and the linework is processed correctly, as shown in Figure 5–59

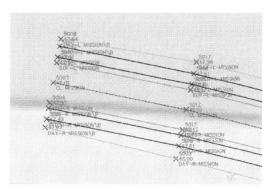

Figure 5–59

20. Save and close the drawing.

Chapter Review Questions

1. When importing points with connectivity codes, you cannot change to the codes used in the field to define figures.

   a. True

   b. False

2. If the Surveyor forgets to put in a connective code after a point description in the field, how do you create a figure from points in the drawing?

   a. You cannot create a figure after importing survey data.

   b. Select the points in the model, right-click and select **Create figure**.

   c. Right-click on **Figures** in the survey database and select **Create figure interactively**.

   d. Right-click on **Figures** in the survey database and select **Create figure from object**.

3. When would you need to translate a survey database?

   a. When the surveyor provides a file format that the Autodesk Civil 3D software cannot read.

   b. When you need to move all of the data in the survey database from an assumed location to a known location.

   c. When you need to correct errors in the data caused by varying measurements.

   d. When the Field book file becomes corrupt and no longer usable.

4. How do you edit errors in survey figures that are generated by imported text files?

   a. Edit the survey figures directly in the drawing.

   b. Edit the survey figures through the Survey Figure Properties.

   c. Edit the text file source that was used during import.

   d. Survey figures cannot be edited.

Command Summary

Button	Command	Location
	Create Points	• **Ribbon**: *Home* tab>Create Ground Data panel
	Import Points from File	• **Ribbon**: *Insert* tab>Import panel • **Toolbar**: Create Points • **Command Prompt:** ImportPoints
	Import Survey Data	• **Ribbon**: *Home* tab>Create Ground Data panel • **Command Prompt:** ImportSurveyData
	Survey User Settings	• **Toolspace**: *Survey* tab
	Zoom To Points	• **Toolbar**: Transparent Commands • **Command Prompt:** 'ZTP

Points

Points are a very important part of every construction project. They help lay out the existing conditions plan, as well as determine where stakes are placed for proposed features of the final design. In this chapter, you will learn how to effectively create various points in the model and assign styles to points. This is done by importing points and creating points manually.

Learning Objectives in This Chapter

- Set the appropriate point creation values and next available point number.
- Create additional COGO points using the Create Points toolbar for points that were not imported from the survey data.
- Assign point symbols, labels, layers, and other items automatically when importing points by setting up Description Key Sets.
- Import points from and export points to ASCII files created from the field survey.
- Group points together using common properties, such as name, elevation, description, etc.
- Review and edit points using the Panorama window to ensure accuracy.
- Prevent unwanted edits to points by locking them.
- Share information about points used for error checking or staking out points using predefined reports.
- Add survey queries to a survey database.

6.1 Point Settings

When creating new COGO points, you must determine the next point number, as well as which elevations and descriptions to assign and how to assign them. To set the current point number, default elevations, descriptions, and other similar settings, use the Create Points toolbar's expanded area. Display this area by clicking ⯆ in the Create Points toolbar. The two areas, *Points Creation* (shown in Figure 6–1) and *Point Identity* (shown in Figure 6–2) contain the most commonly used values.

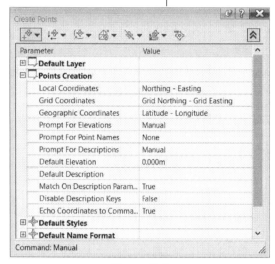

Figure 6–1

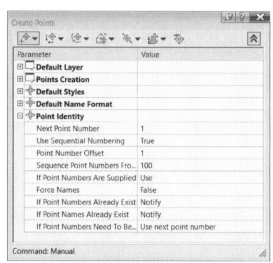

Figure 6–2

- Alternatively, you can select the Toolspace>*Settings* tab and expand the **Commands** collection, under the **Point** collection. Select **Create Points**, right-click, and select **Edit Command Settings**, as shown in Figure 6–3.

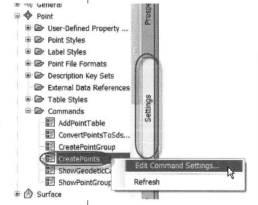

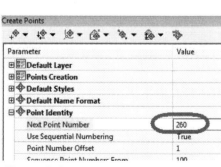

Figure 6–3

Points Creation Values

The *Points Creation* area affects prompting for elevations and descriptions. The two properties in this area are *Prompt For Elevations* and *Prompt For Descriptions*. These properties can be set as follows:

None	Does not prompt for an elevation or description.
Manual	Prompts for an elevation or description.
Automatic	Uses the **Default Elevation** or **Default Description** value when creating a point.
Automatic-Object	Creates points along an alignment whose description consists of the **Alignment name** and **Station**. This description is not dynamic and does not update if the alignment changes or the point is moved. You cannot set *Prompt For Elevations* to **Automatic-Object**.

Point Identity Values

The *Point Identity* area sets the default method of handling duplicate point numbers. If there are duplicate point numbers, there are four ways to resolve the duplication:

- Renumber the incoming point.
- Overwrite the existing point data.
- Merge the incoming point data with existing point data.
- Notify (and await further instructions).

If Notify is selected, then there are five options available:

These options are explained later in this chapter.

- Use next point number
- Add an offset
- Sequence from
- Overwrite
- Merge

This area's most critical property is *Next Point Number*. It is set to the first available number in the point list. If a file of imported point data uses point numbers 1-131 and 152-264, the current point number is 132 after importing the file. This value should be set manually to the next required point number before creating new points with the Create Points toolbar.

6.2 Creating COGO Points

Points can be created using the commands in the Create Points toolbar. These commands include:

- **Miscellaneous - Manual:** Creates a new point at specified coordinates.

- **Alignments - Station/Offset:** Creates a point at an alignment's specific station and offset. These points and their descriptions do not update if the alignment is modified or the point is moved. If you prefer a dynamic station and offset labels, consider using an Alignment label instead.

- **Alignments - Measure Alignment:** Creates point objects at a set interval, which is useful for construction staking. Again, these points do not update if the alignment changes.

- **Surface - Random Points:** Creates points whose elevation is from a specified surface. These points do update, but you must manually force the update. If you prefer a dynamic spot label, consider a Surface label instead.

Each icon in the Create Points toolbar has a drop-down list. If expanded, a command from the list can be selected to run, as shown in Figure 6–4.

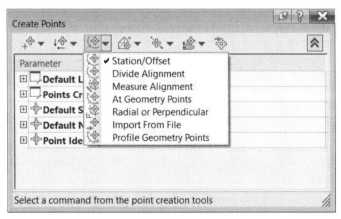

Figure 6–4

6.3 Transparent Commands

Several methods of placing points can use other existing points to help define the location of a new point. For example, you might want to locate a new point at specific distances from two existing points. The Autodesk Civil 3D software uses the point filters to reference point objects in a drawing. These commands (shown in Figure 6–5) are accessed in the *Transparent* ribbon tab, the *Transparent Commands* toolbar, or through the right-click menu when the AutoCAD or Autodesk Civil 3D software is searching for a point.

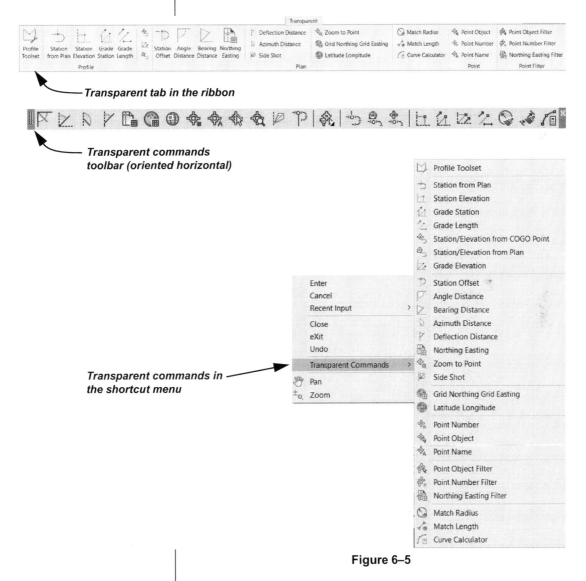

Figure 6–5

The point filters reference points by Point Name or Point Number, or by selecting a point on the screen (Point Object). You can access the transparent commands from their respective toolbars or type one of the following apostrophe letter pairs:

- **'PA** for Point Name

- **'PN** for Point Number

- **'PO** for Point Object

- **'ZTP** for Zoom to Point

Point Object is the easiest, because you only need to select a point or point label on the screen.

The Autodesk Civil 3D transparent commands work with most Autodesk Civil 3D and AutoCAD commands that can use a point's coordinates. AutoCAD commands using transparent commands include **Line**, **Pline**, and **Circle**. To exit a transparent command, press <Esc> or <Enter>.

Practice 6a

Creating Autodesk Civil 3D Points

Practice Objective

- Create a point manually, and then zoom to it using transparent commands.

In this practice, a fire hydrant was located by GPS. You will add a point object to locate it manually.

Task 1 - Add a point object to the drawing.

1. Continue working with the drawing from the previous practice, or open **Points-A-Survey.dwg** from the *C:\Civil 3D for Survey*ors*Worki*ng*Survey* folder.

2. If you are greeted with a splash screen about using Online Map Data, select **Remember my choice** and click **No**, as shown in Figure 6–6. (Since you have captured an online map in a previous chapter, you do not need to use Online Map Data.)

Figure 6–6

3. In the *Home* tab>Create Ground Data panel, select **Points-Point Creation Tools** to display the Create Points toolbar.

4. Expand the toolbar by clicking ⏷ , as shown in Figure 6–7.

Figure 6–7

---

5. In the *Point Identity* area in the dialog box, set the *Next Point Number* to **260** and collapse the toolbar by clicking ⬆.

6. Select the **Manual** option in the miscellaneous group in the toolbar, as shown in Figure 6–8.

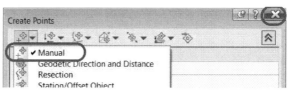

Figure 6–8

7. When prompted for a location, in the Command Line, type **6256069.30,2036634.25** and press <Enter> (or select the endpoint of the large red arrow).

8. When prompted for a description, type **HYD** and press <Enter>.

The period is a placeholder for the elevation field. Typing a zero is incorrect because 0 is a valid elevation.

9. When prompted for an elevation, press <Enter> to accept the default value of **<.>** (period), because the height is unknown.

10. Press <Enter> again to finish the command.

11. Close the Create Points toolbar by clicking the red **X** in the top right corner.

12. In the ribbon, in the *Transparent* tab, click 🔍 (Zoom to Point) and type **260**.

13. In the Toolspace>*Prospector* tab, select the **_All Points** group, right-click, and select **Apply Description Keys**. The point updates to display the Hydrant symbol and its new description, as shown in Figure 6–9.

Before applying Description Keys

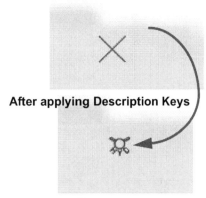

After applying Description Keys

Figure 6–9

14. Save the drawing.

Task 2 - Update the Description Key Set to use parameters.

In this task, you will use the Parameters feature to control the display properties of symbols in your drawings. The most common parameter is the **Scale** parameter. With this parameter, a surveyor will enter the size of a tree as part of the description and the description key file will insert a symbol scaled to the value provided by the surveyor. In this case, you want the pumpers on the hydrant to display correctly (i.e., running parallel to the road).

1. Continue working with the drawing from the previous task.

2. In the Toolspace>*Settings* tab, expand the **Point** collection and expand the **Description Key Sets** collection. Select **Ascent**, right-click, and select **Edit Keys**, as shown in Figure 6–10.

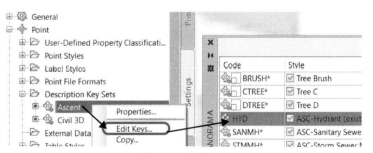

Figure 6–10

3. In the *HYD* row, *Code* column, type **HYD***. The asterisk symbolizes a wildcard, (i.e., any character after the letters HYD). In this example it is -5, parameter1, which you will enter in Step 6.

4. In the *HYD* row, select the checkbox in the *Marker Rotate* column, select the cell, and then select **Parameter1** in the drop-down list. The selected parameter is shown in Figure 6–11.

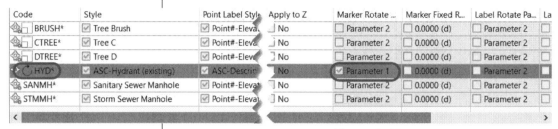

Figure 6–11

5. Click in the top right corner of the dialog box to close the Panorama view.

The -5 indicates the required rotation.

6. In Model Space, select the Hydrant point object, right-click, and select **Edit Points**. Change the *Raw Description* from *HYD* to **HYD -33** and press <Enter>.

7. Select the row, right-click, and select **Apply Description Keys**, as shown in Figure 6–12.

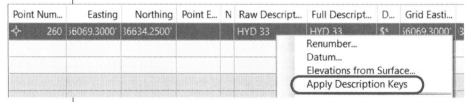

Figure 6–12

8. Click in the top right corner of the dialog box to close the Panorama view.

9. Note that the hydrant has been rotated to display the hydrant pumpers following the rotation of the road, as shown in Figure 6–13.

Figure 6–13

The label also displays the rotation angle text -5, which you do not want.

10. In the Toolspace>*Settings* tab, expand the **Point** collection and expand the **Description Key Sets** collection. Select **Ascent**, right-click, and select **Edit Keys**.

11. In the *HYD* row, change the *Format* from *$*$* to **HYDRANT**, as shown in Figure 6–14.

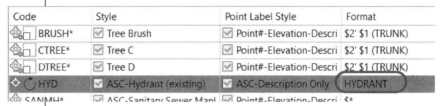

Code	Style	Point Label Style	Format
BRUSH*	Tree Brush	Point#-Elevation-Descri	$2' $1 (TRUNK)
CTREE*	Tree C	Point#-Elevation-Descri	$2' $1 (TRUNK)
DTREE*	Tree D	Point#-Elevation-Descri	$2' $1 (TRUNK)
HYD	ASC-Hydrant (existing)	ASC-Description Only	HYDRANT
SANMH*	ASC-Sanitary Sewer Manl	Point#-Elevation-Descri	$*

Figure 6–14

12. Click [✓] in the top right corner of the dialog box to close the Panorama view.

You still need to apply the changes.

13. In Model Space, select the Hydrant point object, right-click, and select **Apply Description Keys**. The changes are now applied, as shown in Figure 6–15.

Figure 6–15

14. Save the drawing.

6.4 Importing and Exporting Points

The Autodesk Civil 3D software has methods to import point data from ASCII text files, AutoCAD Land Desktop point databases, and Autodesk LandXML. The *Survey* tab also inserts points into a survey database, and from a survey database into a drawing.

Importing Points

There are two methods of launching the import point feature, one is by using the *Insert* tab and the other is using the **Points** creation toolbar in the Toolspace>*Prospector* tab.

Alternatively, you can click (Import Points) in the Create Points toolbar.

How To: Use the Insert Tab Method

1. In the *Insert* tab, select **Points from File**.
2. In the Import Points dialog box, do the following:
   - Set the file format.
   - Select the files to import.
   - Set any advanced options.
   - Click **OK** to import the points.

How To: Use the Point Creation Tools Method

1. In the *Home* tab>Create Gound Data panel, expand the Points drop-down list and select **Point Creation Tools**, as shown in Figure 6–16.
   - Alternatively, in the Toolspace>*Prospector* tab, select **Points**, right-click and select **Create**, as shown in Figure 6–17.

Figure 6–16

Figure 6–17

- Many commands in the Points drop-down list can also be accessed in the Create Points toolbar, as shown in Figure 6–18.

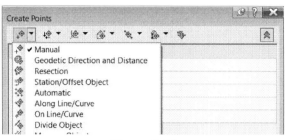

Figure 6–18

2. Click 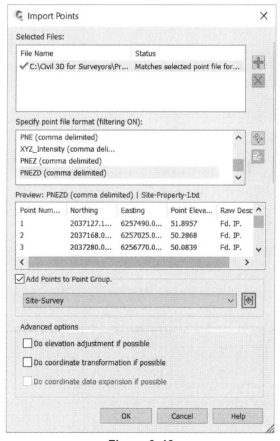 (Import Points) to open the Import Points dialog box. The Import Points dialog box is shown in Figure 6–19.
3. In the Import Points dialog box, expand the Format drop-down list and select a point file format.

Figure 6–19

4. After setting the format, click ✛ on the right to open the Select Source File dialog box.
5. In the Select Source File dialog box, browse to the import point file, select it, and select **Open**.
   - You can select multiple files with the same file format.
   - You can assign the imported points to a new or existing point group by selecting the **Add Points to Point Group** option and selecting the point group in the drop-down list.
   - Select any **Advanced options**, as required.
6. Click **OK** when done. Note that the Duplicate Point Number dialog box displays if there is a conflict between point numbers in the ASCII file and the drawing (e.g., both contain Point Number 101).

Duplicate Point Numbers

If an imported file creates duplicate point numbers, the Autodesk Civil 3D software overwrites, merges, or reassigns them during the import process. When encountering duplicate point numbers, the Autodesk Civil 3D software can do any of the following:

- Use the next available number.

- Add an offset (e.g., add 5000 to each point number that conflicts, so point number 123 becomes 5123).

- Sequence from (e.g., sequence from 7000, so point number 123 becomes 7001, if it is the first point number that is a duplicate).

- Overwrite (replaces the current point values with the file's values).

- Merge (add the file's values to an existing point's values).

If using the offset method, the new point numbers are kept unique in the drawing. If using the next available number method, the new points blend into the original points and are difficult to identify.

The offset method is preferred when resolving duplicate point numbers. When importing points that can potentially duplicate point numbers, the Create Points toolbar's *Point Identity* settings (shown in Figure 6–20) is the default when handling duplicate point numbers.

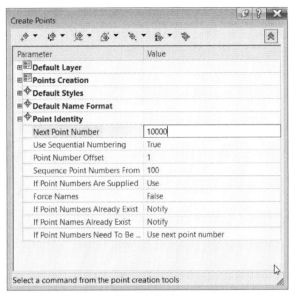

Figure 6–20

In the *Point Identity* settings, set the duplicate point resolution method for the *If Point Numbers Already Exist* variable. The four methods are **Renumber**, **Merge**, **Overwrite**, and **Notify**, as shown in Figure 6–21. The import process never overwrites point data unless you specify that it should do so.

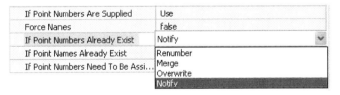

Figure 6–21

When encountering a duplicate point, the Duplicate Point Number dialog box opens. After you define a resolution, it can be assigned to the current duplicate point or to all encountered duplicate points.

Transforming Points on Import or Export

When importing points, the assumption is that the file's and drawing's points are in the same coordinate system. When the file's points are in a different coordinate system, you must define a point file format identifying the point file's coordinate system.

To identify that a point file contains coordinates from a different system, you must define a new point file format. When using this file to import points, the import routine knows that the points are from one system and that the drawing is assigned another. Therefore, when importing the points, it transforms them to the drawing's coordinate system.

When using the file format to export points, the export routine transforms the points from the drawing's coordinate system to the point file format's coordinate system.

The point file format must have two values: the coordinate system, and the keywords **Grid Northing** and **Grid Easting** (or **Latitude** and **Longitude,** if working in a Lat / Long coordinate system.).

The coordinate system assignment is similar to assigning a system to a drawing. In the Point File Format dialog box, toggle on the **Coordinate zone transform** option and click 🌐 next to the *Zone* field. In the Select Coordinate Zone dialog box, set the category and coordinate system, as shown at the bottom in Figure 6–22.

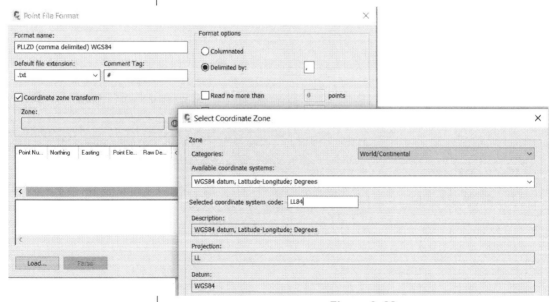

Figure 6–22

You then need to change the Northing and Easting headings to Grid Northing and Grid Easting. Select the heading and, in the Select Column Name dialog box, select the new heading: **Grid Northing** or **Grid Easting**, as shown in Figure 6–23. Remember that if you are working in a Lat / Long coordinate system, you need to use the **Latitude** and **Longitude** keywords instead.

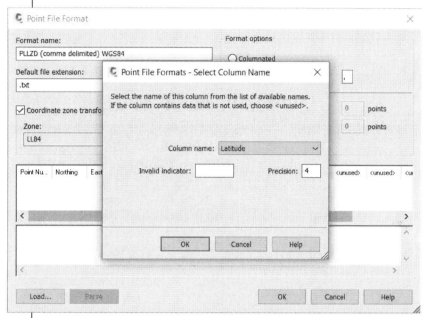

Figure 6–23

Practice 6b

Importing and Exporting Points Part I

Practice Objective

- Import points from and export points to ASCII files created from the field survey.

In this practice, you will import an ASCII file that was created in the field.

Task 1 - Import an ASCII file using the Create Points toolbar.

---

1. Continue working with the drawing from the previous practice or open **Points-B-Survey.dwg** from the *C:\Civil 3D for Surveyors\Working\Survey* folder.

2. In the *Home* tab, click ⚙ (Points) and in the drop-down list, select the **Point Creation tools**.

3. Click ⬆ (Import Points) in the toolbar.

4. Click ➕ and in the *Selected Files* area in the dialog box, browse to the ASCII file's location in the *C:\Civil 3D for Surveyors\Survey Databases\Data\Level 1* folder. Select the survey of the property pins, **Site-Property-I.txt**, as the file you want to import. Double-click on the file name or click the **Open** button to select the file.

You might need to set the Files of Type to *.txt or *.* to display the text files in the list.

5. In the Import Points dialog box, scroll to the bottom of the *Specify point file format (filtering ON)* list and select **PNEZD (comma delimited)**, as shown in Figure 6–24. This is usually found at the bottom of the list.

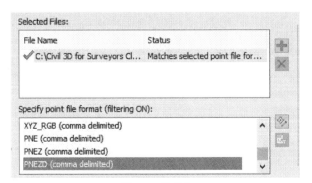

Figure 6–24

6. Click **OK** to import the file. When done, click **X** to close the Create Points toolbar.

7. Zoom out to see the newly created points.

8. In the Toolspace>*Prospector* tab, select **Points** to preview the points in the *Prospector's* preview area.

9. In the Transparent Command toolbar, click (Zoom to Point) and type **249**.

10. In the model, select point **249** and press <Delete>. COGO points can be deleted directly in the drawing; survey points cannot.

11. Use the **Zoom Previous** command to restore your previous zoom level.

12. Save the drawing.

Task 2 - Create a new point file format and export points.

In the Autodesk Civil 3D software, you can create an output format based on an independent coordinate system. Using this output file, you can then open multiple drawings that each have their own coordinate systems and export the points to one common coordinate system.

1. Continue working with the drawing from the previous task.

2. Select the Toolspace>*Settings* tab.

3. Expand the **Point** collection until the **Point File Formats** collection and its format list display.

4. Expand the Point File Formats drop-down list, select **PNEZD (Comma delimited)**, then right-click and select **Copy**.

5. In the Point File Format dialog box, change the format name to **PLLZD (Comma delimited) WGS84**.

6. Select the **Coordinate zone transform** option and click

   next to the *Zone* field.

7. In the Select Coordinate Zone dialog box, set the following, as shown in Figure 6–25:

   • *Categories*: **World/Continental**
   • *Available coordinate systems*: **WGS84 datum, Latitude-Longitude; Degrees**

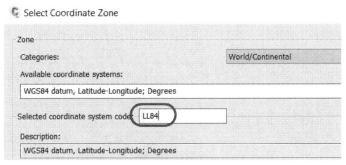

Figure 6–25

8. Click **OK** to return to the Point File Format dialog box.

   Note that there are two WG84 Coordinate Systems. Verify that the selected coordinate system code is set to **LL84** after selecting the coordinate system.

   Alternatively, you can type **LL84** directly into the *Coordinate system code* field (as shown in Figure 6–25), rather than selecting it from the list.

9. Select the **Northing** heading. In the Select Column Name dialog box, expand the Column name drop-down list, select **Latitude**, and click **OK**.

10. Select the **Easting** heading. In the Select Column Name dialog box, expand the Column name drop-down list, select **Longitude**, and click **OK**.

11. Click **OK** to create the new point file format.

12. Select the Toolspace>*Prospector* tab. If required, expand the **Point Groups** collection.

13. Expand the list of point groups, select **_All Points**, right-click, and select **Export Points** to open the Export Points dialog box.

14. In the Export Points dialog box, change the file format to **PLLZD (Comma delimited) WGS84**.

15. Click to open the Select Destination File dialog box.

16. Browse to the *C:\Civil 3D for Surveyors\Survey Databases\Data\Level 1* folder. Type **Road-Lat-Long** for the file name and click **Open**.

17. In the Export Points dialog box, select the **Limit to Points in Point Group** option, expand the drop-down list on the left, and select **Mission_Ave-I.csv**, as shown in Figure 6–26.

18. Select the **Do coordinate transformation if possible** option, as shown in Figure 6–26.

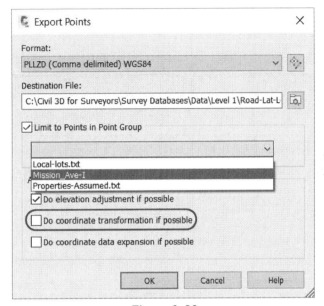

Figure 6–26

19. Click **OK** to export the points to the point file.

20. Open Windows Explorer and browse to the *C:\Civil 3D for Surveyors\Survey Databases\Data\Level 1* folder. Open the file **Road-Lat-Long.txt** using a text editor and review it. Note that the point coordinates are now in latitude and longitude.

Practice 6c

Importing and Exporting Points Part II

Practice Objective

- Import points from an ASCII file into the survey database.

One method of importing points is to import a points file directly into the Autodesk Civil 3D software. In this practice, you will examine another method. You will use the Survey Database features to import a points file.

Task 1 - Set the Survey Database and import points.

1. Continue working with the drawing from the previous practice.

2. In the *Survey* tab, right-click on **Survey Databases** and select **Set working folder**.

3. Browse and select the *C:\Civil 3D for Surveyors\Survey Databases\Ascent-Development* folder.

4. Click **Select Folder**.

5. In the *Home* tab>expanded Create Ground Data panel, click 🖳 (Import Survey Data).

6. On the Specify Database page, click **Create New Survey Database**, as shown in Figure 6–27 (1).

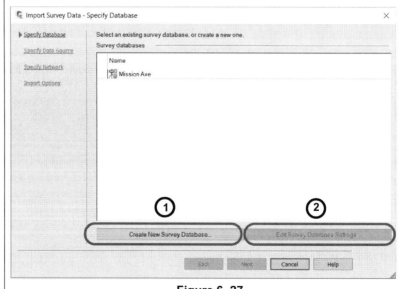

Figure 6–27

7. Type **Survey South** for the name and click **OK**.

8. Click **Edit Survey Database Settings,** as shown above in Figure 6–27 (2).

9. In the Survey Database Settings dialog box, for the *Coordinate zone*, click ⋯ (Browse). In the Select Coordinate Zone dialog box, verify that **NAD83 California State Planes, Zone VI, US Foot** is set. If necessary, change it as shown in Figure 6–28. Click **OK** twice, and then click **Next**.

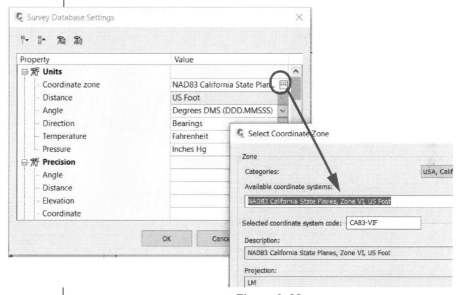

Figure 6–28

10. On the Specify Data Sources page, do the following, as shown in Figure 6–29:

- Expand the Data source type drop-down list and select **Point File**.

*You might need to set the Files of Type to *.csv* or *.** to display the .CSV files.*

- Click ⊞ (Add file), browse to *C:\Civil 3D for Surveyors\Survey Databases\Data\Level 1* and select **Field-Survey-I.csv**. Double-click on the file name or click the **Open** button to select the file.

- For the file format, select **PNEZD (comma delimited)**.

- Click **Next**.

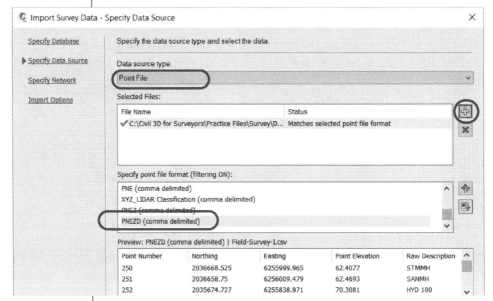

Figure 6–29

11. On the Survey Network page, click **Next**. Note that when you are importing point files, networks are optional.

12. On the Import Options page, set the following (as shown in Figure 6–30), then click **Finish**:

- *Process linework during import*: **Yes**
- *Insert figure objects*: **Yes**
- *Insert survey points*: **Yes**
- *Current linework code set*: **ASCENT**

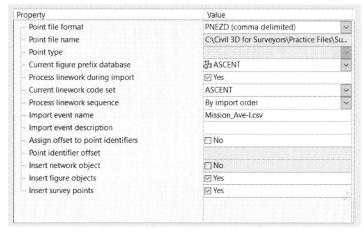

Property	Value
Point file format	PNEZD (comma delimited)
Point file name	C:\Civil 3D for Surveyors\Practice Files\Su...
Point type	
Current figure prefix database	ASCENT
Process linework during import	☑ Yes
Current linework code set	ASCENT
Process linework sequence	By import order
Import event name	Mission_Ave-I.csv
Import event description	
Assign offset to point identifiers	☐ No
Point identifier offset	
Insert network object	☐ No
Insert figure objects	☑ Yes
Insert survey points	☑ Yes

Figure 6–30

13. In the Import Point File dialog box, select **OK** to accept the defaults and import the points.

14. Zoom in and review the tree symbols, shown in Figure 6–31. Note that the vegetation is correctly scaled (to the trunk diameter).

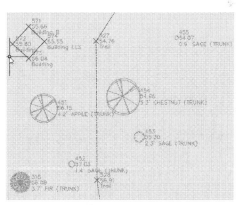

Figure 6–31

15. In the Status Bar, change the view scale to **1"=10'**, as shown in Figure 6–32. Note that the tree symbols remain the same size, but the labels adjust according to the view scale.

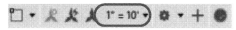

Figure 6–32

16. Note that the linework has been imported designating the centerlines of trails. In the south west corner of the property, note that another figure was imported designating a rock pile, as shown in Figure 6–33.

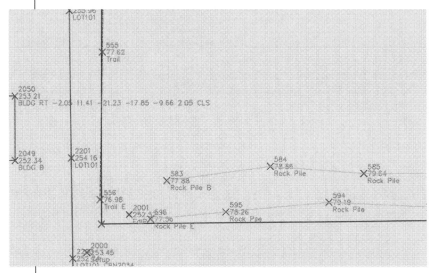

Figure 6–33

17. Rather than importing points via the **Import Survey Data** wizard, you will now use the Toolspace>*Survey* tab. Right-click on the **Survey South** survey database and select Import point file, as shown in Figure 6–34.

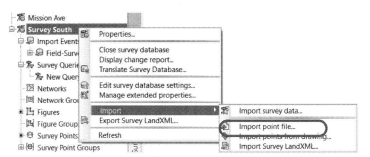

Figure 6–34

*You might need to set the Files of Type to **.txt** or *.* to display the text files.*

18. In the *C:\Civil 3D for Surveyors\Survey Databases\ Data\Level 1* folder, select **Groundshots.txt**. Double-click on the file name or click the **Open** button to select the file.

19. On the Import Options page, select **Insert survey points**. Click **Finish**.

20. Zoom to the extents, if required.

21. Save the drawing.

6.5 Point Groups

Point groups organize points that share common descriptions and characteristics (such as existing storm, gas lines, building corners, etc.). Point groups also enable points to display different point or label styles. For example, a Landscape Architect needs to display different symbols for each tree species, while an Engineer only needs to display a generic tree symbol. The **Description Key Set** enables you to assign the tree species symbols for the Landscape Architect, and a point group enables generic tree symbols to override the symbols for the Engineer. Another function of a point group is to hide all of the points.

In the Autodesk Civil 3D software, point groups can be defined in the template along with a Description Key Set. When creating a new drawing from this template and importing points, they are assigned their symbols and can be sorted into point groups.

All points in a drawing belong to the **_All Points** point group. Consider this point group as the point database. It cannot be deleted and initially is not in a drawing until you add points. All new point groups include all drawing points or a subset of drawing points (copied points from the **_All Points** point group).

Defining Point Groups

To create a new point group, select the Toolspace>*Prospector* tab, right-click on the **Point Groups** collection and select **New**. Alternatively, in the *Home* tab, expand **Points** and select **Create Point Group**.

When you select **New** or **Create Point Group**, the Point Group Properties dialog box opens. It has nine tabs, most of them affecting the point group's definition.

- The *Point Groups*, *Raw Desc Matching*, *Include*, and *Query Builder* tabs add points to the point group. The *Exclude* tab removes points from a point group.

- The *Information* tab defines the point group's name. The *Point style* and *Point label style* should remain at their defaults, unless you want to use either style to override the assigned styles of the points in the point group. The points in the point group display their originally assigned styles until you toggle on the override.

A point group can be locked by toggling on the **Object locked** option to prevent any changes to the group. The Point Group Properties dialog box opens as shown in Figure 6–35.

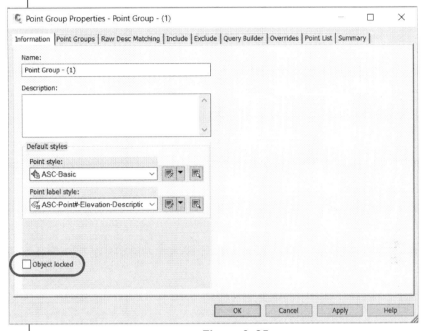

Figure 6–35

- The *Point Groups* tab lists the drawing's groups. A point group can be created from other point groups. When you select a point group name, the group and its points become members of the new point group. For example, the point group **Trees** is created from the point groups *Maple*, *Walnut*, *Oak*, etc.

- The *Raw Desc Matching* tab lists codes from the Description Key Code set. When you toggle on the code, any point matching the code becomes part of the point group.

- If you cannot select a point with the previous two methods, the *Include* tab enables you to include points by specifically entering in the selection criteria. The criteria include the point number (point number list or by selection), elevation, name, raw description, full description, and all points.

With numbers matching	Selects points by a point number range or list. When creating a list, sequential point numbers are hyphenated (1-20) and individual numbers are in a comma delimited list. A point list can include sequential and individual points (1-20, 14, 44, 50-60). Select **Selection Set in Drawing** to select the points in the drawing and list their point numbers at the top of the *Include* tab.
With elevations matching	Enables you to select points by entering a specific elevation or by specifying a minimum and maximum elevation. For example, valid entries include >100,<400, and >100. The first entry only includes points whose elevation is above 100, but less than 400. The second entry only includes points whose elevation is greater than 100. A point without an elevation cannot be selected using this method. An elevation range, defined by separating the start and end numbers with a hyphen, includes points whose elevation falls within the range (1-100). This can be combined with greater or less than symbols.
With names matching	Selects points based on matching their point names. Enter one or more point names separated by commas.
With raw/full descriptions matching	Selects points based on matching an entered raw or full description. Enter one or more descriptions separated by commas. You can use the same wildcards as the Description Key Set. Generally, this method uses the asterisk (*) as the wildcard after the description (e.g., PINE*, CTV*, CL*, etc.).
Include all points	Assigns all points in the drawing to the point group. When this option is toggled on, all other **Include** options are disabled.

- The *Exclude* tab has the same options as the *Include* tab, except for the **Include All Points** option.

- The *Query Builder* tab creates one or more expressions to select points. Each query is a row selecting points. As with all SQL queries, you combine expressions using the operators AND, OR, and NOT. You can also use parentheses to group expressions.

- The *Overrides* tab overrides the points in the point group's raw description, elevation, point style, and point label style. For example, you can override specific tree species symbols with a generic tree symbol, override a label style when displaying this group, or override the point and label style with none (to hide all points).

  The point group display order affects points and their overrides. To change how the point groups display, modify the point group display order.

- The *Point List* tab displays the point group's points. This tab enables you to review points that are currently in the point group. The *Summary* tab displays the point group's settings. You can print this tab as a report by cutting and pasting it into a document.

Updating Out of Date Point Groups

After defining point groups and adding points to a drawing, the group becomes out of date before assigning the points to the group. This enables you to verify that the points should become part of the group.

To review why a group is out of date, select the group, right-click, and select **Show Changes**. If the changes are correct, select **Update** to add the points to the group.

If you know that all of the groups displaying as out of date should be updated, right-click on the **Point Groups** collection and select **Update**. At this level, the command updates all of the point groups.

Overriding Point Group Properties

If a Description Key Set exists in the file, the points take on the symbol and label style assigned by the Description Key Set unless a point group override is toggled on. When working with points, you might want them to display different labels, have them not be visible, or display different symbols. Each required change is a function of a point group override.

A point group that contains all of the points and overrides their symbols and labels with none does not display any points. This is similar to freezing all of the layers involved with points.

A point group that changes the symbols that a group displays overrides the label styles assigned to the point in the point group. To display a different symbol, the point group overrides the assigned point styles.

To set the style and override the assigned styles, toggle on the point group in the *Overrides* tab and set the styles in the *Override* column of the point group, as shown in Figure 6–36.

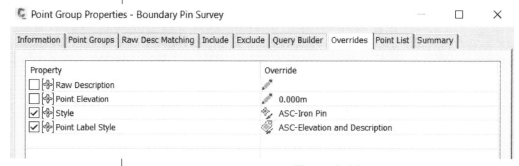

Figure 6–36

Point Groups Display Properties

When creating a point group, it is placed at the top of the point group list. The point group list is more than a list of point groups, it is also the Autodesk Civil 3D's point draw order. The Autodesk Civil 3D software draws the point groups starting from the bottom of the list to the top. If **_All Points** is the first drawn point group and the remaining point groups are subsets of all points, the individual point group does not display, but all of the points display.

To display point groups that are a subset of all points, you must create a point group whose purpose is to hide all points. This popular point group is commonly called **No Display**. With this group, any point group drawn after it displays its members without *seeing* the other points.

The Autodesk Civil 3D software draws point groups from the bottom to the top of the list. To manipulate the display order, right-click on the **Point Groups** collection in the Toolspace> *Prospector* tab and select **Properties**. The Point Groups dialog box opens, enabling you to modify the point group display order using the arrows on the right, as shown in Figure 6–37.

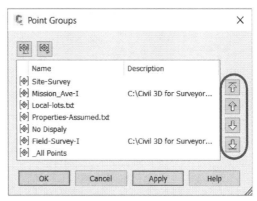

Figure 6–37

These arrows enable you to select the required point group and move it up or down in the list (or all of the way to the top or bottom of the list with one click, ⬆) in the hierarchy for display purposes. The Point Groups dialog box has two additional icons at the top. The first icon displays the difference between point groups and the second icon updates them all.

If you use Description Key Sets, a point displays the assigned point and label style when it is part of any point group. The only time the point displays another style is when you override the style (in the Point Group Properties dialog box, in the *Overrides* tab).

With the Description Key Set and display order shown in Figure 6–38, the points display their originally assigned point styles and point label styles.

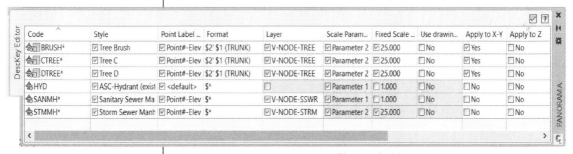

Figure 6–38

The **No Display** point group includes all of the points, but overrides the originally assigned point style and point label styles with **<none>**. When **No Display** is moved to the list's top, no points display. The Point Groups dialog box is shown in Figure 6–39.

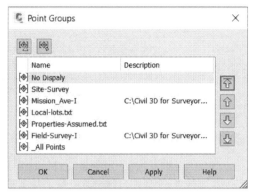

Figure 6–39

Survey Point Groups

Survey has the ability to create its own point groups. The points DO NOT need to reside in the drawing to produce survey point groups.

You can create these groups using one of the following three methods: There are three methods that create these groups:

1. **Survey Point Group by Import:** Import a survey file into a survey at the same time as the points are imported into a drawing. The Survey Toolspace automatically creates a point group that is the same name as the imported file.

2. **Manual selection:** Grouping the points in the drawing and selecting the points in the drawing to populate the survey point group. The issue with this method is that the points need to be grouped in the drawing, and that only those points display for the group being defined.

3. **Manual toggling:** Manually toggling what survey points are included in the survey point group. This method is the least desirable, because you have to toggle on each point in each group

Each method defines groups based on how you use the survey point database.

Practice 6d

Creating Point Groups

Practice Objectives

- Create a point group.
- Rearrange the order of the point groups for display purposes.

In this practice, you will create point groups and change their properties and their display order.

Task 1 - Create point groups (Boundary Pin Survey).

1. Continue working with the drawing from the previous practice or open **Points-C-Survey.dwg** from the *C:\Civil 3D for Surveyors\Working\Survey* folder.

2. In the Toolspace>*Prospector* tab, select **Point Groups**, right-click, and select **New**, as shown in Figure 6–40.

Figure 6–40

3. In the Point Group Properties dialog box, in the *Information* tab, set the following, as shown in Figure 6–41:
   - *Name:* **Boundary Pin Survey**
   - *Point style*: **ASC-Iron Pin**
   - *Point label style*: **ASC-Elevation and Description**

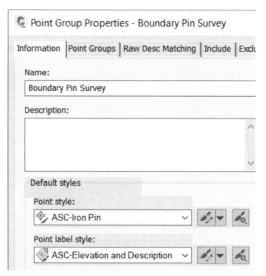

Figure 6–41

4. Select the *Include* tab. Select the **With raw description matching** option. Type ***IP.** (verify that a period follows IP) in the field to select all of the points that have the last three characters *IP.* (iron pin). You can confirm this in the *Point List* tab, as shown in Figure 6–42.

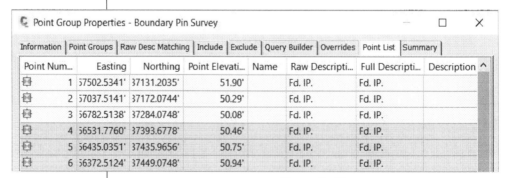

Figure 6–42

5. Click **OK** to close the dialog box and apply the changes.

Task 2 - Create point groups (No display).

Continue working with the drawing from the previous task. In this task, you will use the point group to control the points display. Not only will you be able to display the same point differently, but you will also be able to control the visibility of the points. This eliminates needing to use the Layer command to thaw and freeze layers.

1. Select **Point Groups**, right-click, and select **New** to create a new point group. In the *Information* tab, set the *Name* to **No display**.

2. Select **<none>** for both the *Point style* and the *Point label style*, as shown in Figure 6–43.

Figure 6–43

3. Select the *Overrides* tab and select **Style** and **Point Label Style**, as shown in Figure 6–44.

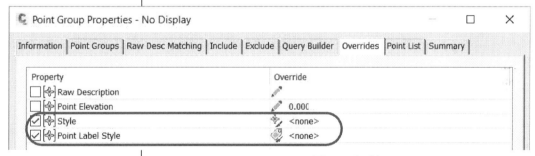

Figure 6–44

4. In the *Include* tab, select the **Include all points** option. Select the *Point List* tab to confirm that all of the points have been included.

5. Click **OK** to create the point group. Note that the points have disappeared because the newly created point group is at the top of the display order.

6. To control the hierarchy and the display of the point group style, select the Toolspace>*Prospector* tab, select **Point Groups**, right-click, and select **Properties**.

7. In the Point Groups dialog box, select the **No display** point group and move it to the top of the list by clicking 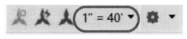. Select the **Boundary Pin Survey** point group and move it to the top of the list by clicking 🔼. Click **OK** to apply the changes. Only the points in the Boundary Pin point group are displayed. You might need to type **regen** in the Command Line (type **RE**, and press <Enter>).

8. In the Status Bar, ensure that the *Annotation Scale* is set to **1"=40'** (as shown in Figure 6–45) to change the point size in the drawing.

Figure 6–45

9. Save the drawing.

Task 3 - Modify the point group's properties.

With each Import Event in a survey database, a point group is generated automatically that contains the points that are imported. You will take the groundshots that were imported in the previous practice and change the properties of the point group.

1. In the Toolspace>*Prospector* tab, under **Point Groups**, select **Groundshots**, then right-click and select **Properties**, as shown in Figure 6–46.

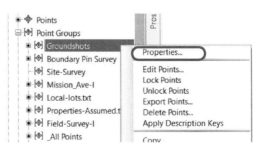

Figure 6–46

2. Note the description that was generated automatically by importing the points, as shown in Figure 6–47.

3. For the *Point style*, select **ASC-Bound**, and for the *Point label style*, select **ASC-Elevation Only**, as shown in Figure 6–47.

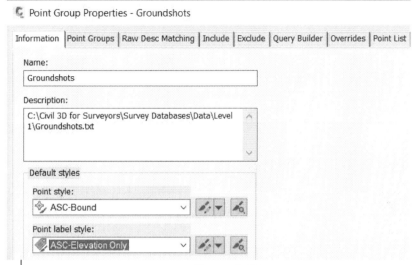

Figure 6–47

4. In the Point Groups dialog box, select the **Groundshots** point group and move it to the top of the list by clicking ⬆.

5. Select the **Boundary Pin Survey** point group and move it to the top of the list by clicking ⬆.

6. Click **OK** to apply the changes. You might need to type **regen** in the Command Line (type **RE**, and press <Enter>).

7. Experiment with moving point groups up and down the list to control the display of points. When done, select the **No display** point group and move it below the **Boundary Pin Survey** point group.

8. Save the drawing.

6.6 Reviewing and Editing Points

Reviewing and editing point data occurs throughout the Autodesk Civil 3D environment. It is as simple as selecting a point in the drawing, right-clicking, and selecting **Edit Points** You can also edit points using the right-click menu in the *Points* heading in the Toolspace>*Prospector* tab, as shown in Figure 6–48. Alternatively, you can select a point entry in the *Prospector's* preview area.

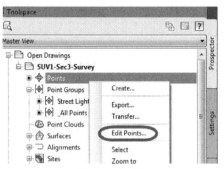

Figure 6–48

When selecting **Edit Points**, the Autodesk Civil 3D software displays the *Point Editor* tab inside the Panorama, as shown in Figure 6–49.

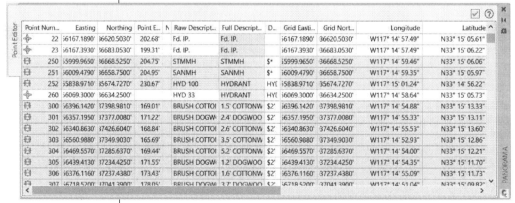

Point Num...	Easting	Northing	Point E...	N	Raw Descript...	Full Descript...	D...	Grid Easti...	Grid Nort...	Longitude	Latitude
22	56167.1890'	36620.5030'	202.68'		Fd. IP.	Fd. IP.		56167.1890'	36620.5030'	W117° 14' 57.49"	N33° 15' 05.61"
23	56167.3930'	36683.0530'	199.31'		Fd. IP.	Fd. IP.		56167.3930'	36683.0530'	W117° 14' 57.49"	N33° 15' 06.22"
250	55999.9650'	36668.5250'	204.75'		STMMH	STMMH	S*	55999.9650'	36668.5250'	W117° 14' 59.46"	N33° 15' 06.06"
251	56009.4790'	36658.7500'	204.95'		5ANMH	SANMH	S*	56009.4790'	36658.7500'	W117° 14' 59.35"	N33° 15' 05.97"
252	55838.9710'	35674.7270'	230.67'		HYD 100	HYDRANT	HYI	55838.9710'	35674.7270'	W117° 15' 01.24"	N33° 14' 56.22"
260	56069.3000'	36634.2500'			HYD 33	HYDRANT	HYI	56069.3000'	36634.2500'	W117° 14' 58.64"	N33° 15' 05.73"
300	56396.1420'	37398.9810'	169.01'		BRUSH COTTO!	1.5' COTTONW	$2'	56396.1420'	37398.9810'	W117° 14' 54.88"	N33° 15' 13.33"
301	56357.1950'	37377.0080'	171.22'		BRUSH DOGW	2.4' DOGWOO	$2'	56357.1950'	37377.0080'	W117° 14' 55.33"	N33° 15' 13.11"
302	56340.8630'	37426.6040'	168.84'		BRUSH COTTO!	2.6' COTTONW	$2'	56340.8630'	37426.6040'	W117° 14' 55.53"	N33° 15' 13.60"
303	56560.9880'	37349.9030'	165.69'		BRUSH COTTO!	3.5' COTTONW	$2'	56560.9880'	37349.9030'	W117° 14' 52.93"	N33° 15' 12.86"
304	56469.5570'	37285.6370'	169.44'		BRUSH COTTO!	5.2' COTTONW	$2'	56469.5570'	37285.6370'	W117° 14' 54.00"	N33° 15' 12.21"
305	56439.4130'	37234.4250'	171.55'		BRUSH DOGW	1.2' DOGWOO	$2'	56439.4130'	37234.4250'	W117° 14' 54.35"	N33° 15' 11.70"
306	56376.1160'	37237.4380'	173.43'		BRUSH COTTO!	1.6' COTTONW	$2'	56376.1160'	37237.4380'	W117° 14' 55.09"	N33° 15' 11.73"
307	56718.5200'	37041.3900'	178.05'		BRUSH DOGW	3.7' DOGWOO	$2'	56718.5200'	37041.3900'	W117° 14' 51.04"	N33° 15' 09.82"

Figure 6–49

Repositioning Point Objects and Labels

When selecting a point, it displays multiple grips. The grips have different functions depending on their state (original vs. dragged).

Original State refers to a point label that has not been dragged from its original position. In this position, there are two grips available.

- Use the **rectangle** grip to:
  - Move the label
  - Rotate the label

  These options become available when you hover over the rectangle grip, as shown in Figure 6–50.

Figure 6–50

- Use the **diamond** grip to:
  - Move the point
  - Rotate both the label and marker
  - Rotate just the marker
  - Reset marker rotation (only available if the marker and/or the label have been rotated)
  - Reset all (only available if the marker and/or the label have been rotated)

  These options become available when you hover over the diamond grip, as shown in Figure 6–51.

Figure 6–51

Dragged State refers to a point label that has been moved from its original position. In this position, the following grips are available.

- Use the **rectangle** label grip to:
  - Move the point
  - Rotate just the marker
  - Reset marker rotation
  - Reset all

These options become available when you hover over the rectangle grip, as shown in Figure 6–52.

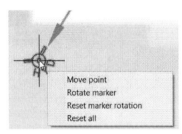

Figure 6–52

- Use the **diamond point object** grip to:
  - Move the label
  - Rotate the marker
  - Reset the label
  - Reset the label location
  - Reset all

These options become available when you hover over the diamond grip, as shown in Figure 6–53.

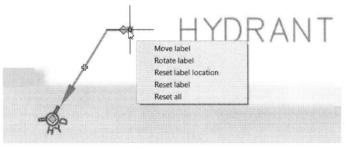

Figure 6–53

- Use the **+** (plus) grip to add vertices to the leader, as shown in Figure 6–54.

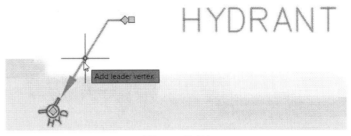

Figure 6–54

- Use the - (minus) grip to delete vertices from the leader, as shown in Figure 6–55.

Figure 6–55

Each label component can be modified and the change is only for that point.

Point objects can be set to automatically rotate to match the current view using style settings. If this is not preferred, they can have a rotation assigned directly through the AutoCAD Properties dialog box.

You can reset a label to its original position by selecting the point, right-clicking, and selecting **Reset Label**.

Each point label style has **Dragged State** parameters. These parameters affect the label's behavior when moving the label from its original label position. Depending on the **Dragged State** parameters, a label can change completely (Stacked text) or display as it was originally defined (As composed). Select the move point grip when you want to relocate the label.

An example of a dragged label is shown in Figure 6–56.

Figure 6–56

Practice 6e | Manipulating Points

Practice Objective

- Modify the label position for points to ensure that the plan is readable.

1. Continue working with the drawing from the previous practice or open **Points-D-Survey.dwg** from the *C:\Civil 3D for Surveyors\Working\Survey* folder.

2. In the Toolspace>*Prospector* tab, right-click on **Point Group** and select **Properties**.

3. Select the **No display** point group and click the <Down Arrow> or <Bottom> icon to move it to the bottom of the list, as shown in Figure 6–57.

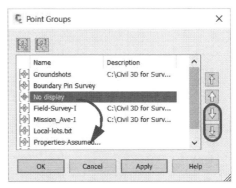

Figure 6–57

This positions the point at the center of the screen.

4. In the preview point list, scroll down until the point number **260** displays. Select it, right-click, and select **Zoom to**.

5. In the Status Bar, ensure that the *Annotation Scale* is set to **1"=40'** (as shown in Figure 6–58) to change the point size in the drawing.

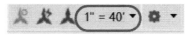

Figure 6–58

6. Select point **260** to display its grips. Select the Drag Label grip, as shown in Figure 6–59, to relocate the label.

Figure 6–59

When selecting the cyan grip, it turns red.

7. With the label still displaying grips, hover on the Rectangle grip and select **Reset Label**.

8. With the label still displaying grips, hover over the Square label grip to display the options for moving, rotating, and additional sub item grips, as shown in Figure 6–60. Select **Rotate label** and rotate the label.

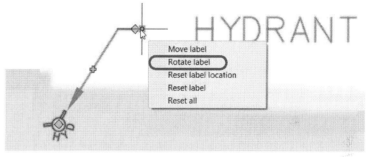

Figure 6–60

9. With the label still displaying grips, click the + (plus) grip to add a vertex to the leader, then select the - (minus) grip to delete the vertex.

10. Save the drawing.

6.7 Locking/Unlocking Points

The Autodesk Civil 3D software has point locking, which protects its properties from edits. A locked point displays 🖉 (Lock).

To lock all of the points, select **Points** in the Toolspace> *Prospector* tab, right-click, and select **Lock**, as shown on the left in Figure 6–61. You can also lock points in a point group. To lock individual points, select the point, right-click, and select **Lock**, as shown on the right. You can also select points in a drawing and use the right-click method to lock them.

You can select a range of points by selecting a point in the list and while holding <Shift>, and then selecting another point in the list. This selects all of the points between the first and second selected points. Select individual points by holding <Ctrl> and selecting points.

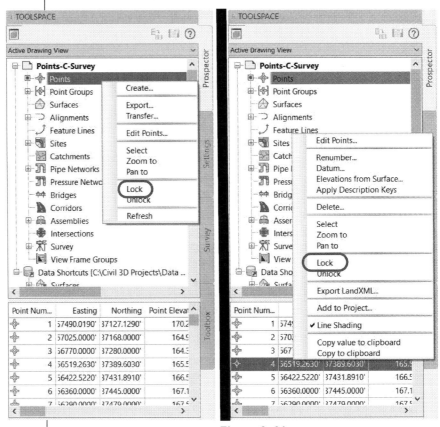

Figure 6–61

Reviewing/Editing Points

Review and edit points using one of the following methods:

- Use the tools in the *Modify* tab>Points panel.

- Select the **Points** heading, right-click, and select **Edit Points**.

- Select points in a drawing, right-click, and select **Edit Points**.

These commands enable you to edit all or selected points, revise the points' elevation, reassign point elevations from a surface, or renumber the points.

In the Point Editor, use <Shift> or <Ctrl> to a select a range or set of individual points. After selecting the points, right-click and select the required editing option, as shown in Figure 6–62. You can also select points graphically and then right-click to edit the points.

Figure 6–62

Practice 6f

Point Locking and Editing

Practice Objective

- Prevent unwanted edits to points by locking them.

1. Continue working with the drawing from the previous practice.

2. In the Toolspace>*Prospector* tab, select **Points** to display a point list in the *Prospector's* preview area.

3. Scroll through the list, select point number **10**, right-click, and select **Zoom to**.

4. In the drawing, select point **10** and note the move grip that displays at its marker, as shown in Figure 6–63.

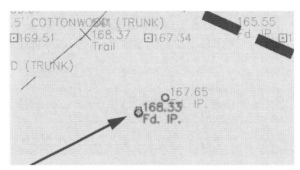

Figure 6–63

5. In the Toolspace>*Prospector* tab, select **Points**, right-click, and select **Lock**, as shown on the left in Figure 6–64. Note that the points in the *Prospector's* preview area now display the **Lock** icon, as shown on the right.

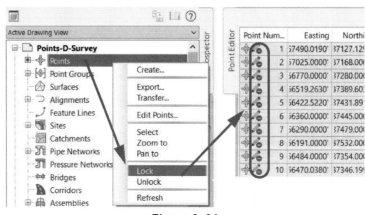

Figure 6–64

6. In the model, select point **10** and note that although the move grip is displayed, you cannot move the point, as shown in Figure 6–65.

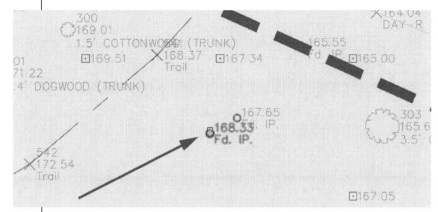

Figure 6–65

7. In the Toolspace>*Prospector* tab, select **Points**. Right-click and select **Edit Points**. The points display the **Lock** icon and the editor now has a gray background, as shown in Figure 6–66.

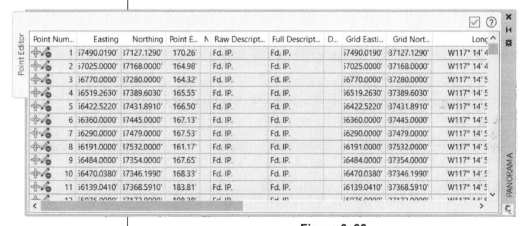

Figure 6–66

8. Select point **5** from the list of points. Scroll down the list, press <Shift> and select point **10**.

9. With points **5** to **10** highlighted right-click, and select **Unlock**. Note that the points no longer display the **Lock** icon and have a white background, as shown in Figure 6–67. These two things indicate that the points are available for editing.

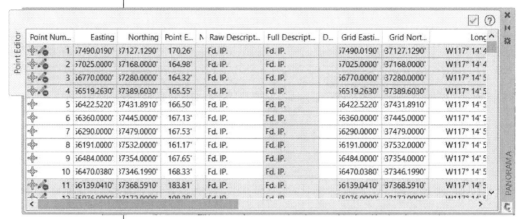

Point Num...	Easting	Northing	Point E...	N	Raw Descript...	Full Descript...	D...	Grid Easti...	Grid Nort...	Lonç
1	57490.0190'	37127.1290'	170.26'		Fd. IP.	Fd. IP.		57490.0190'	37127.1290'	W117° 14' 4
2	57025.0000'	37168.0000'	164.98'		Fd. IP.	Fd. IP.		57025.0000'	37168.0000'	W117° 14' 4
3	56770.0000'	37280.0000'	164.32'		Fd. IP.	Fd. IP.		56770.0000'	37280.0000'	W117° 14' 5
4	56519.2630'	37389.6030'	165.55'		Fd. IP.	Fd. IP.		56519.2630'	37389.6030'	W117° 14' 5
5	56422.5220'	37431.8910'	166.50'		Fd. IP.	Fd. IP.		56422.5220'	37431.8910'	W117° 14' 5
6	56360.0000'	37445.0000'	167.13'		Fd. IP.	Fd. IP.		56360.0000'	37445.0000'	W117° 14' 5
7	56290.0000'	37479.0000'	167.53'		Fd. IP.	Fd. IP.		56290.0000'	37479.0000'	W117° 14' 5
8	56191.0000'	37532.0000'	161.17'		Fd. IP.	Fd. IP.		56191.0000'	37532.0000'	W117° 14' 5
9	56484.0000'	37354.0000'	167.65'		Fd. IP.	Fd. IP.		56484.0000'	37354.0000'	W117° 14' 5
10	56470.0380'	37346.1990'	168.33'		Fd. IP.	Fd. IP.		56470.0380'	37346.1990'	W117° 14' 5
11	56139.0410'	37368.5910'	183.81'		Fd. IP.	Fd. IP.		56139.0410'	37368.5910'	W117° 14' 5
12	56076.0000'	37171.0000'	108.30'		Fd. IP.	Fd. IP.		56076.0000'	37171.0000'	W117° 14' 5

Figure 6–67

10. In the Point Editor Panorama, double-click on point **10**. The cell switches to edit mode now that it has been unlocked.

11. Close the Panorama by clicking ☑ in the top right corner without making any changes.

12. In the drawing, select point **10**, right-click, and review the editing options in the right-click menu.

13. Press <Esc> to deselect the point.

14. Review the commands displayed in the ribbon. Because this is a contextual object, all of the entries are tools that are applicable to a point.

15. In the Toolspace>*Prospector* tab, select **Points**, right-click, and select **Unlock**.

16. Do not save the drawing.

6.8 Point Reports

The surveyor needs to produce point reports. These can include a record list for the project, a checklist to find errors, reference for field crews, stakeout, etc. Incorporating survey data with an Autodesk Civil 3D engineering project is unique in that it relies on connection and communication with third party survey equipment and software.

Autodesk Civil 3D points can be exported and then uploaded to the survey equipment without relying on manually created lists. However, a documented point list might be required. There are several ways to create reports about points.

Reports Manager

The Autodesk Civil 3D Reports Manager produces several point reports. To create reports from the Reports Manager, the *Toolbox* tab must be available in the Toolspace. To display the *Toolbox* tab, go to the *Home* tab, expand the Palettes drop-down list, and select **Toolbox**. Then select the *Toolbox* tab and expand the **Reports Manager** collection to display a list of object type reports, as shown in Figure 6–68.

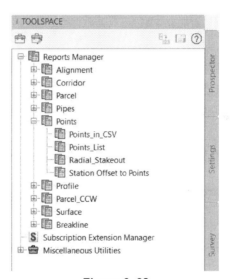

Figure 6–68

Points are easily organized into a convenient, legible list that displays the point number, northing, easting, elevation, and full description (as shown in Figure 6–69). Another point report lists the points' station and offset values relative to an alignment. Another report calculates distances and angles from an occupied and a backsight. You can transfer points to Microsoft Excel spreadsheets using a CSV report.

To create these reports, select the report's name, right-click, and select **Execute**.

Number	Northing	Easting	Elevation	Description
1	632055.919	2208068.041	900.655	MON
2	631396.467	2207989.483	900.171	MON
3	630834.659	2207979.534	898.369	MON
4	631382.131	2207989.229	900.174	MON

Figure 6–69

Point Editor Reports

Another report method is to use the *Point Editor* tab of the Panorama. In the Toolspace>*Prospector* tab, select **Points**, right-click, and select **Edit** to display the *Point Editor* tab of the Panorama, as shown in Figure 6–70.

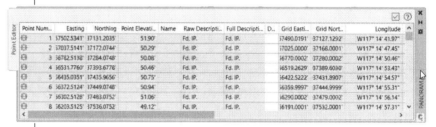

Figure 6–70

In the Panorama, you can select individual points using <Ctrl> or select blocks of points using <Shift>. When done selecting points, right-click and select **Copy to clipboard**. You can then paste the copied points into Microsoft Excel, a text editor, or any application that accepts the points, as shown in Figure 6–71.

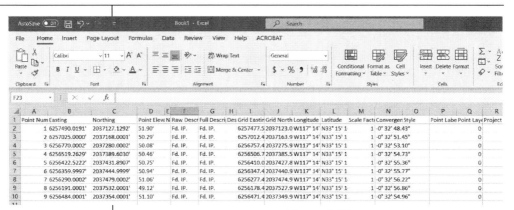

Figure 6–71

Practice 6g	Point Reports

Practice Objective

- Share information about points used for error checking or staking out points using predefined reports.

1. Continue working with the drawing from the previous practice.

2. If the *Toolbox* tab is not displayed in the Toolspace, select the *Home* tab and click  (Toolbox), as shown in Figure 6–72, to display the *Toolbox* tab.

Figure 6–72

3. Select the *Toolbox* tab and expand the **Reports Manager** collection to display the list of object type reports. Expand the **Points** collection, as shown in Figure 6–73.

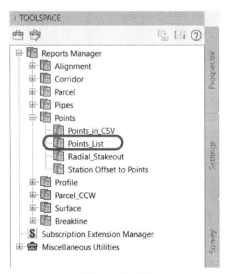

Figure 6–73

4. Select **Point List**, right-click, and select **Execute**.

5. In the Export to LandXML dialog box, click **OK** to generate the report. In the Save As dialog box, type a filename or accept the default **CivilReport.html**, and save the file. If the file exists, you will be prompted to replace it.

6. The point list is displayed in Internet Explorer. Review the report and when done, close it.

7. Close but do not save the drawing.

6.9 Filtering a Survey Database

Many civil engineering projects can become quite large depending on the scope of the project or the area that it covers. The larger the project area or scope, the larger the drawing size. This is especially true when designing or modifying long corridor projects, such as trails or freeways. That is why you can filter the survey database and only import the part of the project you are working on into the current drawing. Queries can be defined for both points and figures and can use general properties or extended properties that are either user-defined or imported from LandXML.

General properties available for Points include: elevation, number, description, name, control point, non-control point, station point, easting, and northing, as shown in Figure 6–74.

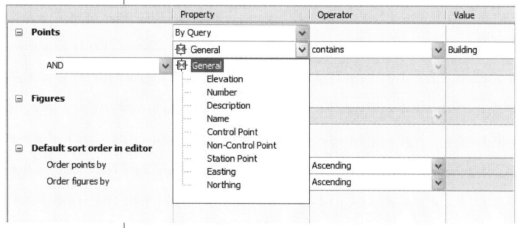

Figure 6–74

General properties available for Figures include: vertices, description, layer, name, site, style, breakline, closed, auto generated, lot line, first point X and Y, and last point X and Y, as shown in Figure 6–75.

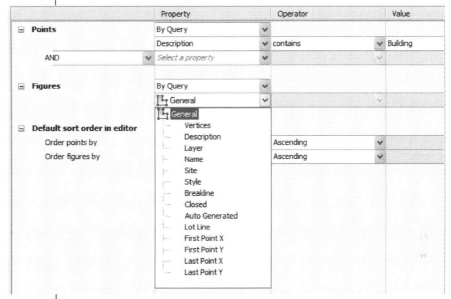

Figure 6–75

Both point and figure queries enable specific operators to help limit the data that you import into the drawing. The operators include: is equal to, is not equal to, is less than, is greater than, is less than or equal to, is greater than or equal to, contains, does not contain, starts with, does not start with, ends with, and does not end with, as shown in Figure 6–76.

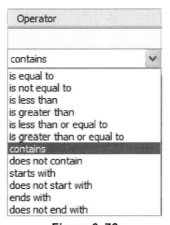

Figure 6–76

You can also include two boolean operators: **And** and **Or**. Each time you create a query, a new line is created below the current line on which you are working, as shown in the top of Figure 6–77.

- Selecting **And** for the boolean operation limits the data even more because it has to meet both conditions to be included in the query, similar to the results shown in the red area of the two circles on the left in Figure 6–77.

- Selecting **Or** for the boolean operation expands the included data because can meet either condition to be included in the query, similar to the results shown in the red area of the two circles on the right in Figure 6–77.

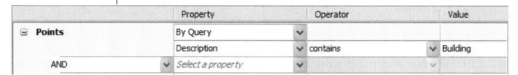

Figure 6–77

Individual survey queries can be saved to QML files that can be opened and reused or imported into another survey database. This can be done in the Survey Query Builder or by right-clicking on the query name under the **Survey Queries** collection and selecting **Save Query to File**.

How To: Filter a Survey Database

1. Expand the survey database in which you are working.
2. Right-click on **Survey Queries** and select **New**, as shown in Figure 6–78.

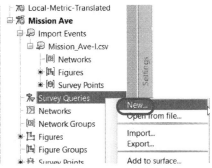

Figure 6–78

3. Select the property that you want to query under points or figures.
4. Select the operator to use on the data.
5. Type the value that you want the conditions to meet.
6. Add additional conditions using the **And** or **Or** operators to expand or limit the data even more.
7. To ensure that you are getting all of the information you want in the query, you can preview it in the drawing by selecting **Preview in Drawing**, as shown in Figure 6–79.

Figure 6–79

8. Finally, save the query for a later use, add the data to a surface, or import it into the drawing. To add it to a surface, right-click on **Survey Queries** and select **Add to surface**, as shown in Figure 6–80.

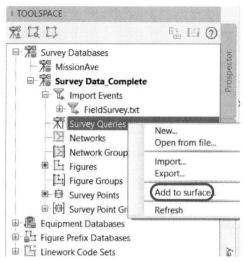

Figure 6–80

Practice 6h

Filter a Survey Database

Practice Objective

- Filter a survey database to isolate only the points or figures required for the tasks being completed in the project to reduce file sizes.

1. Continue working with the drawing from the previous practice or open **Points-Final.dwg**, from the *C:\Civil 3D for Surveyors\Working\Survey* folder.

2. Open the **Mission Ave** survey database for editing.

3. Expand the survey database, right-click on Survey Queries, and then select **New**, as shown in Figure 6–81.

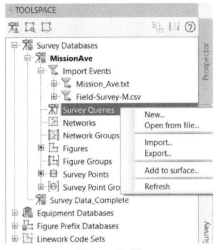

Figure 6–81

4. Name the new survey query **Road Lines**, and then enter **Breaklines for Mission Ave** as a description.

5. In the *Figures* area, set the following, as shown in Figure 6–82:
    - *Property:* **Name**
    - *Operator:* **starts with**
    - *Value:* **DAY**
    - **OR** (as operator)
    - *Property:* **Style**
    - *Operator:* **starts with**
    - *Value:* **ASC-**

6. Click **Preview in Drawing** to ensure that you have captured the correct figures.

7. Click **Save Query**, as shown in Figure 6–82.

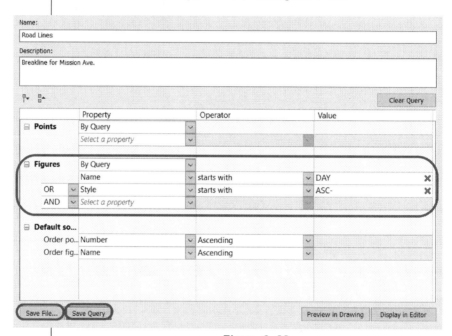

Figure 6–82

8. Click **Save File** and browse to the *C:\Civil 3D for Surveyors\Ascent-Config* folder. Accept the default file name (**Road Lines.qml**) and click the **Save** button.

9. Click the **Save Query** button.

10. Exit the Survey Query Builder palette by clicking the X in the top corner.

11. Open the **Survey South** survey database for editing.

12. Expand the survey database, right-click on **Survey Queries**, and select **New**.

13. Name the new query **Building Corners**.

14. In the *Points* area, set the following:
    - *Property:* **Description**
    - *Operator:* **Contains**
    - *Value:* **Building**

15. Click **Preview in Drawing**.

16. Click **Save Query** to save the query and then close the Survey Query Builder palette.

17. Save the drawing as **<Your Initials>-Survey-Complete.dwg** in the *C:\Civil 3D for Surveyors\References\DWG\Survey* folder.

18. While any changes are stored in the **Mission Ave** survey database, save the drawing to ensure any other changes are captured.

Chapter Review Questions

1. How do you control the next point number to be used in a drawing?

    a. The Point Identity parameters located in the expanded area in the Create Points toolbar.

    b. Under Label Styles, in the Toolspace>*Settings* tab.

    c. In the *Survey* tab, right-click on **Survey Points**.

    d. In the Toolspace>*Prospector* tab, right-click on **Survey Points**.

2. Can the **_All Points** point group be deleted?

    a. Yes

    b. No

3. Can a point group be made out of other point groups?

    a. Yes

    b. No

4. When points are locked, the point label can still be dragged to another location.

    a. True

    b. False

5. Survey points must reside in the current drawing in order to add them to a surface.

    a. True

    b. False

Command Summary

Button	Command	Location
	Create Points	• **Ribbon**: *Home* tab>Create Ground Data panel
	Import Points from File	• **Ribbon**: *Insert* tab>Import panel • **Toolbar**: Create Points • **Command Prompt**: ImportPoints
	Import Survey Data	• **Ribbon**: *Home* tab>Create Ground Data panel • **Command Prompt**: ImportSurveyData
	Survey User Settings	• **Toolspace**: *Survey* tab
	Toolbox	• **Ribbon**: *Home* tab>Palettes panel
	Zoom To Points	• **Toolbar**: Transparent Commands • **Command Prompt**: 'ZTP

Surfaces

In this chapter, you will learn how to create a surface from survey data. Then, you will learn to effectively refine the surface by using breaklines and boundaries and making other edits. Finally, you will analyze the surface and annotate it to communicate the existing conditions.

Learning Objectives in This Chapter

- Learn the steps required to build a surface in the Autodesk® Civil 3D® software.
- Adjust and edit a surface using surface properties and various commands.
- Add drawing objects to a surface to improve the accuracy of a TIN model.
- Add breaklines and boundaries to a surface to improve its accuracy.
- Analyze a surface using the object viewer.
- Label contour elevations, slope values, and spot elevations.
- Analyze a surface to determine the buildable area for the project conditions.

7.1 Surface Process

The surface building process can be divided into the following steps:

1. Assemble the data.
2. Assign the data to a surface.
3. Evaluate the resulting surface.
4. Add breaklines, assign more data, modify the data, or edit the surface as required.

1. Assemble data.

The first step in surface building is to acquire the initial surface data. This can be:

- Points

- Contours

- 3D polylines

- Feature lines

- AutoCAD® objects

- ASCII coordinate files

- Boundaries

Each data type provides specific information about a surface.

2. Assign data to a surface.

Acquired data is assigned to a surface. Once assigned, the Autodesk Civil 3D software immediately processes this data and a surface object is created.

Surfaces are listed individually in the **Surfaces** collection in the Toolspace>*Prospector* tab. Each surface contains content information, as shown in Figure 7–1. The surface content includes **Masks**, **Watersheds**, and **Definition** elements. The **Definition** contains a list of all of the surface data that has been applied, including boundaries, breaklines, and points. The Toolspace>*Prospector* tab displays data for each type of surface data in the list view when one of these types is selected.

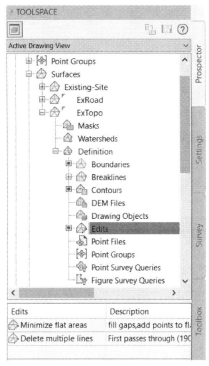

Figure 7–1

The Autodesk Civil 3D software processes the initial data into one of two types of surfaces. The first type, the **Triangulated Irregular Network** (TIN) surface, is the most common. With triangulated surfaces, surface points are connected to adjacent points by straight lines, resulting in a triangular mesh. Surfaces generated from contour lines have surface points created at their vertices, modified by weeding and supplementing factors. An example of this type of surface is shown in Figure 7–2.

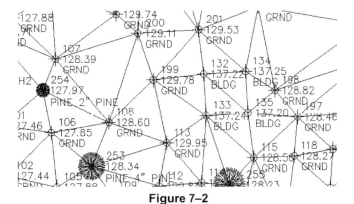

Figure 7–2

The second type of surface is a *Grid* surface. This surface interpolates and assigns an elevation from the surface data to each regular grid intersection. Most of the elevations at grid intersections are interpolated. **Digital Elevation Models** (DEMs) are a type of grid surface used in GIS applications. An example of this type of surface is shown in Figure 7–3.

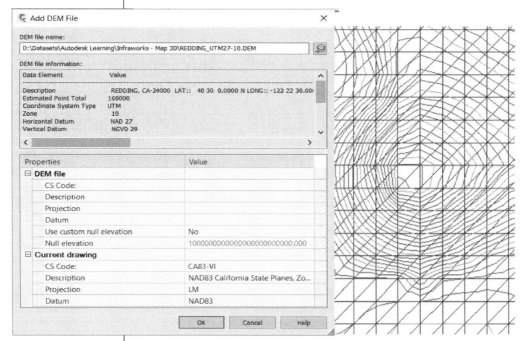

Figure 7–3

3. Evaluate the resulting surface.

Surfaces, especially ones created from points, typically need some attention to represent them as accurately as possible. For any four adjacent surface points, there are two possible triangulations, as shown in Figure 7–4.

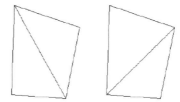

Figure 7–4

The differences can be difficult to envision when viewing the triangles from the TOP view, but these two configurations provide entirely different geometries. For example, note the surface shown in Figure 7–5.

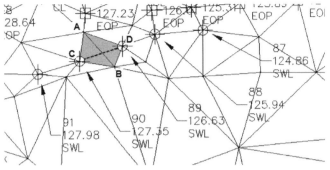

Figure 7–5

The triangulated points A, B, C, and D have a TIN line running from A to B. This configuration ignores the fact that C and D are both part of a continuous swale (SWL), indicated by the dashed line. In a 3D view, this configuration would resemble the example shown on the left in Figure 7–6. The correct triangulation has the triangle line *following* the linear feature rather than *crossing* it, as shown on the right.

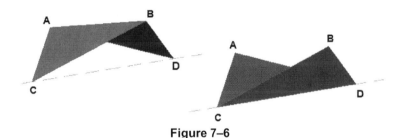

Figure 7–6

When creating surfaces, representing linear features correctly is important. Examples of linear features include road center lines, edges-of-pavement, road shoulders, swales, berms, tops and bottoms of banks, and headwalls. Adding breaklines that follow linear features ensures that a terrain model is triangulated correctly along the features, rather than across them.

Other types of issues to watch out for include bad elevations (blown shots), elevations at 0 where there should be no chance of such elevation values, and points that were surveyed above or below the ground (e.g., the tops of fire hydrants). Unwanted triangles along the edges of the surface might connect points that should not be connected, which could also present problems.

In addition to the casual inspection of the triangles, surfaces can be evaluated by creating contour lines, reviewing the surface in 3D, and using the **Quick Profile** command.

4. Add breaklines, assign more data, modify the data, or edit the surface as required.

After you have evaluated the surface, you can add the required breaklines or edit the surface directly to make adjustments. If the triangulation errors are isolated, editing the surface directly might be faster than creating and applying breaklines. For example, the triangulation issue in the previous *swale* example could be addressed by *swapping* the edge that crossed the swale center line. To do so, in the Toolspace>*Prospector* tab, under a Surface's **Definition**, right-click on **Edits** and select **Swap Edge**, as shown in Figure 7–7.

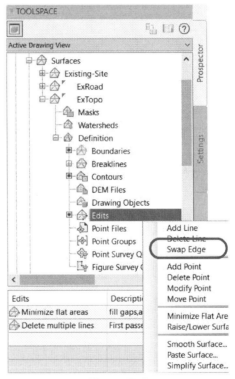

Figure 7–7

Other options enable you to add, move, modify, or remove points from the surface (but not change or erase the point object on which they were based), as well as add or remove triangle lines directly. **Minimize Flat Areas** is a group of algorithms that can be used to minimize the number of flat areas created by contour data. **Raise/Lower Surface** enables you to raise and lower the entire surface by a set amount, and a **Smooth Surface** enables you to smooth surfaces using the **Natural Neighbor** or **Kriging** method. (Contour smoothing is handled through surface styles. These techniques smooth the actual surface geometry.)

7.2 Surface Properties

The *Definition* tab in the Surface Properties dialog box displays the **Build**, **Data**, and **Edit** operations for a surface. The *Operation Type* column is a record of the surface data addition and edits. Using the checkboxes, you can toggle off individual actions in the history and display the resulting changes to the surface. The entries can be toggled on or off. This helps to isolate possible errors or review features (such as surface slopes) that are greatly affected by the addition of a headwall or retaining wall.

You can change the order of items in the list of operations. Operations higher in the list are applied to the surface before items further down in the list. Open this dialog box by right-clicking on the surface name in the Toolspace>*Prospector* tab (or by selecting the surface in the drawing and right-clicking) and selecting **Surface Properties**. It is also featured prominently in the contextualize ribbon when the surface is selected. The dialog box is shown in Figure 7–8.

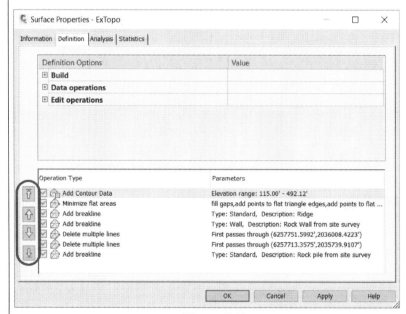

Figure 7–8

The *Information* tab enables you to rename the surface, edit the description, apply a surface object style, and render material, which controls how the surface displays in a rendered view or when the surface is exported to another (rendering) program.

The *Statistics* tab displays the current surface slope, elevation, and triangulation. It contains three areas:

- **General:** Provides an overall view of the surface. The **Minimum**, **Maximum**, and **Mean** elevations are the important entries in this area and provide the first hint of bad or incorrect data.

- **Extended:** Reports the **2D** and **3D** surface areas and **Minimum**, **Maximum**, and **Mean** slope values.

- **TIN:** Reviews the number of triangles, minimum and maximum triangle areas, and leg lengths in the surface.

The areas of triangles, along with the minimum and maximum triangle side lengths are indicators of data consistency. Generally, the longest triangles form around the perimeter of the surface. Limiting the length of triangle edges removes these types of triangles from the surface. You can delete these lines rather than try to set an optimum length, or you can create a boundary to prevent these types of triangles from being created.

When surfaces are created, they are assigned properties based on the *Build Options* area in the Edit Command Settings dialog box, as shown on the right in Figure 7–9. To open this dialog box, right-click on the **CreateSurface** command and select **Edit Command Settings**, as shown on the left in Figure 7–9.

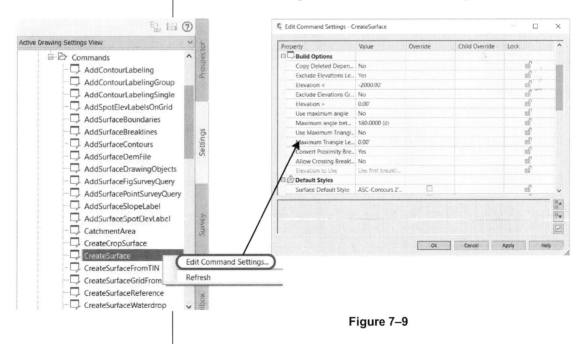

Figure 7–9

Surface Rebuilding

Some surface edits and point modifications can render a surface out of date. At that point, the surface is flagged as being out of date in the Toolspace>*Prospector* tab, as indicated by the **Drawing Item Modifier** icon shown in Figure 7–10.

Figure 7–10

When this occurs, you can right-click on the surface in the Toolspace>*Prospector* tab and select **Rebuild**. This updates the surface to reflect the recent changes. Alternatively, you can right-click on the surface in the Toolspace>*Prospector* tab and select **Rebuild-Automatic**, which updates the surface automatically without input from you. However, note that toggling this option on increases the strain on the computer resources and graphics capabilities.

7.3 Surface Data

Contours

In the Autodesk Civil 3D software, polylines with elevation are useful as custom contour objects. Whether using polylines or AutoCAD Land Desktop contour objects, the Autodesk Civil 3D software builds a surface by triangulating between contours. The end of each triangle side connects to a vertex of two different contours.

When processing contours for surface data, the Autodesk Civil 3D software inspects the contour vertices for two conditions: too many data points representing similar data (e.g., 10 vertices on 15 units of contour length in an almost straight line) and not enough data points over the length of a contour.

You can set the values for these conditions in the Add Contour Data dialog box (as shown in Figure 7–11) when you add contour data.

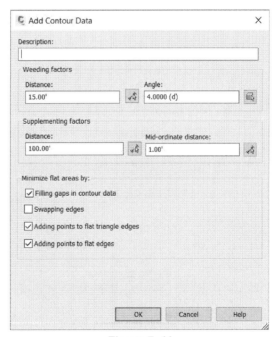

Figure 7–11

Weeding Factors

The *weeding* process removes redundant vertices from contours. The first step in the weeding process is to inspect three adjacent contour vertices, whose overall distance is shorter than a user-specified distance (e.g., three vertices in less than 15 units of contour). When encountering this situation, the weeding process prompts you about the change in direction between the three vertices.

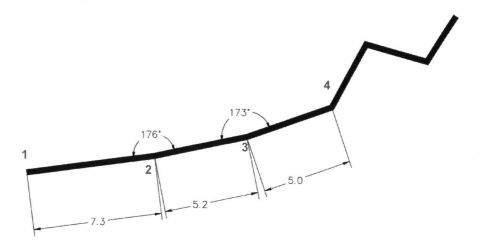

Figure 7–12

For example, in Figure 7–12 above, does the direction from vertex 1 to vertex 2 change more than four degrees when going from vertex 2 to vertex 3? If not, the vertices are almost in a straight line and are too close. The Autodesk Civil 3D software considers vertex 2 to be redundant and removes it from the surface data. This process repeats for the next three vertices. If the distance is under 15 units and the change of direction is less than four degrees, the next vertex 2 is removed from the data.

If a contour has three vertices in less than 15 units and turns more than four degrees, vertex 2 is kept because the change in direction is significant. If there are more than 15 units between the three vertices, the Autodesk Civil 3D software moves on to the next group.

Therefore, the higher the number of distances and angles, the more vertices that are removed.

An important feature of weeding is not what it removes from the data, but what is left over. If not enough data remains, the numbers for the weeding factors should be set to lower values.

Supplementing Factors

When the Autodesk Civil 3D software inspects contour data, it uses supplementing factors to add vertices to the surface data. The first supplementing factor is the distance between contour vertices. When the distance between vertices is over 100 units, the Autodesk Civil 3D software adds a vertex to the data along the course of the contour, as shown in Figure 7–13.

Figure 7–13

The second supplementing factor is a mid-ordinate distance for the curve segments of a contour. If the length of a line from the midpoint of the chord length of the arc to perpendicular to the arc is more the desired distance, a new vertex is inserted at the midpoint of the arc and the process is repeated, as shown in Figure 7–14.

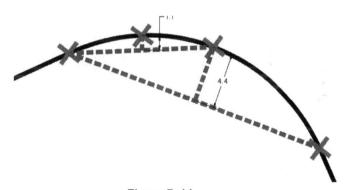

Figure 7–14

If curves are distributed throughout the contour data, a setting of 0.1 is a good starting point.

- All weeding and supplementing factors are user-specified.

- Weeding and supplementing does not modify the contours or polylines in a drawing, only their data.

- There is no *correct* setting for weeding and supplementing. Varying the values creates more or less surface data.

DEM Files

Digital Elevation Models (DEMs) are grid-based terrain models primarily used by GIS applications to represent large areas. Since they are large-scale and grid-based, they are generally only used in the Autodesk Civil 3D software for preliminary design and other approximate tasks.

Drawing Objects

AutoCAD points, text, blocks, and other objects can be used as surface data. Individual Autodesk Civil 3D point objects can also be selected using the **Drawing Objects** option. Selected objects need to have a valid elevation value.

- All data added as drawing objects is considered point data.

- You can add 3D lines and polyfaces using this method, but each end point is treated as if it were a point object. Linework is not treated as contours or breaklines. The Add Points From Drawing Objects dialog box is shown in Figure 7–15.

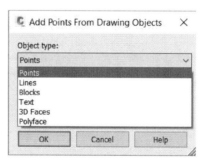

Figure 7–15

Point Files

Points in an ASCII point file can be used as surface data.

- You can use any import/export file format.

- This is an excellent way to create a large surface from a massive number of points, as it bypasses creating point objects, thereby reducing drawing overhead.

Point Groups

Using previously defined points groups in a surface definition enables you to isolate only the points on the ground. This helps you ensure that the tops of walls and invert elevations do not distort the surface, by omitting them in from the point group definition.

Point Survey Queries

Select points in a survey database can be used as surface data by creating a survey query. The point data is used, but point objects are not created in the current drawing.

- Dynamic references to the points provide a more seamless update if changes to the database or query are made.

- This is an excellent way to create a large surface from a massive number of points, as it bypasses creating point objects, thereby reducing drawing overhead.

- You can query the survey points required for creating a surface (similar to the point groups described previously).

- Points from a survey query display under point groups in the surface definition.

Figure Survey Queries

Select figures in a survey database can be used as surface data, as shown in Figure 7–16. The figures are used as breaklines, but 3D polylines are not created in the drawing.

- Dynamic references to the figures provide a more seamless update if changes to the database or query are made.

- This is an excellent way to create a large surface from a massive number of figures, as it bypasses creating 3D polylines and turning them into breaklines, thereby reducing drawing overhead.

- Figures from a survey query display under breaklines in the surface definition.

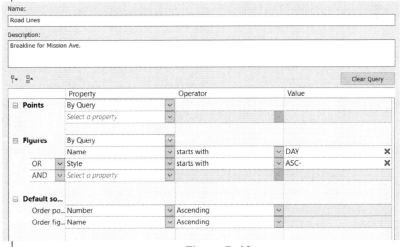

Figure 7–16

Practice 7a

Creating an Existing Ground Surface

Practice Objective

- Add point data to a surface that already exists in the drawing.

The final step in the Existing Condition phase is to create an existing ground terrain model that can be used in the design development phase of a project. In this practice, you will define the surface with surface data. You will use this model to create existing ground contours and for reference during the design phase. You will create the initial surface from ground shots, then supplement it with the Mission Avenue survey.

1. Open **SUF1-A.dwg** from the *C:\Civil 3D for Surveyors\ Working\Surface* folder.

2. If you are greeted with a splash screen about using Online Map Data, select **Remember my choice** and click **No**, as shown in Figure 7–17. (Since you have captured an online map in a previous chapter, you do not need to use Online Map Data.)

Figure 7–17

3. Although the point group that you use In this practice, has been created, you should change the display order of the point groups to display them clearly. To do so, in the Toolspace>*Prospector* tab, right-click on **Point Groups** and select **Properties**. Move the **_No Display** point group to the top, and then move the following point groups above it:

- **Groundshots**
- **Boundary Pin Survey**
- **Field-Survey-I.csv**

4. In the Toolspace>*Prospector* tab, select the **Surfaces** collection, right-click, and select **Create Surface**.

5. In the Create Surface dialog box, set the following:
   - *Surface type*: **TIN surface**
   - *Surface Name*: **ExTopo**
   - *Description*: **Existing Topography**
   - *Style*: **ASC-Contours 2' and 10' Background**

6. Click **OK** to accept the changes and close the dialog box.

7. In the Toolspace>*Prospector* tab, expand the **Surfaces** collection and expand the **ExTopo** collection.

8. Expand the **Definition** collection, select **Point Groups**, right-click, and select **Add**, as shown in Figure 7–18.

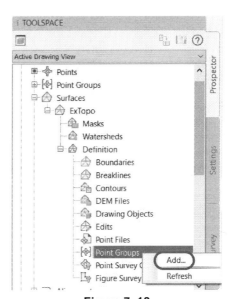

Figure 7–18

9. In the Point Groups dialog box, select the **Groundshots** point group, as shown in Figure 7–19. Click **OK** to accept the changes and close the dialog box.

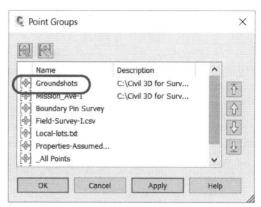

Figure 7–19

10. Select the new surface. In the contextual *Surface* tab>Modify panel, expand the **Add Data** command and select **Point Groups**, as shown in Figure 7–20.

You could have selected all of the point groups at once in the previous step. These steps demonstrate another way of adding data to the surface.

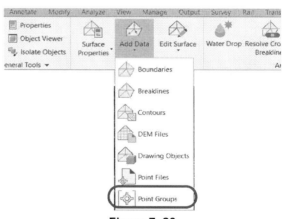

Figure 7–20

11. While holding <Ctrl>, select **Boundary Pin Survey** and **Field Survey-I.csv** from the list, and then click **OK**.

12. Review the surface, and then save the drawing.

7.4 Breaklines and Boundaries

A surface can include data from boundaries, breaklines, contours, Digital Elevation Model files (DEMs), drawing objects (AutoCAD points, individual Autodesk Civil 3D points, lines, 3D faces, etc.), and point files. The **Boundaries** collection displays above the **Breaklines** collection under the surface's **Definition** (in the Toolspace>*Prospector* tab), as shown in Figure 7–21. However, you should generally add boundaries after adding breaklines to a surface. If you use the Data Clip boundary type, any data that you add to the surface (point file, DEM file, or breakline) is only added to the area in the boundary. In that case, breaklines can be added to the surface after a Data Clip boundary type. Surface edit operations are not affected by the Data Clip boundary.

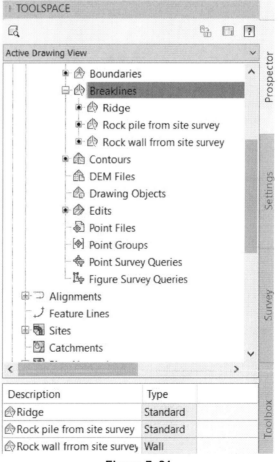

Figure 7–21

Breaklines

Breaklines affect surface triangulation and are important in point-based surfaces. Think of breaklines being a fold in a surface, much like a fold in a piece of paper. They ensure that terrain models are triangulated correctly along linear features, as shown in Figure 7–22.

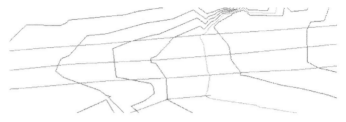

Surface before breaklines have been applied along the center line of a road.

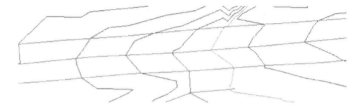

Surface after breaklines have been applied along the center line of a road.

Figure 7–22

- When adding a breakline to a surface, the Autodesk Civil 3D software creates an entry under the **Breakline>Definition** collections, based on a description that you supply.

- When you define multiple breaklines at the same time, the Autodesk Civil 3D software creates a single entry under the **Breaklines** collection. However, they are listed separately in the Toolspace>*Prospector* tab's List View.

- Breaklines can be defined as one of four types: **Standard**, **Proximity**, **Wall**, and **Non-Destructive**.

Standard Breaklines

A standard breakline is one that has valid elevations assigned at each vertex.

- Standard breaklines can be defined from 3D lines, 3D polylines, survey figures, or grading feature lines.

- The number of points generated along a breakline can be reduced by specifying a *Weeding* factor or increased by specifying a *Supplementing* factor, similar to weeding and supplementing factors for contour data.

- Curves in standard breaklines are approximated through the use of a mid-ordinate distance, similar to the way curved boundaries are resolved.

- When drawing 3D lines, polylines, or feature lines, you can use Autodesk Civil 3D's transparent commands. For example, using the **Point Object ('PO)** transparent command to select a point as a vertex of a 3D polyline prompts the Autodesk Civil 3D software to assign the point's elevation to the vertex of the polyline.

- Standard breaklines can also be defined from ASCII breakline data files (.FLT file extension).

Proximity Breaklines

Proximity breaklines do not need to have elevations at their vertices. A polyline at elevation 0 could be used as a proximity breakline. When a proximity breakline is defined, the Autodesk Civil 3D software automatically assigns vertex elevations from the nearest TIN data point, such as a nearby point object or contour line vertex.

- The Autodesk Civil 3D software can define proximity breaklines from 2D polylines or grading feature Lines.

- The Autodesk Civil 3D software does not support curves in proximity breaklines. Arc segments are treated as if they were straight line segments.

- One of the default options in the surface *Build* area enables the conversion of all proximity (2D) breaklines into standard (3D) breaklines. After conversion, the breakline is listed as a standard breakline and has the same elevations as the point objects that are at each vertex.

Non-Destructive Breaklines

Non-destructive breaklines are rarely used in Civil 3D. They are created from either a grading feature line or any AutoCAD open or closed polyline. At each vertex of the breakline, the elevation is assigned from the surface triangle edge and a surface point is created. By creating new surface points from the original surface triangle, the integrity of the original surface is maintained.

- They are used when deleting surface areas that lack TIN edges.

- They preserve the TIN composition before adding new data to that surface.

- They create new vertices when they cross an existing TIN line.

Wall Breaklines

- A wall breakline can be used to represent both the top and bottom of a wall, curb, or other sheer face.

- Wall breaklines are defined by 3D lines, 3D polylines, or feature lines. When defining them from linework, the object itself is meant to define either the top or bottom of the wall.

- The other end of the wall (top or bottom) is defined interactively by entering the absolute elevations or height differences from the defining line.

- If a wall breakline starts as a 2D polyline or feature line, it can contain curve segments.

- The number of points generated along a breakline can be reduced by specifying a *Weeding* factor or increased by specifying a *Supplementing* factor.

Survey Figures as Breaklines

Figures created by surveyors can be used as breaklines if a connection exists between the drawing and the survey database.

How To: Add Survey Figures as Breaklines

1. Open the survey database for editing.
2. In the *Survey* tab, expand the **Survey Data** collection and select **Figures**. The list of figures in the grid view displays at the bottom of the Toolspace.
3. Select the figures, right-click, and select **Create breaklines**, as shown in Figure 7–23.

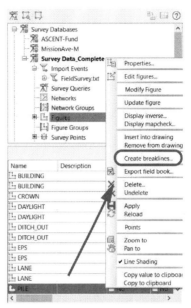

Figure 7–23

4. In the Create Breaklines dialog box, select the surface on which to place the breaklines, and then, in the *Breakline* column, select the **Yes** option to create the breaklines, as shown in Figure 7–24. Click **OK** to close the dialog box.

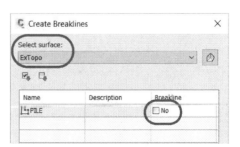

Figure 7–24

Boundaries

Boundaries provide interior or exterior limits to the surface triangulation. Boundaries are typically created from 2D closed polylines. There are four types of boundaries: **Outer**, **Hide**, **Show**, and **Data Clip**. An outer boundary should be one of the last items added to a surface, because adding data outside an existing boundary extends the surface past the boundary.

- An **Outer** boundary hides or excludes data outside its edge.

- A **Hide** boundary hides an interior portion of a surface to delineate features (such as water bodies and building footprints).

- A **Show** boundary displays a portion of a surface within a Hide boundary (e.g., to display an island in a pond).

- A **Data Clip** boundary acts as a filter on all data, including points, DEMs, and breaklines added to the surface after the creation of the Data Clip boundary. If a data clip boundary is used, any data added after it, that falls outside the data clip boundary, is ignored.

A boundary can contain arc segments. To better represent surface elevations around an arc, the Autodesk Civil 3D software uses a mid-ordinate value to calculate where the triangles interact with the boundary. The mid-ordinate value is the distance between the midpoint of the cord and the arc. The smaller the mid-ordinate value, the closer the surface data is to the original arc. An example is shown in Figure 7–25.

Figure 7–25

A boundary can limit a surface to the data in it. When you want to extend the triangulation exactly to a boundary line, select the **Non-destructive breakline** option in the Create Boundary dialog box. A non-destructive breakline fractures triangles at their intersection with the boundary. The resulting triangles preserve the original elevations of the surface at the boundary intersection as close as possible.

The example in Figure 7–26 shows the following:

1. The surface with a polyline is used as an outer boundary.
2. The boundary is applied without the **Non-destructive breakline** option. This is typically used when the boundary polyline is approximate and not meant to represent a hard edge. Triangles that lie under the boundary are removed from the surface, resulting in a jagged edge.
3. The boundary is applied with the **Non-destructive breakline** option. Non-destructive breaklines are often used to create a specific termination limit for the surface (such as at a parcel boundary). Triangles that lie under the boundary are trimmed back to the boundary, resulting in a smooth edge.

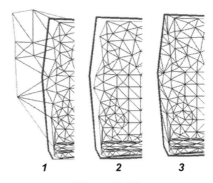

Figure 7–26

Practice 7b

Add Additional Data to an Existing Ground Surface

Practice Objectives

- Build a surface directly from breaklines.
- Create a new surface style.
- Improve the accuracy of a surface by adding various breaklines, such as standard breaklines, wall breaklines, and breaklines from survey figures.

Task 1 - Define a surface with breaklines.

In examining the **ExTopo** surface more closely, note that although the internal site contours correctly reflect the surveyed point elevations, in the area of the existing road, **Mission Avenue** (the road running east to west at the top of the site), the data is a bit sparse. However, you have a detailed survey of the road. Using this data, you will generate a surface from breaklines stored within the survey database.

1. In the Toolspace>*Prospector* tab, select the **Surfaces** collection, then right-click and select **Create Surface**.

2. In the Create Surface dialog box, set the following:
   - *Surface type*: **TIN surface**
   - *Surface Name*: **ExRoad**
   - *Description*: **Mission Ave**
   - *Style*: **Contours 2' and 10' (Background)**

3. Click **OK** to close the Create Surface dialog box.

4. In the Toolspace>*Survey* tab, right-click on the **Mission Ave** survey database and select **Open for edit** to open it for editing.

*If **Mission Ave** is not listed under Survey Databases, change your working folder to C:\Civil 3D for Surveyors\ Survey Databases\ Ascent Pointfiles.*

5. Expand the **Survey Queries** branch, select the **Road Lines** query, then right-click and select **Add to Surface**, as shown in Figure 7–27.

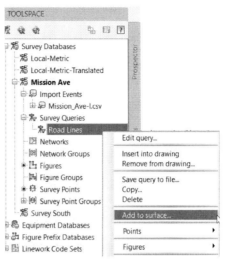

Figure 7–27

The Reference the survey database for dynamic query results option would permit dynamic updates of the surface if the road is re-surveyed for updated conditions.

6. In the Add Survey Query Results to Surface dialog box, select **ExRoad** for the surface. Select the *Insert query results into drawing as point groups and figures* option, as shown in Figure 7–28.

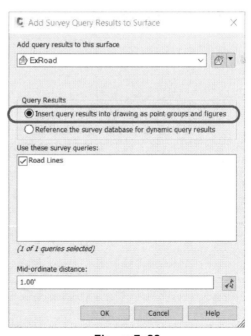

Figure 7–28

7. Click **OK** to close the dialog box.

8. Exit the *Survey Query* contextual ribbon by clicking the green checkmark, as shown in Figure 7–29.

Figure 7–29

9. Review the surface and save the drawing.

Task 2 - Create a surface contour style.

---

1. Since there is very little grade change along the road, the frequency of the contours is small, making the surface difficult to see. Expand the **Surfaces** collection, right-click **ExRoad**, and select **Surface Properties**.

2. In the Surface Properties dialog box, in the *Information* tab, expand 🖉🔽 to the right of the *Surface style* field and select **Copy Current Selection**, as shown in Figure 7–30.

3. In the *Information* tab, set the style *Name* to **ASC-Contours 0.5' and 2.5' (Background)**, as shown in Figure 7–31. Edit the description appropriately.

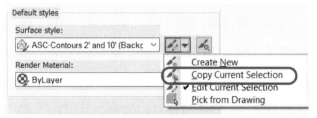

Figure 7–30

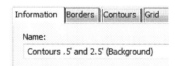

Figure 7–31

4. In the *Contours* tab, expand the **Contour Intervals** collection and set the following, as shown in Figure 7–32:
   - *Minor Interval:* **0.5'**
   - *Major Interval:* **2.5'**

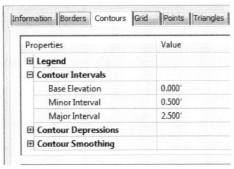

Figure 7–32

5. Click **OK** to accept and close the Edit Style dialog box, and click **OK** to close the Surface Properties dialog box.

6. Zoom into the **ExRoad** surface at the north end of the site and note the detail contours identifying the crown of the road.

7. Save the drawing.

Task 3 - Add surface breaklines.

TIN lines are generally created using the shortest distance between points. To further define a surface, you might need to supplement it with breaklines of ridges, ditches, walls, etc., that accurately define the surface. These breaklines prevent the software from triangulating directly between points that are bisected by a breakline. The breakline becomes part of the triangulation between the two adjacent points.

1. Continue working with the drawing from the previous practice or open **SUF1-B.dwg** from the *C:\Civil 3D for Surveyors\ Working\Surface* folder.

The contextual tab displays.

2. Select any part of the **ExTopo** surface in Model Space.

3. In the contextual *Surface* tab>Modify panel, select **Surface Properties**, as shown in Figure 7–33. The Surface Properties dialog box opens.

Figure 7–33

4. In the *Information* tab, expand the Surface style drop-down list and select **ASC-Contours and Triangles**, as shown in Figure 7–34. Click **OK** to close the dialog box.

Figure 7–34

Now that the triangulations are displayed, you will examine how adding a feature line impacts the surface.

5. In the *View* tab>Views panel, expand the drop-down list and select **Surf-Breakline**. This zooms into the breakline that is located north of the existing road as shown in Figure 7–35. If you do not see the red 3D polyline, toggle on the **A-BREAKLINE** layer.

Note that the triangulation crosses the breakline.

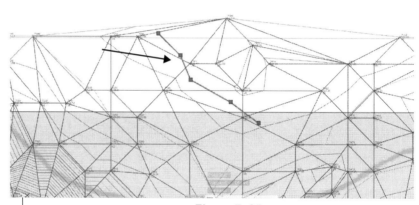

Figure 7–35

Be sure you select the ExTopo surface!

6. In the Toolspace> *Prospector* tab, expand the **Surfaces>ExTopo>Definition** collection. Select **Breaklines**, right-click, and select **Add**, as shown in Figure 7–36.

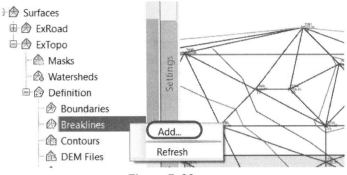

Figure 7–36

7. Set the *Description* to **Ridge** and ensure that **Standard** is set for *Type*, as shown in Figure 7–37. Accept all of the defaults and then click **OK** to close the dialog box.

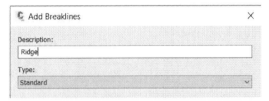

Figure 7–37

8. When prompted to select objects, select the red 3D polyline and press <Enter> to complete the command.

9. The surface should rebuild automatically. Note that the triangulation now takes the breakline into consideration, as shown in Figure 7–38.

*If the **ExTopo** surface is marked as out of date*

*( ), select the **ExTopo** surface, right-click, and select **Rebuild Automatic**.*

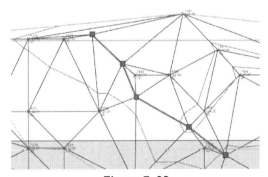

Figure 7–38

10. Save the drawing.

Task 4 - Add field book figures as breaklines.

In the task, you will add breaklines to the surface from figures that were created when the field books were imported.

1. In the Toolspace>*Survey* tab, right-click on the **Survey South** survey database and select **Open for edit** to open it for editing.

2. Expand the **Survey South** collection and select **Figures**. The list of figures in the grid view displays at the bottom of the Toolspace.

3. Select the figure **PILE**, then right-click and select **Create breaklines**, as shown in Figure 7–39.

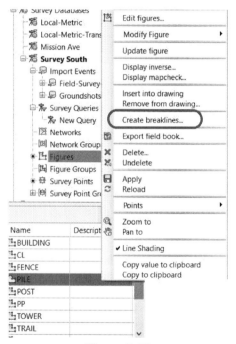

Figure 7–39

4. In the Create Breaklines dialog box, select **ExTopo** for the surface, and select the **Yes** option in the *Breakline* column to create breaklines, as shown in Figure 7–40. Click **OK** to close the dialog box.

5. The Autodesk Civil 3D software zooms in to the location of the breakline, and opens the Add Breaklines dialog box. Type **Rock pile from site survey** in the *Description* field, and ensure that **Standard** is selected in the Type drop-down list, as shown in Figure 7–41. Click **OK** to close the dialog box.

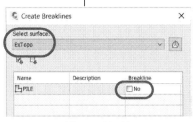

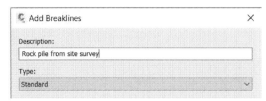

Figure 7–40   Figure 7–41

6. Save the drawing.

Task 5 - Add a wall breakline.

In the task, you will add a wall breakline to the surface from figures that were created when the field books were imported.

1. In the *Survey* tab, expand the survey data collection and select **Figures**. Note the list of figures in the grid view at the bottom of the Toolspace.

2. Select the **Wall** figure, then right-click and select **Create breaklines**.

3. In the Create Breaklines dialog box, select the **ExTopo** surface and select the **Yes** option in the *Breakline* column to create breaklines. Click **OK** to close the dialog box.

4. The Autodesk Civil 3D software zooms in to the location of the breakline, and opens the Add Breaklines dialog box. Type **Retaining wall from site survey** in the *Description* field, and ensure that **Wall** is selected in the Type drop-down list, as shown in Figure 7–42. Click **OK** to close the dialog box.

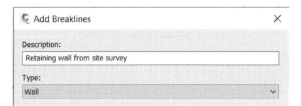

Figure 7–42

5. At the prompt to pick the offset side, select a point to the south of the wall break line, as shown in Figure 7–43.

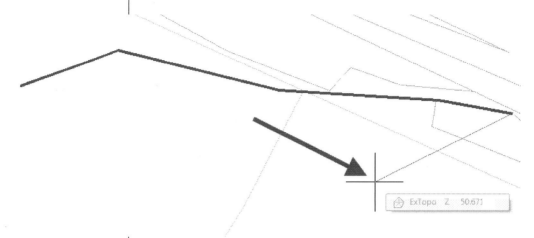

ExTopo Z 50.671

Figure 7–43

6. When prompted to select the option for the wall height, select the default **All** option because the wall has a constant height of 1.5' from the base.

7. When prompted for the elevation difference or elevation, type **1.5** and press <Enter>.

8. Save the drawing.

7.5 Surface Editing

There are three ways of adjusting surfaces graphically: using lines, points, and area edit tools (such as **Minimize Flat Areas** and **Smooth Surface**). All of these tools are available by right-clicking on the *Edits* heading in a surface's *Definition* area (Toolspace>*Prospector* tab), as shown in Figure 7–44.

* The Autodesk Civil 3D software considers each graphical surface edit to be additional data that can be removed later.

* Most surface edits apply immediately. If the drawing item modifier icon displays (as shown in Figure 7–45), then an edit has rendered the surface out of date. When this happens, a surface should be rebuilt by right-clicking on the surface name in the Toolspace>*Prospector* tab and selecting **Rebuild**.

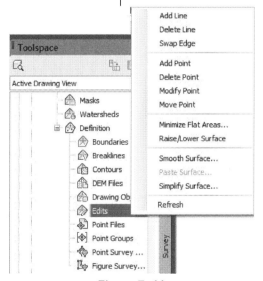

Figure 7–44

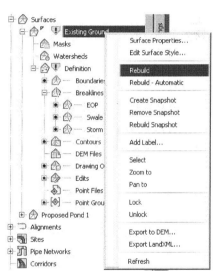

Figure 7–45

* To have a surface automatically rebuild as required, right-click on the surface name in the Toolspace>*Prospector* tab and select **Rebuild-Automatic**. However, toggling this option on increases the use of computer resources and graphics capabilities.

* To delete an edit from a surface permanently, remove it from the *Edits* list in Toolspace>*Prospector* tab's preview area or from the *Operations Type* list in the *Definition* tab in the Surface Properties dialog box.

Line Edits

The line editing commands include **Add Line**, **Delete Line**, and **Swap Edge**. The **Add Line** and **Delete Line** commands add or remove triangle lines. The **Delete Line** command is often only applied around the outside edge of a surface to remove unwanted edge triangulation. Deleting lines in the interior of a surface causes both of the triangles next to the removed line to be deleted, leaving a hole in the surface that needs to be repaired by adding another line.

If you are considering deleting a line only to replace it with the opposite diagonal, such as the central line shown in Figure 7–46, using the **Swap Edge** command instead might be more efficient.

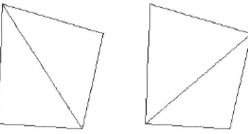

Figure 7–46

Adding an interior line that crosses many existing triangles swaps them where possible to adhere to the geometry represented by the added line. This method can be a good way of swapping multiple edges at the same time.

Point Edits

The Point editing commands can **Add**, **Delete**, **Modify**, or **Move** surface points. They do not affect point objects in the drawing, but rather the surface points created from them. Surface points can be adjusted or deleted as required.

When an Autodesk Civil 3D point object is adjusted (i.e., moved), the surface containing that point data might not be identified as being out of date nor update automatically. In this situation, you should rebuild the surface.

Simplify Surface

As the collection methods of surface data continue to evolve, yielding significantly larger data sets, the drawing file size increases in proportion to the surface data contained in the drawing. The Autodesk Civil 3D software has a limit of 2.5 million vertices for a surface. Once it exceeds this limit, the software prompts you to store surface data to an external file with an .MMS extension. The resulting external surface files can be quite large. To avoid this, you can simplify your surface using the Simplify Surface wizard. Extra points can be removed from a surface without compromising its accuracy. Points that you might want to remove include points that are in an external point file or database, or redundant points in areas of high data concentration where the value of this extra information is minimal. There are two simplification methods available.

- **Edge Contraction:** This method simplifies the surface by using existing triangle edges. It contracts triangle edges to single points by removing one point. The location of the point to which an edge is contracted is selected so that the change to the surface is minimal.

- **Point Removal:** This method simplifies the surface by removing existing surface points. More points are removed from denser areas of the surface.

When you simplify a surface, you specify which regions of the surface the operation should address. The region options include using the existing surface border, or specifying a window or polygon. The **Pick in Drawing** icon enables you to select the region from the drawing. If a closed line exists in the drawing that you want to use as the region boundary, you can select the **Select objects** option and then use the **Pick in Drawing** icon to select the boundary. Curves in the boundary are approximated by line segments. The line segment generation is governed by a *Mid Ordinate Distance* value that you determine.

Once you have selected the region, the dialog box displays the *Total Points Selected In Region* value. You can refine the surface reduction options by setting a percentage of points to remove, the maximum change in elevation, or the maximum edge contraction error.

Smooth Contours

Although not a true surface edit, Autodesk Civil 3D surface contours can be smoothed to reduce their jagged appearance using the Surface Object Style settings. There are two approaches to this: the *Add Vertices* method and the *Spline Curve* method. The *Add Vertices* method enables you to select a relative smoothness from the slider bar at the bottom of the Surface Style dialog box, as shown in Figure 7–47.

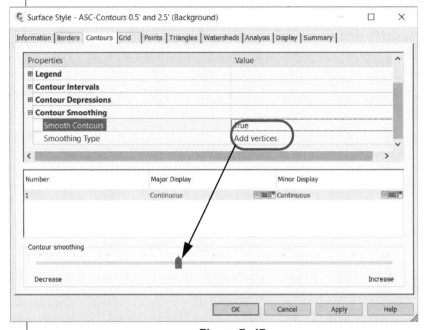

Figure 7–47

The *Spline Curve* method generates very smooth contours, but the contours are more liberally interpolated and might overlap where surface points are close together. This approach is best applied to surfaces with relatively few data points or in areas of low relief, as shown in Figure 7–48.

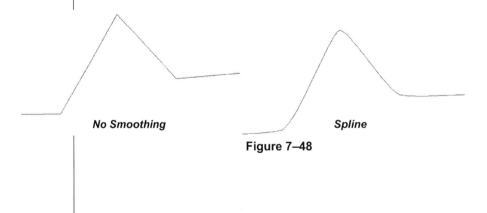

No Smoothing   *Spline*

Figure 7–48

Smooth Surface

The Smooth Surface edit introduces new, interpolated elevations between surface data. It is used to create a more realistic-looking terrain model, though not necessarily a more accurate one. Generally, surface smoothing works best with point-based surface data.

The Autodesk Civil 3D software has two smoothing methods: *Natural Neighbor* and *Kriging*.

- *Natural Neighbor* interpolates a grid of additional data points that produce a smoother overall terrain model.

- *Kriging* reads surface trends to add additional data in sparse areas.

Surface smoothing is applied by right-clicking on the **Edits** collection under a surface's *Definition* and selecting **Smooth Surface**. The Smooth Surface dialog box and example of surface smoothing are shown in Figure 7–49.

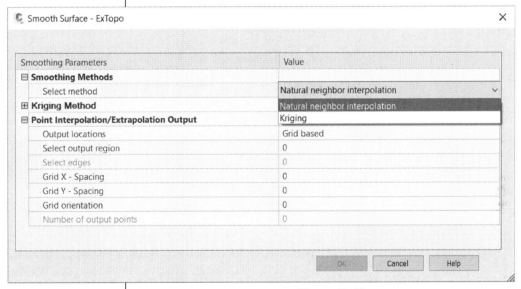

Figure 7–49

Copy Surface

The Autodesk Civil 3D software does not have a copy surface command, but surface objects can be copied using the AutoCAD **Copy** command (**Modify>Copy**). When copying surface objects, select the same base and then a second point to ensure that the surface is not moved during the copy. Another option is to not specify a base point, but give the surface a Displacement distance of 0,0,0, which means there is no displacement.

After a copy, a duplicate surface is created and displays in the Toolspace>*Prospector* tab. The copy has the same name as the original, followed by a number in parenthesis, such as (1). These copied surfaces can be renamed as required. Surface copies are independent of each other and can be individually edited.

Surface Paste

The **Surface Paste** command enables the Autodesk Civil 3D software to combine multiple surfaces into a single surface. You might want to paste into a copy of a surface if you want to keep the original unmodified. For example, a finished condition surface is required that includes a proposed surface (*Proposed*) along with the existing ground (EG) around its periphery. In this situation, you would first create a new surface and name it **Finished Ground**. In the **Surfaces** collection in the Toolspace>*Prospector* tab, right-click on the Finished Ground surface's **Edit** collection and select **Paste** to merge in the **Existing ground (EG)** and **Proposed** surfaces.

Once the command has executed, the surface's **EG** and **Proposed** surfaces are left unchanged, and the **Finished Ground** surface represents a combination of the two. If you did not create the **Finished Ground** surface, but pasted the **Proposed** surface into the **EG** surface, you would not have the original **EG** surface for reference in profiles and other places (unless you copied the EG surface, as explained above). If surfaces are pasted in the wrong order, the order can be rearranged using the *Definition* tab in the Surface Properties dialog box.

Surfaces remain dynamically linked after pasting. Therefore, if the **Proposed** surface changes, the **Finished Ground** surface updates to display the change the **Finished Ground** surface is set to **Rebuild Automatically**.

Raise/Lower Surface

The **Raise/Lower Surface** command adds or subtracts a specified elevation value. This adjustment is applied to the entire surface. It is useful for modeling soil removal and changing a surface's datum elevation.

Adjusting Surfaces Through Surface Properties

In addition to the graphical edit methods, you can adjust surfaces by changing their surface properties. Surface property adjustments include setting a *Maximum triangle length* or *Exclude elevations* greater or less than certain values. You can also enable or disable the effects of certain surface data (such as breaklines and boundaries) by disabling them in the dialog box.

The *Copy deleted dependent objects* option copies the definition of dependent objects if these objects are deleted from the drawing. Examples of dependent objects includes polylines used for contour definitions or breaklines, or any AutoCAD objects used to define a surface. Without this option, the surface loses the definition those objects had provided.

To locate these options (as shown in Figure 7–50), right-click on a surface in the Toolspace>*Prospector* tab and select **Surface Properties**.

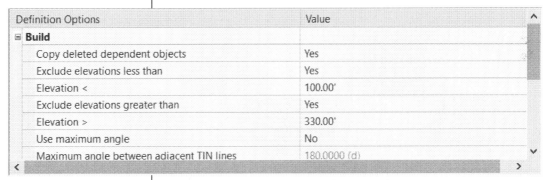

Definition Options	Value
Build	
Copy deleted dependent objects	Yes
Exclude elevations less than	Yes
Elevation <	100.00'
Exclude elevations greater than	Yes
Elevation >	330.00'
Use maximum angle	No
Maximum angle between adjacent TIN lines	180.0000 (d)

Figure 7–50

7.6 Surface Analysis Tools

Viewing a Surface in 3D

AutoCAD's default view, the overhead or plan view, is not the only way to view a surface. The AutoCAD **3D Orbit** command and the Autodesk Civil 3D **Object Viewer** tilt the coordinate space to display a 3D surface model. How the surface displays is dependent on the assigned style. You can view a surface in 3D using the Object Viewer or directly in the drawing window using the **3D Orbit** command. Both have similar navigation controls, but the Object Viewer enables you to review only your surface in 3D without changing your current view.

Both methods can display a wireframe (3D Wireframe and 3D Hidden), conceptual, or realistic view. By default, a Conceptual display is a cartoon-like rendering without edge lines, while a Realistic display has material styles with edge lines. Both viewing methods use the AutoCAD ViewCube, which uses labels and a compass to indicate the direction from which you are viewing a model.

The Object Viewer method is shown in Figure 7–51.

Figure 7–51

Quick Profile

Understanding the affect of breaklines and other data on a surface is critical to generating an accurate surface. The **Analyze>Ground Data>Quick Profile** command enables you to produce an instant surface profile with minimal effort. It is also accessible through the **Home>Profile** drop-down list.

A *Quick Profile* is a temporary object, which disappears from the drawing when you save or exit. If you need a more permanent graphic, you should create an alignment and profile.

Quick Profiles can be created along lines, arcs, polylines, lot lines, feature lines, or survey figures, or by selecting points. In addition to the command being located in the *Analyze* tab, you can select one of the previously mentioned objects, right-click, and select **Quick Profile**. Two examples of the Quick Profile are shown in Figure 7–52.

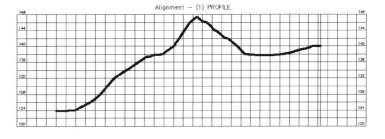

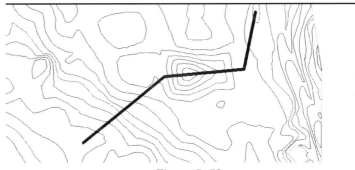

Figure 7–52

Practice 7c | Surface Edits

Practice Objective

- Edit a surface using definition options in the surface properties and commands found in the Toolspace.

In this practice, you will refine a previously created surface. The **ExTopo** surface has some triangulations that are not valid. You will eliminate these TIN lines using three methods: you will set options for the surface properties, delete TIN lines (triangle edges), and add a boundary to the surface. Each of these methods has advantages and disadvantages and should be used appropriately.

Task 1 - Copy deleted dependent objects.

1. Continue working with the drawing from the previous practice or open **SUF1-C.dwg** from the *C:\Civil 3D for Surveyors\ Working\Surface* folder.

2. Zoom in to the lower South-east area of the project, as shown in Figure 7–53.

*Ensure that the **ExTopo** surface is using the **Contours and Triangles** surface style.*

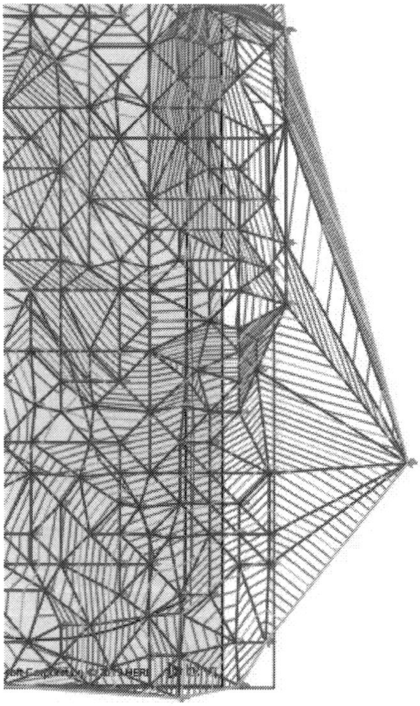

Figure 7–53

3. In Model Space, select the **ExTopo** surface. The *Tin Surface ExTopo* contextual tab displays. In the *Modify* panel, select **Surface Properties**, as shown in Figure 7–54.

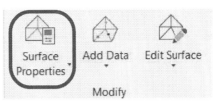

Figure 7–54

4. The Surface Properties dialog box opens. Select the *Definition* tab and expand the **Build** options in the *Definition Options* area.

This step copies the definition of dependent objects if these objects are deleted from the drawing.

5. Set the *Copy deleted dependent objects* value to **Yes**, as shown in Figure 7–55. Click **OK** to close the dialog box and accept the changes.

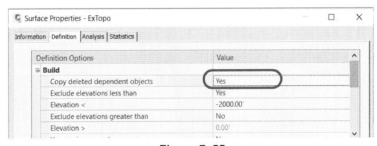

Figure 7–55

6. When prompted to *Rebuild the surface* or *Mark the surface as out-of-date*, select **Rebuild the surface**.

7. Save the drawing.

Task 2 - Delete lines.

Some triangles along the eastern edge of the surface need to be removed.

1. In Model Space, select the **ExTopo** surface. The *Tin Surface ExTopo* contextual tab displays. In the *Modify* panel, expand the 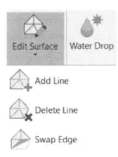 (Edit Surface) drop-down list, and select **Delete Line**, as shown in Figure 7–56.

Figure 7–56

Another option would be simply to delete the extraneous point to the far east, rather than deleting TIN lines.

2. Select each of the required TIN lines in Model Space, as shown in Figure 7–57. When you have finished, press <Enter> to end the selection and then press <Enter> again to end the command.

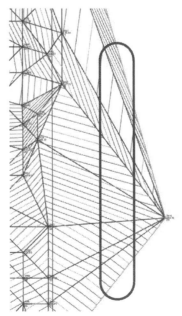

Figure 7–57

3. Save the drawing.

Task 3 - Add a boundary.

The **Delete Line** command can be effective, but might not efficiently clean up the edges of large surfaces. A surface boundary is useful if you have a well-defined boundary.

1. In Model Space, select the **ExTopo** surface. The *Tin Surface ExTopo* contextual tab will display. In the *Modify* panel, click

    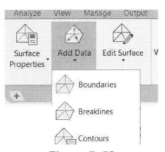 (Add Data), expand the drop-down list, and select **Boundaries**, as shown in Figure 7–58.

Figure 7–58

2. The Add Boundaries dialog box opens, as shown in Figure 7–59. Type **Limits** in the *Name* field, and select **Outer** in the Type drop-down list.

3. Select the **Non-destructive breakline** option (as shown in Figure 7–59) because you do want to trim to this polyline shape. Otherwise, the dialog box options will erase all of the triangle lines that cross or are beyond the boundary, resulting in a more jagged edge. Click **OK** to accept the changes and close the dialog box.

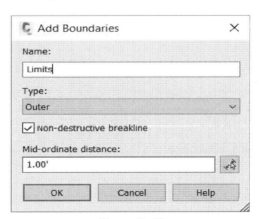

Figure 7–59

You might have to regen the screen to display the boundary.

4. When prompted to select an object, select the red polyline that represents the boundary, as shown in Figure 7–60.

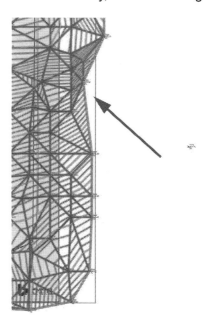

Figure 7–60

5. Examine how this boundary affected the surface. The boundary only trimmed the surface to the selected rectangle, but it did not extend the surface to the rectangle. This boundary is a dynamic part of the **ExTopo** surface.

6. Select the red boundary polyline and move the grips. In the Prospector, note that the **ExTopo** surface is marked as being *Out of Date.* Right-click on the **ExTopo** surface and set it to **Rebuild - Automatic**, as shown in Figure 7–61.

Figure 7–61

7. Note that when you change the polyline defining the boundary, the surface expands or contracts to match the change in the boundary. Restore the polyline to its original position.

8. Press <Esc> to deselect the red boundary polyline.

9. Save the drawing.

Task 4 - Set the elevation range.

It is a best practice to set the elevation range in the Surface Properties to avoid errors from invalid data that might get transferred to the surface.

1. In Model Space, select the **ExTopo** surface, then right-click and select **Object Viewer**.

2. Examine the surface to check for any errors, as shown in Figure 7–62.

Figure 7–62

3. Exit the object viewer by clicking the **X** in the upper right corner of the Object Viewer window.

4. Right-click on the **ExTopo** surface and select **Surface Properties**. On the *Statistics* tab, expand the **General** branch. Note that the site ranges from an elevation of roughly 100' to 330', as shown in Figure 7–63.

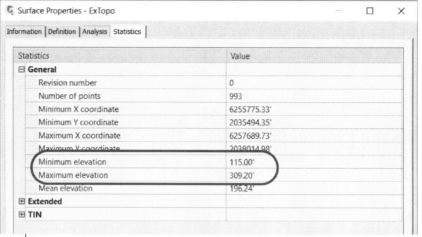

Figure 7–63

5. To safeguard the surface from receiving data beyond this elevation range, select the *Definition* tab. Expand the **Build** properties and set the following, as shown in Figure 7–64:
   - *Exclude elevation less than*: **Yes**
   - *Elevation <*: **100'**
   - *Exclude elevation greater than:* **Yes**
   - *Elevation >*: **330'**

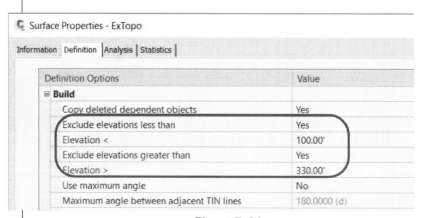

Figure 7–64

6. Click **OK** to accept the changes and close the dialog box.

7. When prompted to *Rebuild the surface* or *Mark the surface as out-of-date*, select **Rebuild the surface**.

8. Save the drawing.

Task 5 - Create a composite surface.

In the preceding tasks, you created a surface from available point data. However, the data around the existing road, **Mission Avenue** (the road running east to west at the top of the site), was inaccurate, so you surveyed the road and created a surface from breaklines (directly from the survey database). Now you need to create a composite surface that represents the site condition combined with the road.

1. In the Toolspace>*Prospector* tab, right-click on the **Surfaces** collection and select **Create Surface**.

2. In the Create Surface dialog box, set the following:

    - *Surface Type:* **TIN surface**
    - *Surface Name:* **Existing-Site**
    - *Description:* **Composite surface of ExTopo and ExRoad**
    - *Style*: **ASC-Contours 2' and 10' (Background)**

3. Click **OK** to close the dialog box and create the surface.

4. In the Toolspace>*Prospector* tab, select the Surfaces category. In the preview list area, select the **ExRoad** and **ExTopo** surfaces. Right-click on the *Style* column heading and select **Edit**, as shown in Figure 7–65.

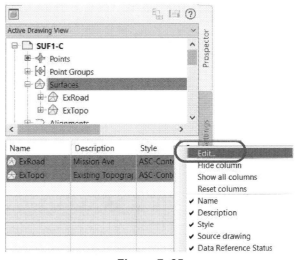

Figure 7–65

5. Set the surface style to **_No Display** and click **OK** to accept the changes and close the dialog box.

6. In the Toolspace>*Prospector* tab, expand the **Surfaces> Existing-Site>Definition** collections for that surface and select **Edits**. Right-click and select **Paste Surface**, as shown in Figure 7–66.

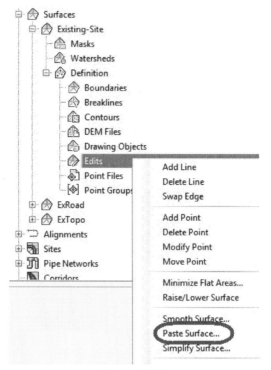

Figure 7–66

To select both surfaces, hold <Ctrl> when selecting the second surface.

7. In the Select Surface to Paste dialog box, select the **ExTopo** and **Ex Road** surfaces, as shown in Figure 7–67. Once selected, click **OK** to close the dialog box.

Figure 7–67

Using the Object Viewer on the new **Existing-Site** surface, note that the **ExRoad** surface was pasted first, followed by the **ExTopo** surface. In the area of overlap along the road, the **ExTopo** surface data takes precedence. This is not the required result.

8. In Model Space, select the **Existing-Site** surface from the surfaces listed in the **Surfaces** collection in the Toolspace> *Prospector* tab. The contextual tab for the surface object displays. Select **Surface Properties** in the ribbon panel. The *Surface Properties - Existing Site* dialog box opens. In the *Definition* tab, note the order of the paste operations, as shown in Figure 7–68.

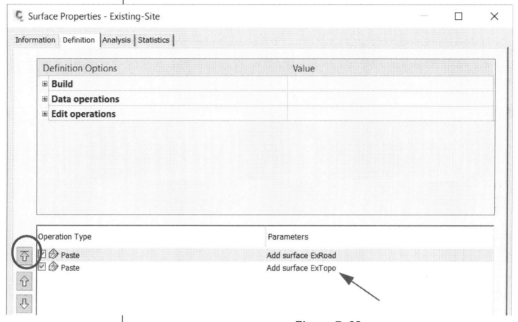

Figure 7–68

9. Select the **Paste** operation with the value **Add surface ExTopo** and move it to the top of the list by clicking [⬆].

10. Click **Apply**. When prompted to *Rebuild the surface* or *Mark the surface as out-of-date*, select **Rebuild the Surface**.

11. Click **OK** to exit the dialog box.

    As a consequence of the Autodesk Civil 3D software's dynamic abilities, any changes to either the **ExTopo** or **ExRoad** surface are reflected in the **Existing-Site** surface.

12. Save the drawing.

7.7 Surface Labels

Surface labels can be used to label contour elevations, slope values, spot elevations, and watershed delineations. Label values update when the surface changes.

To create surface labels, in the *Annotate* tab>Labels & Tables panel, expand Add Labels and select **Surface** to access the surface label flyout menu, as shown in Figure 7–69.

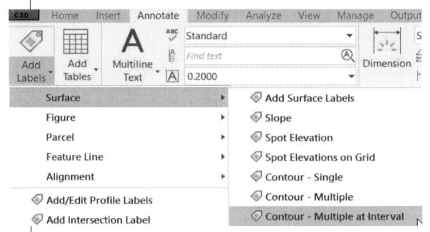

Figure 7–69

You can also click  (Add Labels) to open the Add Labels dialog box, as shown in Figure 7–70. This dialog box enables you to select the feature and label type while being able to control the label style on the fly.

Figure 7–70

Contour Labels

Contour labels can be created individually, as multiples along a linear path, or as multiples along a linear path with repeated labels at a set interval. Multiple contours are aligned along an object called a *Contour Label Line*, which can be repositioned as required, and in turn updates the position of its labels. These label lines have a selectable property that can make them visible only when an attached label is selected. If they are left visible, they should be placed on a non-plotting layer.

Spot and Slope Labels

Spot elevation and slope labels can be created as required to annotate a surface. These are dynamic surface labels and not point objects, although they might look similar to points. Spot elevations update automatically when the surface changes, whereas points need to be updated manually to reflect changes in a surface. Slopes can be measured at a single point or averaged between two points.

7.8 Surface Analysis Display

The Autodesk Civil 3D software can calculate and display many different surface analyses. These are described as follows:

Surface Analysis	Description
Contours	This analysis can display contours differently based on their elevation ranges.
Directions	This analysis can render surface triangles differently depending on which direction they face.
Elevations	This analysis can render surface triangles differently depending on their elevation ranges.
Slopes	This analysis can render surface triangles differently depending on their slope ranges.
Slope Arrows	This analysis creates a dynamic slope arrow that points downslope for each triangle, colorized by slope range.
User-Defined Contours	This analysis can display user-defined contours differently based on their elevation ranges.
Watersheds	This analysis can calculate watershed areas, and render them according to area type. The Autodesk Civil 3D watershed analysis usually results in a very large number of individual watersheds. Although a Catchment Areas command is available to assist in drawing the catchment areas, it is still up to the engineers to draw their own conclusions on how these should be merged together into catchment areas.

- The above analyses are calculated on demand for each surface and their results are stored under the surface's Surface Properties.

In addition, the following separate utilities might be helpful when analyzing surfaces:

- **Check for Contour Problems:** Used to locate problems with the contour data, including crossing or overlapping contours. To access this command, in the *Surface* tab>expanded Analyze panel, select ⬜ **Check for Contour Problems**, as shown in Figure 7–71.

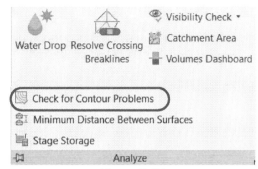

Figure 7–71

- **Resolve Crossing Breaklines:** Identifies and fixes any breaklines that create an invalid condition when two different elevations exist at the intersection point of two breaklines. The breaklines can be found in the drawing, in a survey figure, or in the survey database. To access this command, in the *Surface* tab>Analyze panel, click ⬙ (Resolve Crossing Breaklines).

- **Water Drop:** Draws a 2D or 3D polyline indicating the expected flow path of water across the surface from a given starting point. To access this command, in the *Surface* tab>Analyze panel, click 💧 (Water Drop).

- **Catchment Area:** Draws a 2D or 3D polyline indicating the catchment boundary and catchment point marker for a surface drainage area. To access this command, in the *Surface* tab>Analyze panel, click ◎ (Catchment Area). You should use this command in conjunction with the **Water Drop** command to determine an accurate placement of catchment regions and points.

- **Visibility Check>Zone of Visual Influence:** Analyzes the line of sight for 360 degrees around a single point. To access this command, in the *Surface* tab>Analyze panel, click

  (Visibility Check>Zone of Visual influence). This command is good for analyzing if towers, buildings, and other objects can be seen within a certain radius.

- **Minimum Distance Between Surfaces:** Identifies the (X,Y) location where two overlapping surfaces are the closest elevation. To access this command, in the *Surface* tab>

  Analyze panel, click (Minimum Distance Between Surfaces). If there is more than one location with the shortest distance between the two surfaces (because it is flat), then the location might be represented by a series of points, a line, or a closed polyline.

- **Stage Storage:** Calculates volumes of a basin from a surface, using either a surface or polylines to define the basin. To access this command, in the *Surface* tab>Analyze

  panel, click (Stage Storage). Either the *Average End Area* or the *Conic Approximation* method, or both are used to calculate volumes for the stage storage table.

Analysis Settings

You apply a surface analysis using the *Analysis* tab in the Surface Properties dialog box. In this tab, you can select the number of ranges and a legend table to be used. All of the remaining analysis settings are located in the *Surface Object* style, including whether to display in 2D or 3D, the color scheme, elevations, range groupings, etc. If you want to change the number of ranges or the range values, use the settings in this tab at any time.

Analysis Data Display

Overall visibility, layer, linetype, and related controls for analysis elements are managed using the *Display* tab in the Object Style dialog box, as shown in Figure 7–72. The component entries for *Slopes, Slope Arrows, Watersheds*, etc., display. These can be set to display different settings and combinations of elements in 2D and 3D.

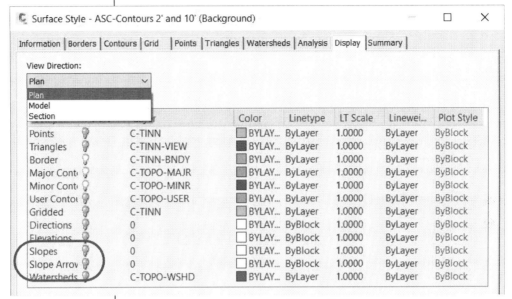

Figure 7–72

Practice 7d

Surface Labeling and Analysis

Practice Objective

- Communicate information about the surface by labeling and analyzing it.

Task 1 - Add surface labels.

1. Continue working with the drawing from the previous practice or open **SUF1-D.dwg** from the *C:\Civil 3D for Surveyors\ Working\Surface* folder.

2. Zoom to the lower South-west area of the project.

3. Select the **Existing-Site** surface in Model Space. In the contextual *Surface* tab>Labels & Tables panel, expand Add Labels and select the **Contour - Multiple**, as shown in Figure 7–73.

Figure 7–73

4. When prompted to select the first point, specify any point. When prompted for the next point, select a second and third point that creates a line intersecting all of the contours that you want to label, as shown in Figure 7–74. Press <Enter> when done.

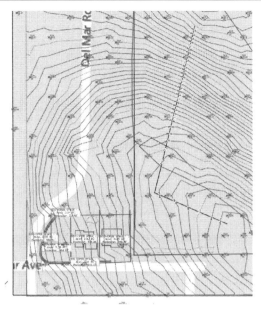

Figure 7–74

5. Move and reorient the contour label line. The labels update.

6. The *Display Contour Label Line* property can be set to only be visible when contour labels are selected. To change the visibility property, select the line in Model Space and select **Properties** in the contextual *Label* tab>General Tools panel. In the Properties dialog box, set the *Display Contour Label Line* property and the *Display Minor Contour Labels* property to **False,** as shown in Figure 7–75.

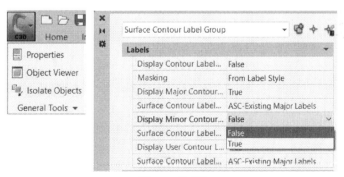

Figure 7–75

Once the grips disappear, the line no longer displays. Select a contour label to have the contour label line temporarily display for editing.

7. Close the Properties dialog box and press <Esc> to cancel your selection.

8. To have all of the future contour label lines behave this way in this drawing, select the Toolspace>*Settings* tab. Select **Surface**, right-click, and select **Edit Feature Settings**, as shown in Figure 7–76.

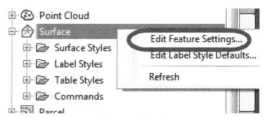

Figure 7–76

9. In the Edit Feature Settings dialog box, expand **Contour Labeling Defaults** and set the *Display Contour Label Line* property to **False** and change *Surface Contour Label Style Minor* to **<none>**, as shown in Figure 7–77. Click **OK** to accept the changes and close the dialog box.

Figure 7–77

10. Select the **Existing-Site** surface again in Model Space. In the contextual *Surface* tab>Labels & Tables panel, expand **Add Labels** and select **Contour - Multiple**.

11. Select two points that draw a line across some contours and press <Enter> when done. The contour label line and minor contour labels do not display.

12. Select the **Existing-Site** surface in Model Space. In the contextual *Surface* tab>Labels & Tables panel, expand **Add Labels** and select **Slope**.

13. To accept the prompt for the default One-point label, press <Enter>, and select a point in Model Space within the surface boundary. The Autodesk Civil 3D software places the slope value at that point. When you finish placing the labels, press <Enter> to exit the command.

14. (Optional) Using the process from Steps 10 and 11, experiment with labeling the surface with spot elevations and two point slopes. Note that you can able to copy a label (with the regular AutoCAD **Copy** command) and place it at a different location. As the labels are dynamic, the values change to reflect the surface information at the location of the label.

Task 2 - Perform a slope analysis.

1. Select the **Existing-Site** surface in Model Space. In the contextual *Surface* tab>Modify panel, select **Surface Properties**.

2. In the *Information* tab in the Surface Properties dialog box, select **ASC-Slope Banding (2D)** as the surface style.

The Autodesk Civil 3D software calculates a range of values to fit within the specified number of ranges.

3. In the *Analysis* tab, set the *Analysis type* to **Slopes**, and the number of ranges to **4**. Click  (Run Analysis).

4. In the *Analysis* tab, change the range values to the following, as shown in as shown in Figure 7–78:

Range	Minimum Slope	Maximum Slope
Range 1	10.000%	15.000%
Range 2	15.000%	20.000%
Range 3	20.000%	30.000%
Range 4	30.000%	(leave as is)

Figure 7–78

5. Change the range of colors for the slope range to match those shown in Figure 7–78. To change the color, click on it to open the Select Color dialog box (shown in Figure 7–79) and select the required color. Click **OK** to close the dialog box.

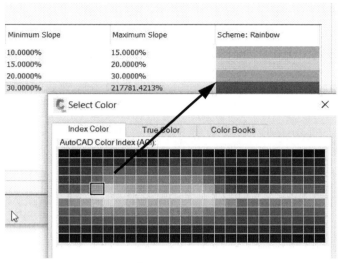

Figure 7–79

6. Click **OK** to close the dialog box and apply the changes. Press <Esc> to exit the surface selection.

7. Review the area that you want to develop. Note that the slope ranges are an issue.

8. You need to create a slope values table. Select the **Existing-Site** surface in Model Space. In the contextual *Surface* tab>Labels & Tables panel, select **Add Legend**.

9. Select **Slopes** from the command options, and then select **Dynamic** for a dynamic table.

10. When prompted for the top corner of the table (top left), select a location in an open area to the right of the surface, as shown in Figure 7–80. Press <Esc> to exit the selection.

   • Because this table is dynamic, any changes made to the surface or to the ranges in the analysis update the table automatically.

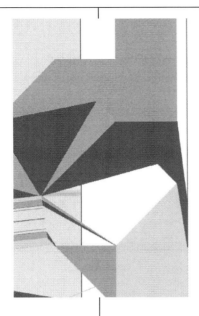

Slopes Table				
Number	Minimum Slope	Maximum Slope	Area	Color
1	10.00%	15.00%	1164837.45	▓
2	15.00%	20.00%	490506.78	░
3	20.00%	30.00%	213490.67	▒
4	30.00%	165974.97%	186357.74	█

Figure 7–80

11. (Optional) Open the Surface Properties dialog box (Steps 3 to 7) and change the number of slope ranges or the values. The Model Space Legend table updates.

12. Save and close the drawing.

Chapter Review Questions

1. Put the following steps in the order suggested for building a surface.

   a. Add Breaklines, assign more data, modify the data, or edit the surface as required.

   b. Assign data to a surface.

   c. Accumulate data.

   d. Evaluate the resulting surface.

2. What controls how an Autodesk Civil 3D surface displays (whether it displays contours, TIN lines, or an analysis)?

   a. Surface Style

   b. Surface Definition

   c. AutoCAD Layers

   d. Surface Boundary

3. Where would you set the lowest and highest acceptable elevations for a surface?

   a. In the Create Surface dialog box when you are first creating the surface.

   b. In the *Definition* tab in the Surface Properties dialog box.

   c. In the *Analysis* tab in the Surface Properties dialog box.

   d. Under **Edits** in the surface definition.

4. Select the type of breakline that the following statement defines:
   This type of breakline is a 3D polyline or Feature Line. It does not need a point object at each vertex because each has its own elevation.

   a. Non-Destructive

   b. Proximity

   c. Wall

   d. Standard

5. A Quick Profile disappears when you save or exit a drawing.

   a. True

   b. False

6. What are the types of edits that can be done to a surface? (Select all that apply.)

   a. Line Edits

   b. Point Edits

   c. Simplify Surface

   d. Grip Edit

7. How do you remove an edit from a surface? (Select all that apply.)

   a. Clear it in the Operations Type list in the Surface Properties in the *Definition* tab.

   b. Remove it from the Edits list in the Toolspace>*Prospector* tab's Preview.

   c. Select it and press <Delete>.

   d. Delete it from the Operations Type list of the Surface Properties in the *Definition* tab.

8. Which type of boundary would you use to ensure that any data that you add to a surface is ignored if it falls outside that boundary?

   a. Hide

   b. Show

   c. Data Clip

   d. Outer

9. Which of the following is not a surface label that is available out of the box in the Autodesk Civil 3D software?

   a. Contour Labels

   b. Spot Elevation Labels

   c. Slope Labels

   d. Cut/Fill Labels

10. To add Survey figures to a surface as a breakline, the Survey figures must reside in the current drawing.

   a. True

   b. False

Command Summary

Button	Command	Location
	Add Data	• **Contextual Ribbon:** *Surface* tab> Modify panel
	Create Surface	• **Ribbon:** *Home* tab>Create Ground Data panel • **Command Prompt:** CreateSurface
	Edit Surface	• **Contextual Ribbon:** *Surface* tab> Modify panel
	Resolve Crossing Breaklines	• **Contextual Ribbon:** *Surface* tab> Analyze panel • **Command Prompt:** BreaklineTool
	Surface Properties	• **Contextual Ribbon:** *Surface* tab> Modify panel • **Command Prompt:** EditSurfaceProperties

8

Field to Finish

The Autodesk® Civil 3D® software is a powerful tool for Civil Engineering and Survey. To fully use the tool requires a lot of setup and optional customization to the *Settings* tab in the Toolspace, as well as to the Survey User Settings for the dedicated *Survey* tab. The previous chapters were dedicated to these setup steps and customizations.

In this chapter, you will examine the available tools used to create an Existing Conditions Plan. Then, with everything in place, you will create the plan to about 75% completion in a very short amount of time.

Learning Objectives in This Chapter

- Understand the five components of a Field to Finish workflow.
- Understand the fieldwork standards that survey crews employ and examine the resulting field data collected.
- Examine the customization and contents of a drawing template used to create an Existing Conditions Plan.
- Examine the Survey User Settings.
- Create an Existing Conditions Plan.
- Understand what is required to further the project workflow.

8.1 Field to Finish Overview

Figure 8–1 provides an overview of the entire workflow for generating existing condition drawings from raw survey data.

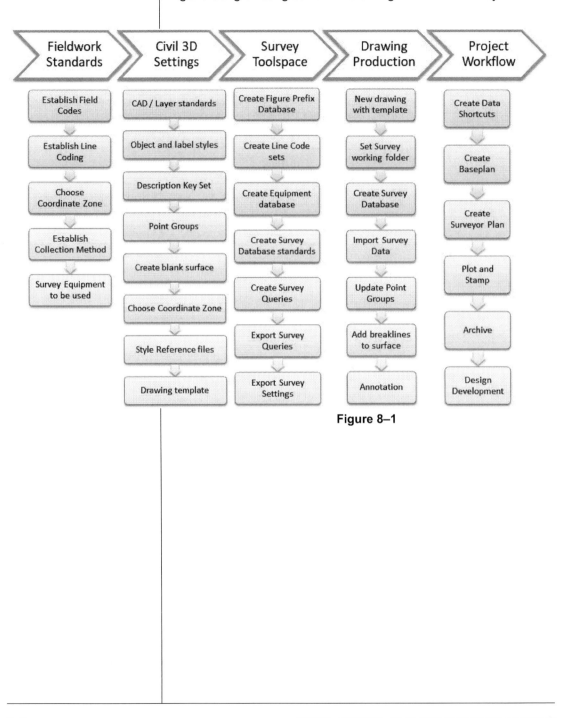

Figure 8–1

8.2 Fieldwork Standards

Figure 8–2 provides an outline of the Fieldwork Standards to be established for efficient survey data collection and processing.

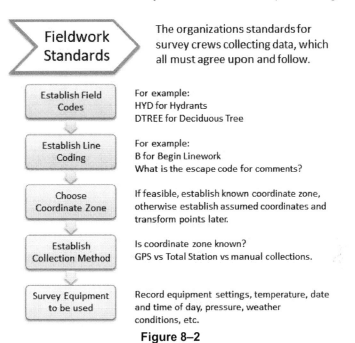

The organizations standards for survey crews collecting data, which all must agree upon and follow.

Establish Field Codes
For example:
HYD for Hydrants
DTREE for Deciduous Tree

Establish Line Coding
For example:
B for Begin Linework
What is the escape code for comments?

Choose Coordinate Zone
If feasible, establish known coordinate zone, otherwise establish assumed coordinates and transform points later.

Establish Collection Method
Is coordinate zone known?
GPS vs Total Station vs manual collections.

Survey Equipment to be used
Record equipment settings, temperature, date and time of day, pressure, weather conditions, etc.

Figure 8–2

Practice 8a

Fieldwork Review

Practice Objective

- Review data submitted by the survey crew.

In this practice, you will review the data available for creating an Existing Conditions Plan. Point files and .CSV files have been supplied by the surveyors, as well as a traverse file that was input into the Autodesk Civil 3D's Traverse Editor.

Task 1 - Review point files.

1. Use the Windows File Explorer to browse to the *C:\Civil 3D for Surveyors\Survey Databases\Data\Finale* folder.

2. Double-click on **Groundshots.txt** to open it a text editor.

3. Note that the point numbers start at 7000, the Northings and Eastings seem to be in the California range, the descriptions are GS (for Groundshots) and the fields are separated by commas, as shown in Figure 8–3. From this, you can determine that the format is PNEZD, comma delimited.

```
Groundshots.txt - Notepad
File  Edit  Format  View  Help
7000,2035634.35,6255775.33,225.30,GS
7001,2035774.35,6255775.33,227.79,GS
7002,2035984.35,6255775.33,228.50,GS
7003,2036054.35,6255775.33,227.32,GS
7004,2036080.30,6255711.53,224.95,GS
7005,2036150.30,6255711.53,223.46,GS
7006,2036264.35,6255775.33,221.88,GS
7007,2036404.35,6255775.33,218.43,GS
7008,2036491.40,6255727.95,216.81,GS
7009,2036544.35,6255775.33,215.18,GS
7010,2036824.35,6255775.33,211.14,GS
7011,2036911.40,6255727.95,212.00,GS
7012,2036964.35,6255775.33,214.93,GS
7013,2037104.35,6255775.33,212.33,GS
7014,2037200.85,6255792.62,206.37,GS
7015,2037244.35,6255775.33,201.90,GS
7016,2037314.35,6255775.33,196.77,GS
7017,2037441.14,6255758.50,178.84,GS
7018,2037524.35,6255775.33,166.40,GS
7019,2037664.35,6255775.33,146.39,GS
7020,2037874.35,6255775.33,119.36,GS
```

Figure 8–3

4. Close the file without saving it.

5. Double-click on **Field-Survey-I.csv** to open it in Microsoft Excel (if required, you can also edit the file in a text editor).

6. Note that the point numbers start at 250, the Northings and Eastings seem to be in the California range, and that some of the descriptions have one parameter while others have two parameters, as shown in Figure 8–4. Since it is a CSV file, it indicates the fields are separated by commas. From this, you can determine that the format is PNEZD, comma delimited.

	A	B	C	D	E
1	250	2036668.525	6255999.965	204.75	STMMH
2	251	2036658.75	6256009.479	204.95	SANMH
3	252	2035674.727	6255838.971	230.67	HYD 100
4	300	2037398.981	6256396.142	169.01	BRUSH COTTONWOOD 1.5
5	301	2037377.008	6256357.195	171.22	BRUSH DOGWOOD 2.4
6	302	2037426.604	6256340.863	168.84	BRUSH COTTONWOOD 2.6
7	303	2037349.903	6256560.988	165.69	BRUSH COTTONWOOD 3.5
8	304	2037285.637	6256469.557	169.44	BRUSH COTTONWOOD 5.2
9	305	2037234.425	6256439.413	171.55	BRUSH DOGWOOD 1.2
10	306	2037237.438	6256376.116	173.43	BRUSH COTTONWOOD 1.6
11	307	2037041.39	6256718.52	178.05	BRUSH DOGWOOD 3.7
12	308	2037225.305	6256553.097	169.44	BRUSH COTTONWOOD 2
13	309	2037164.652	6256568.76	171.38	BRUSH DOGWOOD 3.2
14	310	2037129.704	6256685.128	173.93	CTREE PINE 2.3

Figure 8–4

7. Close the file without saving it.

8. Double-click on **Mission_Ave-l.csv** to open it in Microsoft Excel. (if required, you can also edit the file in a text editor).

9. Note that the point numbers start at 5000, the Northings and Eastings seem to be in the California range, some of the descriptions have a parameter, separated by a space, and that others have two parameters, separated by a space and a slash (|\), as shown in Figure 8–5. Since it is a CSV file, it indicates the fields are separated by commas. From this, you can determine that the format is PNEZD, comma delimited.

	A	B	C	D	E	F
1	5000	2037682.84	6255795.694	156.4	DAY-R MISSION\B	
2	5001	2037687.629	6255796.53	155.59	DITCH-R MISSION\B	
3	5002	2037693.952	6255797.636	157.2	EOS-R MISSION\B	
4	5003	2037708.819	6255800.231	157.5	CL MISSION	
5	5004	2037697.184	6255798.2	157.26	EOP-R MISSION	
6	5005	2037720.453	6255802.265	157.26	EOP-L MISSION	
7	5006	2037723.685	6255802.83	157.2	EOS-L MISSION	
8	5007	2037730.009	6255803.932	155.59	DITCH-L MISSION\B	
9	5008	2037734.268	6255804.677	156.31	DAY-L MISSION\B	
10	5009	2037664.729	6255874.175	157.47	DAY-R MISSION	
11	5010	2037672.218	6255875.779	156.2	DITCH-R MISSION	
12	5011	2037678.494	6255877.124	157.8	EOS-R MISSION	
13	5012	2037693.251	6255880.29	158.1	CL MISSION	
14	5013	2037681.702	6255877.813	157.87	EOP-R MISSION	
15	5014	2037704.799	6255882.764	157.87	EOP-L MISSION	

Figure 8–5

10. Close the file without saving it.

11. From reviewing these files, you now know that:

    • There will be no overlap among points.

    • All points are within the CA83-VIF coordinate zone (however, you should confirm this information with the survey crew chief).

    • The descriptions have parameters and some parameters are separated by a slash.

    • All file formats are PNEZD, comma delimited.

Task 2 - Inspect the traverse file.

---

1. Start a new drawing using the default template. You are only using the drawing to invoke the Traverse Editor.

2. In the *Home* tab>Create Ground Data panel, click

    (Traverse Editor).

3. In the Traverse Editor, click 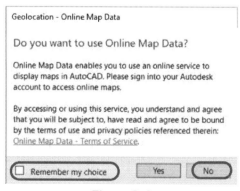 (Load Traverse from File). Browse to the *C:\Civil 3D for Surveyors\Survey Databases\ Data\Finale* folder and select **Boundary-complete.trv2**.

4. If you are greeted with a splash screen about using Online Map Data, select **Remember my choice** and click **No**, as shown in Figure 8–6. (Since you have captured an online map in a previous chapter, you do not need to use Online Map Data.)

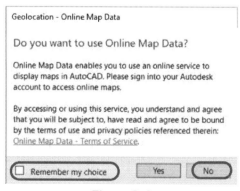

Geolocation - Online Map Data

Do you want to use Online Map Data?

Online Map Data enables you to use an online service to display maps in AutoCAD. Please sign into your Autodesk account to access online maps.

By accessing or using this service, you understand and agree that you will be subject to, have read and agree to be bound by the terms of use and privacy policies referenced therein: Online Map Data - Terms of Service.

☐ Remember my choice   Yes   No

Figure 8–6

5. Review the data table and the outline above it. As you select a data row, note that the corresponding component highlights in the drawing area, as shown in Figure 8–7.

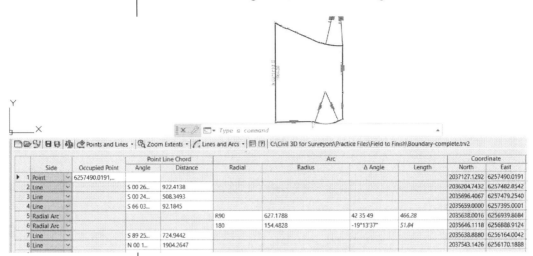

Side		Occupied Point	Point Line Chord		Arc				Coordinate	
			Angle	Distance	Radial	Radius	Δ Angle	Length	North	East
1 Point	˅	6257490.0191,...							2037127.1292	6257490.0191
2 Line	˅		S 00 26...	922.4138					2036204.7432	6257482.8542
3 Line	˅		S 00 24...	508.3493					2035696.4067	6257479.2540
4 Line	˅		S 66 03...	92.1845					2035659.0000	6257395.0001
5 Radial Arc	˅				R90	627.1788	42 35 49	466.28	2035638.0016	6256939.8684
6 Radial Arc	˅				180	154.4828	-19°13'37"	51.84	2035646.1118	6256888.9124
7 Line	˅		S 89 25...	724.9442					2035638.8880	6256164.0042
8 Line	˅		N 00 1...	1904.2647					2037543.1426	6256170.1888

Figure 8–7

6. Close the Traverse Editor without saving.

7. Close the drawing without saving.

8.3 Civil 3D Settings

Figure 8–8 provides an outline of the Autodesk Civil 3D settings to be set in a template for efficient drawing production and standardization.

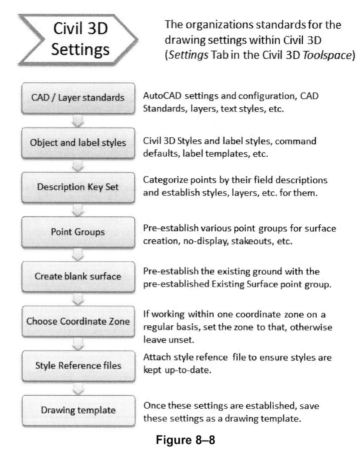

The organizations standards for the drawing settings within Civil 3D (*Settings* Tab in the Civil 3D *Toolspace*)

CAD / Layer standards — AutoCAD settings and configuration, CAD Standards, layers, text styles, etc.

Object and label styles — Civil 3D Styles and label styles, command defaults, label templates, etc.

Description Key Set — Categorize points by their field descriptions and establish styles, layers, etc. for them.

Point Groups — Pre-establish various point groups for surface creation, no-display, stakeouts, etc.

Create blank surface — Pre-establish the existing ground with the pre-established Existing Surface point group.

Choose Coordinate Zone — If working within one coordinate zone on a regular basis, set the zone to that, otherwise leave unset.

Style Reference files — Attach style refence file to ensure styles are kept up-to-date.

Drawing template — Once these settings are established, save these settings as a drawing template.

Figure 8–8

Practice 8b | Civil 3D Settings Review

Practice Objective

- Review the Civil 3D settings found in the template.

In this practice, you will review the various configurations and components in the *Settings* and *Prospector* tabs of the Autodesk Civil 3D Toolspace.

1. Expand the ![icon] (Application Menu) and start a new drawing file based on the **ASC-EG (CA83-VIF) NCS.dwt** template in the *C:\Civil 3D for Surveyors\Ascent-Config* folder, as shown in Figure 8–9.

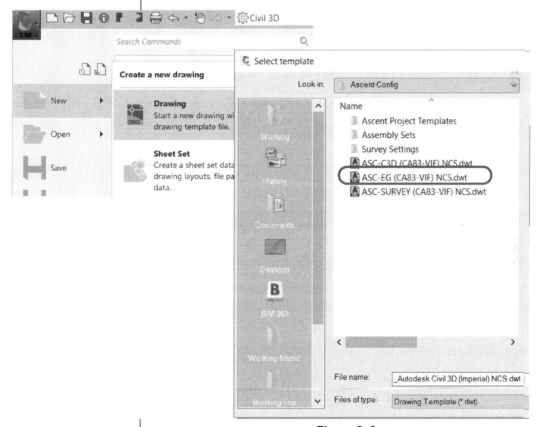

Figure 8–9

2. Note the text in the middle of the screen, which indicates that the drawing is already configured to the CA83-VIF Coordinate System and is the *Existing Ground* template, as shown in Figure 8–10.

Figure 8–10

3. In the Toolspace>*Prospector* tab, expand **Point Groups** and note the point groups that are already present in the new drawing. Also note that there is an **EG** point group for Existing Ground, as well as a **_No Display** point group.

4. Expand **Surface** and note that the **EG** surface has already been created for Existing Ground. Expand **Surface>EG> Definitions** and note that the **EG** surface is defined by the **EG** point group, as shown in Figure 8–11. The **EG** surface is set to **Rebuild-Automatic**.

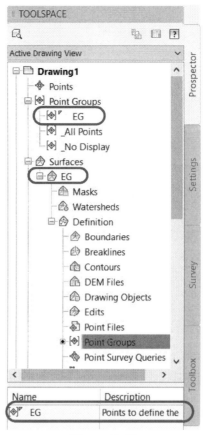

Figure 8–11

The predefined elevation ranges have been established based on typical elevation ranges within the region of work.

5. Right-click on the **EG** surface and select **Surface Properties**. In the *Definitions* tab, note the settings shown in Figure 8–12.

Surface Properties - EG

Information | Definition | Analysis | Statistics

Definition Options	Value
Build	
Copy deleted dependent objects	Yes
Exclude elevations less than	Yes
Elevation <	35.00'
Exclude elevations greater than	Yes
Elevation >	350.00'
Use maximum angle	No
Maximum angle between adjacent TIN lines	90.0000 (d)
Use maximum triangle length	Yes
Maximum triangle length	350.00'

Figure 8–12

6. In the Toolspace>*Settings* tab, expand **Surface>Surface Styles**, as shown in Figure 8–13.

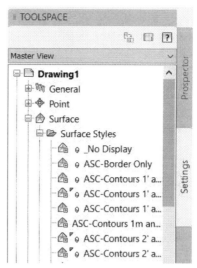

Figure 8–13

7. Note there are customized surface styles, many with a prefix of "ASC-". These styles have a small clip icon (💼) preceding the name, indicating that they are referenced from some templates.

8. In the *Manage* tab>Styles panel, click 💼 (Reference).

9. In the Attach Referenced Template dialog box, note the reference templates that are attached, and the order that they are listed, as shown in Figure 8–14.

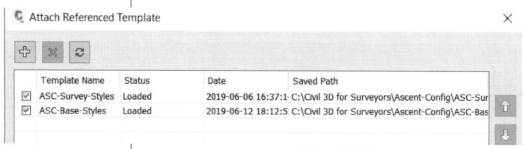

Figure 8–14

10. Close the Attach Referenced Template dialog box.

11. Keep the drawing open for the next practice, but do not save the drawing.

8.4 Survey Toolspace

Figure 8–15 provides an outline of the Survey Toolspace settings and configuration for effective and secure storage of the survey data within a survey database and its incorporation in Civil 3D drawings.

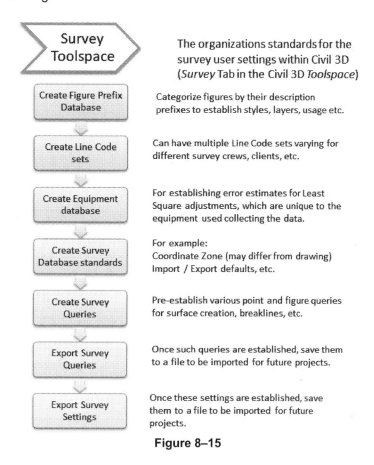

Survey Toolspace — The organizations standards for the survey user settings within Civil 3D (*Survey* Tab in the Civil 3D *Toolspace*)

Create Figure Prefix Database — Categorize figures by their description prefixes to establish styles, layers, usage etc.

Create Line Code sets — Can have multiple Line Code sets varying for different survey crews, clients, etc.

Create Equipment database — For establishing error estimates for Least Square adjustments, which are unique to the equipment used collecting the data.

Create Survey Database standards — For example: Coordinate Zone (may differ from drawing) Import / Export defaults, etc.

Create Survey Queries — Pre-establish various point and figure queries for surface creation, breaklines, etc.

Export Survey Queries — Once such queries are established, save them to a file to be imported for future projects.

Export Survey Settings — Once these settings are established, save them to a file to be imported for future projects.

Figure 8–15

Practice 8c

Survey Toolspace Review

Practice Objective

- Import Survey User Settings and review the changes that occur.

In this practice, you will import Survey User Settings, and then review the various settings and components in the Toolspace>*Survey* tab.

1. If you did NOT complete the previous practice examining the Autodesk Civil 3D settings, expand ![CSD] (Application Menu) and start a new drawing file based on the **ASC-EG (CA83-VIF) NCS.dwt** template in the *C:\Civil 3D for Surveyors\Ascent-Config* folder.

   Otherwise, continue working with the unnamed drawing from the previous practice.

2. In the Toolspace>*Survey* tab, click ![icon] (Survey User Settings), as shown in Figure 8–16.

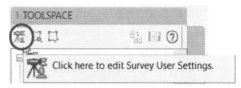

Figure 8–16

3. Click ![icon] (Import User Settings), as shown in Figure 8–17.

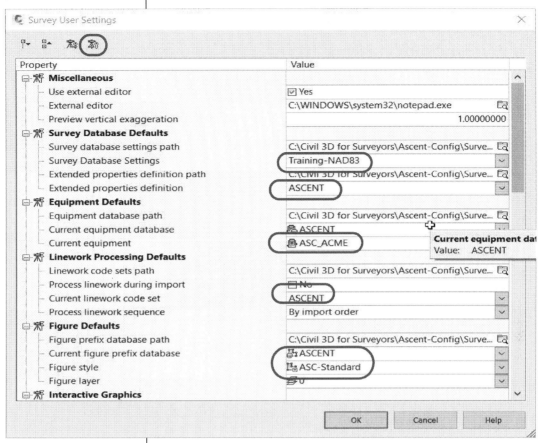

Figure 8–17

4. Browse to *C:\Civil 3D for Surveyors\Ascent-Config\Survey Settings* and select **ASCENT-Settings.usr_set.**

5. Click **Open** or double-click the file to open it.

6. Note that importing User Settings causes all of the branches to contract. The simplest way of expanding them all again is to close and reopen the Survey User Settings window.

7. Note that the paths have changed for the various entries, as shown in Figure 8–17.

8. Click **OK** to exit the Survey User Settings.

9. In the Toolspace>*Survey* tab, expand the various branches and note the different entries. The entries in bold are the defaults, as shown in Figure 8–18.

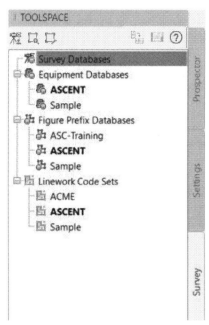

Figure 8–18

10. Exit the drawing without saving it.

8.5 Drawing Production

Figure 8–19 provides an outline of the workflow required to create Existing Conditions drawings or Surveyor's Certificate drawings.

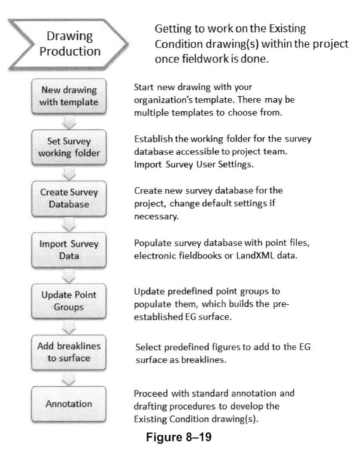

Drawing Production — Getting to work on the Existing Condition drawing(s) within the project once fieldwork is done.

New drawing with template — Start new drawing with your organization's template. There may be multiple templates to choose from.

Set Survey working folder — Establish the working folder for the survey database accessible to project team. Import Survey User Settings.

Create Survey Database — Create new survey database for the project, change default settings if necessary.

Import Survey Data — Populate survey database with point files, electronic fieldbooks or LandXML data.

Update Point Groups — Update predefined point groups to populate them, which builds the pre-established EG surface.

Add breaklines to surface — Select predefined figures to add to the EG surface as breaklines.

Annotation — Proceed with standard annotation and drafting procedures to develop the Existing Condition drawing(s).

Figure 8–19

Practice 8d

Drawing Production

Practice Objective

- Create an Existing Conditions Plan.

In the previous practices in this chapter, you examined data collected in the field or input into a traverse through a legal description. You also examined how the drawing template and Survey User Settings are configured. However, no changes were made.

In this practice, you will to create an Existing Conditions Plan to about 75% completion.

Task 1 - Start a new drawing.

1. Start a new drawing using the **ASC-EG(CA83-VIF) NCS.dwt** template in the *C:\Civil 3D for Surveyors\Ascent-Config* folder.

2. Erase the message about the coordinate system in the middle of the drawing.

3. In the Toolspace>*Survey* tab, click 🔧 (Survey User Settings), as shown in Figure 8–20.

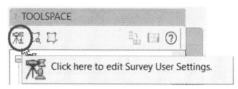

Figure 8–20

4. Click 🔧 (Import User Settings), then browse to *C:\Civil 3D for Surveyors\Ascent-Config\Survey Settings* and select **ASCENT-Settings.usr_set**.

5. Click **Open** or double-click the file to open it, then click **OK** to close the *Survey User Settings* dialog box.

6. Save the drawing as **Existing Conditions.dwg** in the *C:\Civil 3D for Surveyors\Working\Field to Finish* folder. If there is already a drawing there with that name, overwrite it.

Task 2 - Set up the Survey Database.

1. In the Toolspace>*Survey* tab, right-click on **Survey Databases**, and select **Set working folder**, as shown in Figure 8–21.

2. Navigate to the *C:\Civil 3D for Surveyors\Survey Databases\Grand Finale* folder. Select the folder, and then click **Select Folder**, as shown in Figure 8–22.

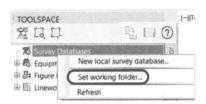

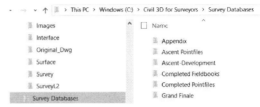

Figure 8–21   **Figure 8–22**

3. In the Toolspace>*Survey* tab, right-click on **Survey Databases** and select **New local survey database**.

4. Set the *Name* to **ASC Existing Conditions**, then click **OK**.

5. Right-click on the **ASC Existing Conditions** database and select **Edit Survey Database Settings**.

6. In the dialog box, under *Units*, for the *Coordinate Zone*, note that it is already set to **NAD83 California State Planes, Zone VI, US Foot**, from the customized default settings.

7. Click **OK**.

Task 3 - Import the survey data.

1. In the *Home* tab>expanded Create Ground Data panel, click (Import Survey Data).

2. On the Specify Database page, ensure that the **ASC Existing Conditions** database is the current one (it should be the only one) and then click **Next**.

3. On the Specify Data Sources page, do the following, as shown in Figure 8–23.

- Expand the Data source type drop-down list and select **Point File**.

You might need to set Files of Type to *.csv or *.* to display the .CSV files.

- Click 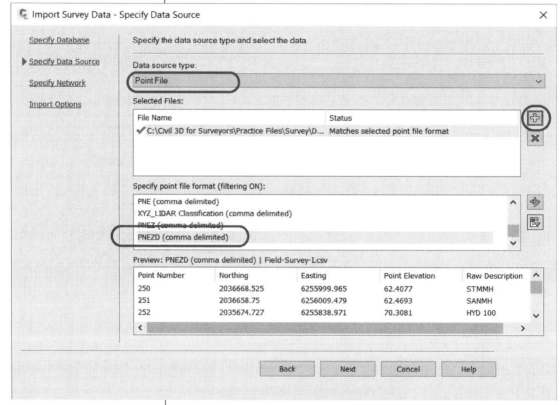 (Add file), browse to *C:\Civil 3D for Surveyors\Survey Databases\Data\Finale*, and open **Field-Survey-I.csv**.
- For the file format, select **PNEZD (comma delimited)**.
- Click **Next**.

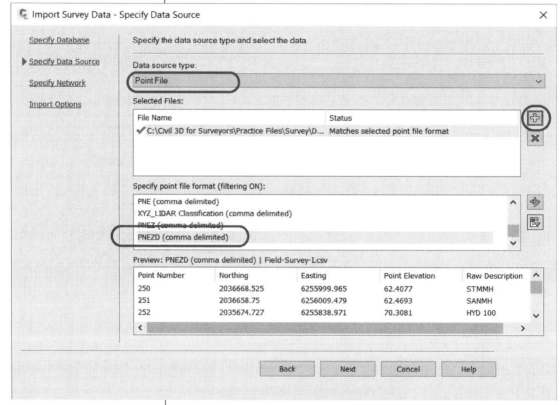

Figure 8–23

4. On the Survey Network page, click **Next**. When importing point files, networks are optional.

5. On the Import Options page, ensure that **Process linework during import**, **Insert figure objects**, and **Insert survey points** are all selected, as shown in Figure 8–24. Ensure that **ASCENT** is the *Current linework code set*.

These are the defaults settings, so should not need to change them, however it is always recommended to double-check these settings.

6. Click **Finish**.

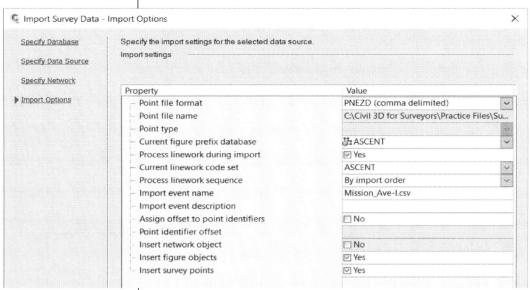

Figure 8–24

7. Save the drawing.

8. Repeat Steps 1 through 5 for the **Groundshots.txt** point file.

9. Save the drawing.

You might have to Zoom Extents to display the results.

10. Repeat Steps 1 through 4 for the **Mission_Ave-I.csv** point file.

11. On the Import Options page, change the *Current linework code set* to **ACME**.

12. Click **Finish**.

13. Save the drawing.

Task 4 - Capture an online map.

1. If not already done, sign into your Autodesk account, which can be accessed through the icon in the upper right corner of the screen, as shown in Figure 8–25

Figure 8–25

2. If the *Terms of Service* splash screen displays, click **Yes** to accept them and dismiss the screen.

3. Go to the *Geolocation* tab.

4. In the *Online Map* panel, expand the Map drop-down list and select *Map Road* as the map style, as shown in Figure 8–26.

Figure 8–26

When an online map is captured, it is added to the current layer. Ensure that the correct layer is current prior to capturing a map.

5. Make the **V-SITE-IMGE** layer current.

6. In the *Online Map* panel, expand the Capture drop-down list and select **Capture Area**, as shown in Figure 8–27.

Figure 8–27

7. Pick two points representing the corners of a rectangular area that includes the extents of the survey data.

8. Make layer **0** current again.

9. Save the drawing.

Task 5 - Importing the Boundary traverse.

A traverse was input previously into the Traverse Editor and saved to an external file. You will load this file into the Traverse Editor so it is included in this drawing.

1. In the *Home* tab>Create Ground Data panel, click

    (Traverse Editor).

2. In the Traverse Editor, click 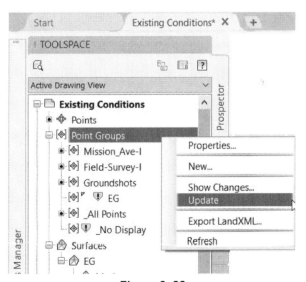 (Load Traverse from File). Browse to *C:\Civil 3D for Surveyors\Survey Databases\ Data\Finale* and select **Boundary-complete.trv2**.

3. Close the Traverse Editor palette and save the drawing. If prompted to save the traverse file, decline the option as no changes have been made.

4. Click on the boundary that was imported and note that it is a polyline.

5. Save the drawing.

Task 6 - Update point groups (build the surface).

The **EG** and **_No Display** point groups, as well as the **EG** surface, are already set up in the template.

1. In the *Toolspace*>Prospector tab, expand **Point Groups** and note that a point group for each import event has been created.

2. The **EG** and **_No Display** point groups need to be updated. Right-click on **Point Groups** and select **Update**, as shown in Figure 8–28.

Figure 8–28

3. Since the **EG** surface is set to be rebuilt automatically (in the template), the surface is built by updating the EG point group.

Task 7 - Import and execute survey database queries.

Queries for the survey database were previously defined and exported to a file. You will import these queries and execute them.

1. If required, in the Toolspace>*Survey* tab, right-click on the **ASC-Existing Conditions** survey database to open it for editing.

2. Expand **ASC-Existing Conditions**, then right-click on **Survey Queries** and select **Open from file**, as shown in Figure 8–29.

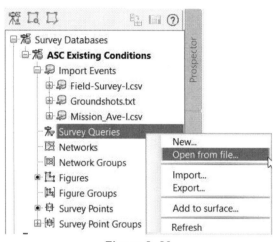

Figure 8–29

3. Browse to *C:\Civil 3D for Surveyors\Survey Databases\ Data\Finale* and select **Road Lines.qml**. Click **Open**.

4. In the *Survey Query Builder,* click **Save Query**, and then exit the *Survey Query Builder*.

5. Exit the *Survey Query* tab by clicking the green checkmark, as shown in Figure 8–30.

Figure 8–30

You will add the road lines to the **EG** surface as breaklines in the next task. Note that it is also possible to add them at this stage in the *Survey Query* tab by using the **Add To Surface** option.

Task 8 - Add survey figures as breaklines.

In this task, you will add breaklines to the surface from figures that were created when the survey data was imported.

1. Expand the **ASC-Existing Conditions** collection and right-click on **Figures**. Select **Create Breaklines**, as shown in Figure 8–31.

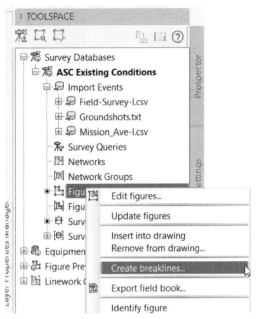

Figure 8–31

2. In the Create Breaklines dialog box, ensure that **EG** is the selected surface. For the **Pile** figure, in the *Breakline* column, select **Yes** to create breaklines, as shown in Figure 8–32. Click **OK** to close the dialog box.

The other figures have been predefined as breaklines in the Figure Prefix database.

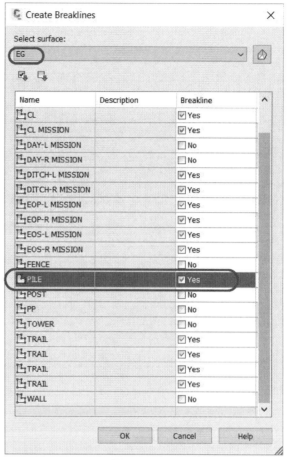

Figure 8–32

3. In the Add Breaklines dialog box, in the *Description* field, type **From Survey Data**. In the Type drop-down list, ensure that **Standard** is selected.

4. Click **OK** to close the dialog box

5. The Event Viewer might open displaying an error, as shown in Figure 8–33. It states that one breakline was not added because it crossed another breakline. You can analyze this at a later stage.

6. You can zoom to the error by selecting **Zoom to** in the far right column. By default, Civil 3D does not allow crossing breaklines. For now, you need to clear these errors from the event log file.

7. Click **Action** in the Panorama and select **Clear All Events**, as shown in Figure 8–33, then close the event viewer by clicking the green checkmark.

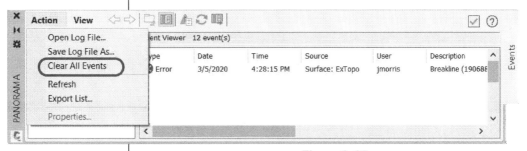

Figure 8–33

8. In the **ASC-Existing Conditions** collection, click **Figures**. Note the list of figures in the grid view at the bottom of the Toolspace.

9. Select the **Wall** figure, then right-click and select **Create breaklines**.

10. In the Create Breaklines dialog box, select the **EG** surface. In the *Breakline* column, select **Yes** to create breaklines. Click **OK** to close the dialog box.

11. The Autodesk Civil 3D software zooms in to the location of the breakline, and opens the Add Breaklines dialog box. In the *Description* field, type **Retaining wall from site survey**. In the Type drop-down list, ensure that **Wall** is selected, as shown in Figure 8–34. Click **OK** to close the dialog box.

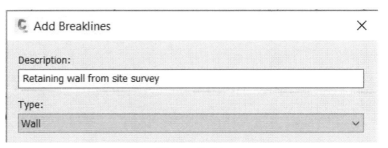

Figure 8–34

12. At the prompt to pick the offset side, select a point to the south of the wall break line, as shown in Figure 8–35.

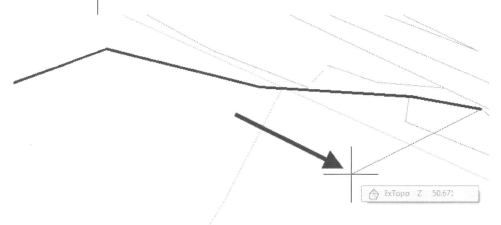

ExTopo Z 50.671

Figure 8–35

13. When prompted to select the option for the wall height, select the default **All** option because the wall has a constant height.

14. When prompted for the elevation difference or elevation, type **1.5** and press <Enter>.

The wall has a constant height of 1.5' from the base.

15. Save the drawing.

Task 9 - Examine the surface.

1. Select the **EG** surface, then right-click, and select **Object Viewer**.

2. Examine the surface to check for any errors, as shown in Figure 8–36.

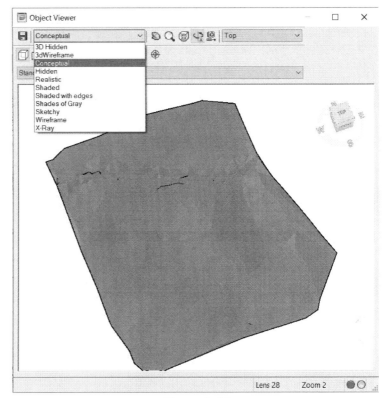

Figure 8–36

3. Exit the object viewer.

4. Select the **EG** surface again. In the contextual tab for the surface object that displays, select **Surface Properties**. The *Surface Properties - EG* dialog box opens.

5. In the *Statistics* tab, examine the statistics of the surface.

6. Exit the *Surface Properties - EG* dialog box, and save the drawing

Task 10 - Drawing development.

From here, the development of the drawing is very much project specific. Use the various labeling tools for the surface as required, using the various AutoCAD tools to complete the drawing.

8.6 Project Workflow

Figure 8–37 provides an overview of the continued workflow downstream, from the creation of existing conditions to the continuation of the project development

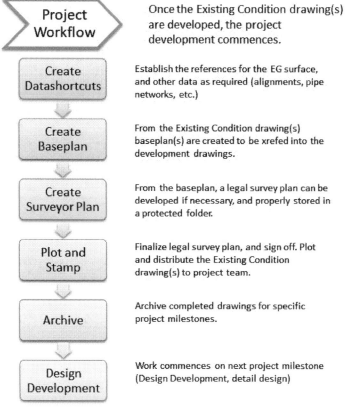

Once the Existing Condition drawing(s) are developed, the project development commences.

Establish the references for the EG surface, and other data as required (alignments, pipe networks, etc.)

From the Existing Condition drawing(s) baseplan(s) are created to be xrefed into the development drawings.

From the baseplan, a legal survey plan can be developed if necessary, and properly stored in a protected folder.

Finalize legal survey plan, and sign off. Plot and distribute the Existing Condition drawing(s) to project team.

Archive completed drawings for specific project milestones.

Work commences on next project milestone (Design Development, detail design)

Figure 8–37

This phase is beyond the scope of this course. It involves multiple designers on multiple teams, referencing data and drawings, and co-operation among all involved staff.

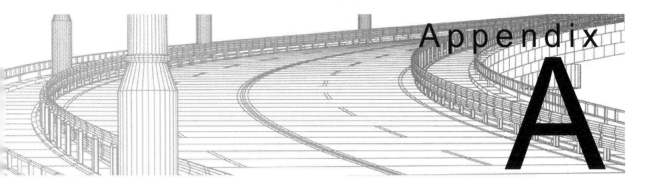

Additional Tools

In the appendix, you will learn a little bit more about the Survey Database and how to manipulate it. You are first reminded how to open a survey database, then you will be able to complete a least squares analysis.

Learning Objectives in This Appendix

- Reduce errors for a more accurate survey by performing a least squares adjustment.
- Create a least squares input file to find the required information for an adjustment.
- Run queries on the Survey Database Points using the Survey Command Window.

A.1 Least Squares

A survey's observations contain errors resulting from internal instrument errors, an unsteady hand holding the prism, poorly maintained equipment, etc. You must adjust the observations to reduce the errors and produce an accurate survey.

The **least squares** adjustment method is a statistical method that resolves a point's statistically most likely location. Observing the same point from different locations produces a slightly different set of point coordinates. Least squares adjust points that have multiple observations from different surveyed locations to resolve the best locations.

A least squares adjustment minimizes the weighted sum squares of residuals for a point's coordinates. The adjustment calculates a point's location based on the least amount of error from all of the point's various measurements. Each observation from a different location and the observation's error produce slightly different point coordinates. The least squares adjustment calculates a single (most likely) location for each point from all of the various field observation (angle/distance) measurements and their errors.

A surveyor can apply least squares to a network or a traverse. A least squares adjustment can be done on any collection of field observations containing redundant observation values.

- A least squares adjustment can be in 2D or 3D.

- The survey must contain points with multiple observations (observed from several locations throughout the survey).

- There must be at least one point with known coordinates (a control point).

- Observations can be points outside the survey area, such as towers, antennas, buildings, etc.

The least squares error estimate values come from the equipment database's current instrument values. You should always have an up-to-date instrument database. If you do not have an equipment database, you should have at least one definition that is general enough to accommodate all instruments.

After setting up the network correctly and importing its data, you need to create a least squares input file. The input file contains all points with redundant observations and breaks down the field book's AD observations to angle and distance measurements. If the data contains elevations, it also includes vertical measurements, such as zenith angles and slope distances.

Practice A1

Creating a Least Squares Survey

Practice Objective

- Prepare to calculate the most probable value for each observation in a survey using the least squares adjustment method.

In this practice, you will reduce the survey notes using the least squares adjustment method. The least squares method calculates the most probable values for each observation. The values are calculated by adjusting each of the observations simultaneously so that the sum of the squares of the residuals (the difference between measured and adjusted observations) is at a minimum.

Task 1 - Set up a network.

1. Open the file **SUV2-A1-Survey.dwg** from the *C:\Civil 3D for Surveyors\Working\SurveyL2* folder.

2. If you are greeted with a splash screen about using Online Map Data, select **Remember my choice** and click **No**, as shown in Figure A–1. (Since you have captured an online map in a previous chapter, you do not need to use Online Map Data.)

Geolocation - Online Map Data

Do you want to use Online Map Data?

Online Map Data enables you to use an online service to display maps in AutoCAD. Please sign into your Autodesk account to access online maps.

By accessing or using this service, you understand and agree that you will be subject to, have read and agree to be bound by the terms of use and privacy policies referenced therein: Online Map Data - Terms of Service.

☐ Remember my choice   Yes   No

Figure A–1

3. In the *Survey* tab, right-click on **Survey Databases** and select **Set working folder**.
   - Browse and select the *C:\Civil 3D for Surveyors\Survey Databases\Appendix* folder.
   - Click **Select Folder**.

4. In the Toolspace>*Survey* tab, right-click on **Survey Databases** and select **New local survey database**.

5. Set the *Name* to **L-Square Data A** and click **OK**.

6. Right-click on the **L-Square Data A** database and select **Edit Survey Database Settings**.

7. In the dialog box, under *Units*, for the *Coordinate zone*, verify that **NAD83 California State Planes, Zone VI, US Foot** is set. If not, click 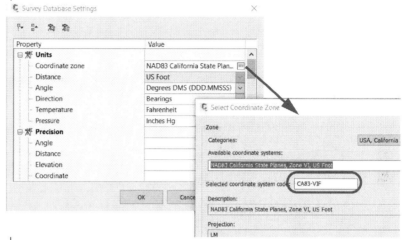 and select it, as shown in Figure A–2, then click **OK**.

Figure A–2

8. Click **OK** to close the dialog box.

9. On the Toolspace>*Survey* tab, right-click on **Networks** (in the currently open survey database) and select **New**.

10. In the New Network dialog box, set the *Name* to **Control Network**. Click **OK**.

Task 2 - Import a survey.

1. Right-click on **Control Network** and select **Import>Import field book**, as shown in Figure A–3.

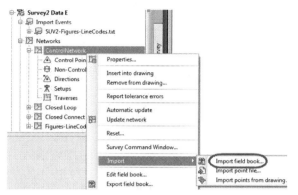

Figure A–3

2. Select the field book file **ControlNetwork.fbk** from the *C:\Civil 3D for Surveyors\Survey Databases\Data\Level 2* folder and click **Open**.

Note that the network is not imported into the drawing because it was not selected in the Import Field Book dialog box.

3. In the *Import Field Book* dialog box, ensure that **ASCENT** is the selected *Current linework code set* (not ACME) and that **Assign offset to point identifiers** is NOT selected. All other checkboxes should be selected as shown in Figure A–4. Click **OK**.

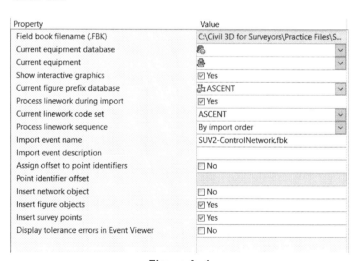

Property	Value
Field book filename (.FBK)	C:\Civil 3D for Surveyors\Practice Files\S...
Current equipment database	
Current equipment	
Show interactive graphics	☑ Yes
Current figure prefix database	☐ ASCENT
Process linework during import	☑ Yes
Current linework code set	ASCENT
Process linework sequence	By import order
Import event name	SUV2-ControlNetwork.fbk
Import event description	
Assign offset to point identifiers	☐ No
Point identifier offset	
Insert network object	☐ No
Insert figure objects	☑ Yes
Insert survey points	☑ Yes
Display tolerance errors in Event Viewer	☐ No

Figure A–4

You might need to zoom extents when the import process completes so that you can see what has been imported.

4. Save the drawing.

Task 3 - Review the survey data.

1. In the Survey Toolspace, in the Networks list, expand the **ControlNetwork** collection, right-click on the **Control Points** heading and select **Edit** to review the control values as shown in Figure A–5.

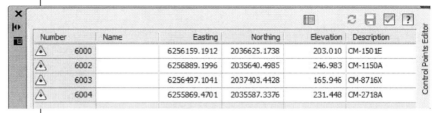

Figure A–5

2. After reviewing the survey control points, click ✖ in the upper left or right corner of the dialog box to exit the Panorama.

3. In the Survey Toolspace, in the Networks list, expand the **ControlNetwork** collection, right-click on the **Setups** heading and select **Edit** to review the control values as shown in Figure A–6.

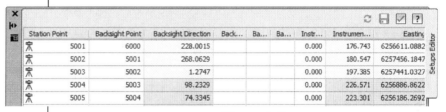

Figure A–6

4. After reviewing the survey setups points, click ✖ in the upper right corner of the dialog box to exit the Panorama.

*If the **ControlNetwork** network is already in the drawing, right-click and select **Remove from drawing**. When prompted whether you are sure, click **Yes**. Note that the network has been removed.*

5. In the Survey Toolspace, in the Networks list, select the **ControlNetwork** network, right-click and select **Insert into drawing**.

6. Save the drawing.

A.2 Creating a Least Squares Input File

When a survey contains redundant point observations and possibly no traverse, you can create a least squares input file that contains the information required for an adjustment. The input file has two parts. The first part lists the control points and the points to be adjusted. The second part breaks down the angle/distance observation values into angle and distance entries. Each entry has a standard deviation (quality estimate) based on the equipment database's current instrument entry.

For example, the following least squares data file contains Angle and Distance values and their error estimates.

!

!	From	At	To			Angle	Distance
!	Point	Point	Point	Angle	Distance	Std Error	Std Error
SD		1153	100		392.761		0.020
VA		1153	100	90.43379		3.9	
A	1151	1153	100	247.30410		9.5	
SD		1153	100		392.761		0.020
VA		1153	100	90.43409		3.9	
A	1151	1153	100	247.30330		9.5	
SD	101	100			440.099		0.022
VA	101	100		90.03042		2.8	
SD	101	100			440.089		0.022
VA	101	100		90.03112		2.8	
SD	101	102			1208.698		0.060

- The angle error is in seconds and the distance error is in feet.

- Control points with known coordinates are not adjusted.

- All observed points with redundant observation data are floating points (points to be adjusted).

- Floating points have a question mark at the beginning of their NEZ line.

- You can make a floating point into a control point by removing its question mark.

- You can add data to the file and enter the estimated error values.

- You can exclude data by placing an exclamation point before the line of data.

Points that are going to be adjusted are listed at the top of the least squares data file and display a question mark at the beginning of their NEZ lines. Points without a question mark are not adjusted. You can change the status of a point by adding or removing the line's question mark.

The following example includes points that are marked to be adjusted.

!3D Input File

!	Least Squares Input File			
!	Generated By Survey			
!	Point	Northing	Easting	Elevation
?NEZ	100	17634.989383	22353.319301	129.766957
?NEZ	101	17472.296414	22762.231891	129.966290
NEZ	1153	17761.182578	21981.405937	134.759730
?NEZ	129	17376.379315	23374.803904	135.564365
NEZ	1151	17622.054456	21859.470581	134.359731
?NEZ	131	17435.520588	23219.865323	133.633393
?NEZ	132	17647.452902	23504.541614	137.079584

Adjustment Analysis

When selecting a **Perform** analysis in the Least Squares flyout, the Autodesk® Civil 3D® software creates data, analyzes the survey, and updates the survey database.

You can perform a preliminary adjustment analysis without affecting the current survey. This enables you to review potential changes and fix any errors or remove data from the analysis.

Right-click on a network name and select **Least squares analysis>Create input file**, **Process input file**, or **Display output file** (as shown in Figure A–7) to analyze a survey and review its results.

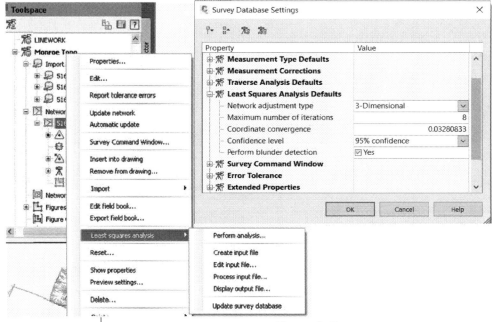

Figure A–7

To adjust the network, right-click and select **Least squares analysis>Update survey database**. Select the file **Network.adj**.

*   When adjusting a survey that contains figures, update the figures after adjusting the survey.

Blunder Detection Analysis

The *Blunder Detection* area of the adjustment identifies the failed measurements because of their high statistical residuals. They indicate errors in the survey that need to be addressed before you continue.

For example, a Blunder Detection analysis includes the following:

****

Blunder Detection/Analysis

****

Reliability Tests

Type	Pnt1	Pnt2	Pnt3	Adjusted	Resid	Redun	Estimate	Marg	Ext
—	—	—	—	—	—	—	—	—	—
SD	101	102		1208.705	0.007	0.956	-0.008	P	P
VA	101	102		89-53-51.06	5.562	0.896	-6.204	P	F
VA	101	102		89-53-53.06	6.562	0.896	-7.319	P	F
ANG	100	101	102	181-00-48.86	1.855	0.525	-3.534	P	P
SD	103	102		1461.861	0.001	0.833	-0.002	P	P
VA	103	102		90-12-07.07	10.367	0.833	-12.440	F	F
SD	103	102		1461.861	-0.009	0.833	0.010	P	P

The adjustment does not affect the control points when you are adjusting a survey. However, it promotes the observed and occupied points to derived control points. All points that were observed from a station and were not promoted to control points, remain as observed points (sideshot points) as shown in Figure A–8.

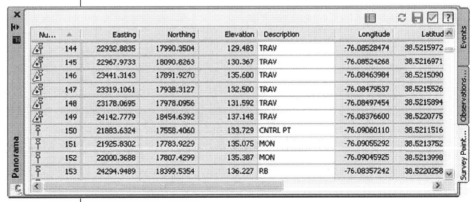

Figure A–8

Updating the Survey

After tweaking and correcting the observations in the data, you must update the survey with the analysis results. This is done from the right-click menu that was used to create and process the survey.

The update routine moves the points to the correct location and adjusts their elevations, if a 3D analysis was done. When updating the survey, the figures become out of date. You must update the figures to their new point attachment locations.

Practice A2

Creating a Least Squares Input File and Adjustment

Practice Objective

*   Perform a least squares analysis of the surveyed network.

In this practice, you will use imported data to perform a least squares analysis of the surveyed network.

Task 1 - Create the least squares input file.

1. Continue working with the drawing from the previous practice or open the file **SUV2-B1-Survey.dwg** from the *C:\Civil 3D for Surveyors\Working\SurveyL2* folder.

2. Continue with the previously opened database or open **L-Square Data B**.

3. Right-click on the survey database and select **Edit Survey database settings**.

4. In the Survey Database Settings dialog box, scroll down to the *Least Squares Analysis Defaults* branch and set the *Network adjustment type* to **2-Dimensional**, as shown in Figure A–9. Click **OK**.

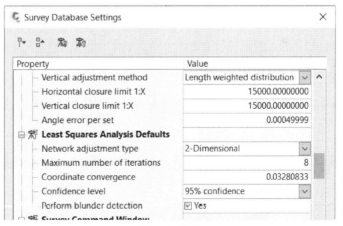

Figure A–9

*If you are prompted that a Network file already exists, click **Yes** to overwrite the file.*

5. In the currently opened survey database, expand the **Networks** collection, right-click on the **ControlNetwork** and select **Least squares analysis>Create input file**, as shown in Figure A–10.

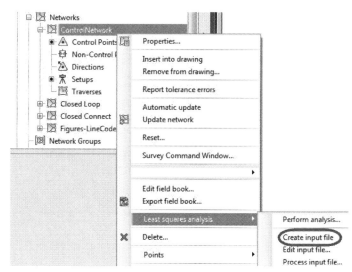

Figure A–10

6. In the currently opened survey database, in the **Network** collection, right-click on the **ControlNetwork** network and select **Least squares analysis>Edit input file**.

7. Review the points that need to be adjusted and the angle (horizontal and vertical) and distance (horizontal and slope) values, as shown in Figure A–11.

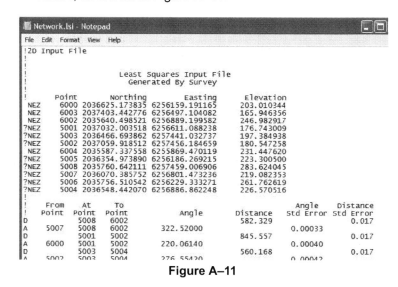

Figure A–11

8. Close the **Network.lsi** in the Notepad file and save the drawing.

Task 2 - Perform a least squares adjustment.

1. In the currently opened survey database, in the **Network** collection, right-click on the **ControlNetwork** network and select **Least squares analysis>Process input file**.

2. In the **Network** collection, right-click on the **ControlNetwork** network and select **Least squares analysis>Display output file**.

   • Note the Measured and Adjusted values as shown in Figure A–12.

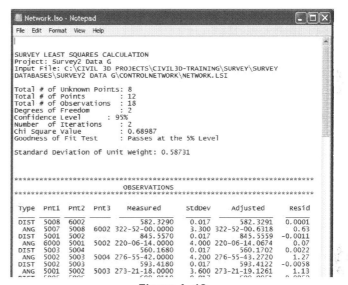

Figure A–12

Task 3 - Update a survey and figures.

If you continued working with the initial survey database, the path will be C:\Civil 3D for Surveyors\Survey Databases\Appendix\ L-Square Data A\ ControlNetwork.

1. In the **Network** collection, right-click on the **ControlNetwork** network and select **Least squares analysis>Update survey database**.

2. In the default folder *C:\Civil 3D for Surveyors\Survey Databases\Appendix\L-Square Data B\ControlNetwork,* select the file **Network.adj** and click **Open**. Note that the default folder path is based on the currently opened survey database.

3. A warning dialog box might open prompted you to process the linework. Close the dialog box. To process the linework, in the Import event, select **ControlNetwork.fbk**, right-click and select **Process Linework**, as shown in Figure A–13. Click **OK**.

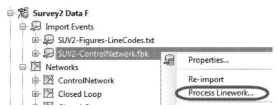

Figure A–13

4. In the **Network** collection, right-click on the **ControlNetwork** network and select **Insert into drawing**.

5. Each adjusted point displays an error ellipse in Model space. To view the point, in the Toolspace>*Survey* tab, select the **Survey Network Control Points** collection. In the list view, right-click on **point 5001** and select **Zoom To**. The drawing zooms to the point and ellipse.

6. Save the drawing.

A.3 Querying Survey Database Points with the Survey Command Window

A network is key to understanding what is going on between points in a survey. When the points are in the drawing, you might typically use the AutoCAD commands rather than the survey tools. By using a survey's network, a surveyor can evaluate, modify, and create survey points.

When points are in a survey network, they are classified as either control points or non-control points. Control and non-control points are points with a known location (i.e., set coordinates), with the difference being that non-control points are unoccupied. If a survey is a traditional survey, the network also includes the initial backsight azimuth and setups.

The best method of evaluating a survey's points is to use the Survey Command Window. To display this tool, right-click on a named network, then select **Survey Command Window**, as shown in Figure A–14.

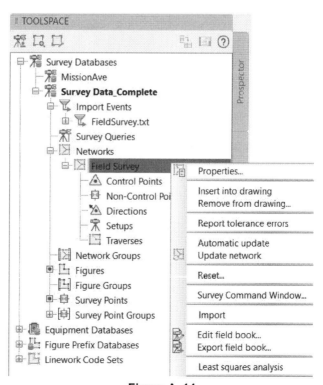

Figure A–14

The Survey Command Window is a user interface to the survey's points and is driven by the Autodesk field book language, as shown in Figure A–15.

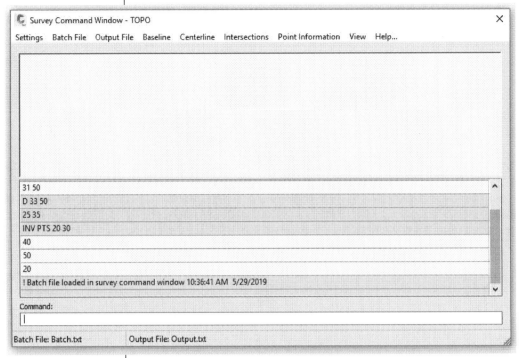

Figure A–15

To use this window effectively, a user needs to be familiar with the field book language, and its shorthand codes (e.g., B for Bearing, D for Horizontal distance, SD for Slope distance, etc.).

One of the field book commands is Ditto. Ditto is on by default and makes a point query repeat without having to use the menu interface or prefix a query with a field book command. For example, in Figure A–15, the user entered **D 33 50**, and then repeated a distance query by entering the next two points (**25 35**) to get a horizontal distance between the points.

Inversing Between Points

To change the current query mode, in the Survey Command Window, open the Point inquiry menu, and select the next query from the list of point queries. In Figure A–15, the next query is to do an inverse between point 20 and point 30 (**INV PTS 20 30**). When the query is run, the Survey Command Window reports the bearing and the distance between points.

If the inverse is around a series of points that define a closed area, enter each succeeding point to get the bearing and distance between each point. To close the inverse, enter the beginning point as the last inversed point. The Survey Command Window reports the bearing and distance to the beginning point and reports the area and perimeter distance.

To start an inverse between points, go to the menu, click **Point Information** to display a list of commands, and then select **Inverse Points**. The Inverse Points dialog box displays the point that starts the inverse process, as shown in Figure A–16.

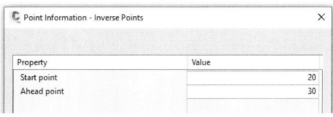

Figure A–16

When you click **OK**, the Survey Command Window grid area displays the inversed points, and the report window displays the inverse values, as shown in Figure A–17.

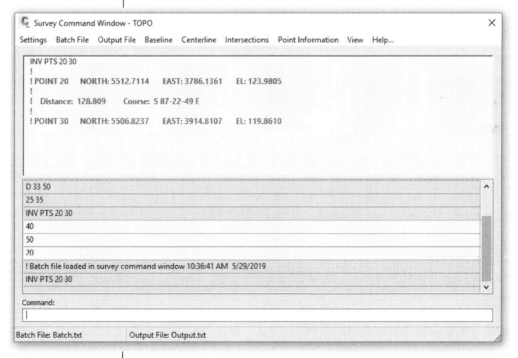

Figure A–17

All subsequent points are entered at the command line. In the command line, each point that is added to the inverse has its inverse values reported in the upper window, as shown in Figure A–18.

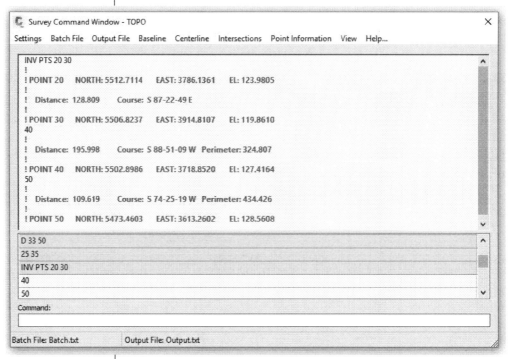

Figure A–18

When you enter the inverse beginning point, the Survey Command Window reports the following, as shown in Figure A–19:

- Final bearing

- Final distance

- Inverse perimeter distance

- Area

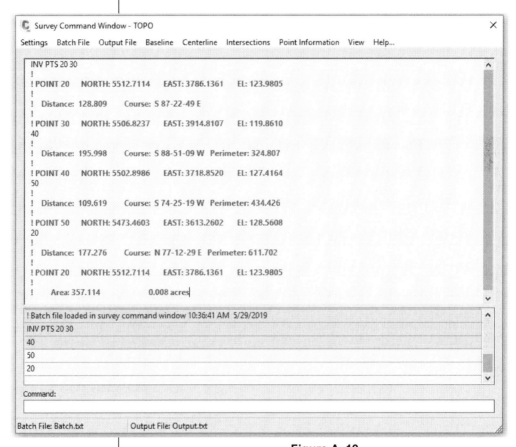

Figure A–19

While the Survey Command Window is reporting the inverse values, an output file saves the reported values to a text file. To view the reported inverse values, in the **Output File** menu, select **View** to open the report. An example report is shown in Figure A–20.

```
Output.txt - Notepad                                    —   □   ×
File  Edit  Format  View  Help
INV PTS 20 30
!
! POINT 20    NORTH: 5512.7114    EAST: 3786.1361    EL: 123.9805
!
!  Distance: 128.809     Course: S 87-22-49 E
!
! POINT 30    NORTH: 5506.8237    EAST: 3914.8107    EL: 119.8610
40
!
!  Distance: 195.998     Course: S 88-51-09 W  Perimeter: 324.807
!
! POINT 40    NORTH: 5502.8986    EAST: 3718.8520    EL: 127.4164
50
!
!  Distance: 109.619     Course: S 74-25-19 W  Perimeter: 434.426
!
! POINT 50    NORTH: 5473.4603    EAST: 3613.2602    EL: 128.5608
20
!
!  Distance: 177.276     Course: N 77-12-29 E  Perimeter: 611.702
!
! POINT 20    NORTH: 5512.7114    EAST: 3786.1361    EL: 123.9805
!
!    Area: 357.114              0.008 acres
```

Figure A–20

The report contains the inverse points that you entered, and the reported distances and angles of each point, as well as the closing point reporting the perimeter and area values. The output file is placed in the survey's *Named Network* folder.

Distance and Bearing Queries

The Survey Command Window can report distances and bearings between points even if there are no points in the drawing. This is because the Survey Command Window is using the survey's point database, and not the drawing.

In the field book language, the letters D and B represent horizontal (2D) distance and bearing quadrant angles. To use these commands, open the **Point Information** menu and select the required command. If you create a query using this method, the point number must be entered in the corresponding command's dialog box. Because the Ditto command is active, after you enter the first point in the dialog box and get the first result, you only need to enter the point number pair in the Survey Command Window command line.

A simpler method to use these commands is to use the codes for distance (D) and bearing (B). In the Survey Command Window command line, set the query mode by entering **D 20 30** to start querying for distances. When you want to change to bearing queries, enter **B 20 30** to change the reporting to bearing. If you want to obtain both the distance and bearing, use the Inverse Point Information command. The report for an inverse is distance and quadrant direction, as shown in Figure A–21.

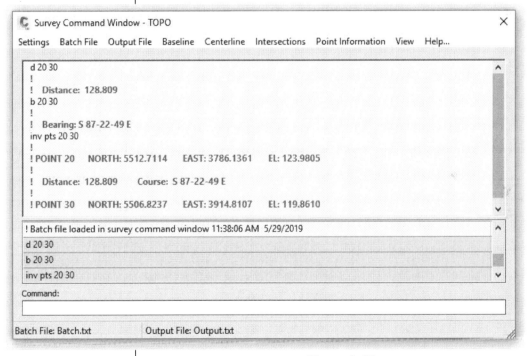

Figure A–21

Baseline or Perpendicular Offsets

A frequent concern of many property owners is building near a shared property line. One example of this is concerning fence posts, and determining which side of the property line they are being placed. To create a query for this example, you would define a baseline (representing the property line) and the baseline's starting station, and then inverse perpendicular to the baseline.

You begin the baseline query by defining the baseline and its starting station, as shown in Figure A–22.

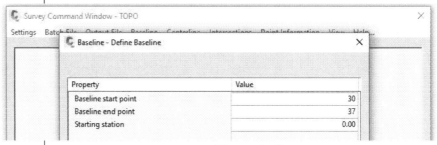

Figure A–22

Then, create a list of points to inverse against the baseline. In this example, the points are **33 38**, as shown in Figure A–23.

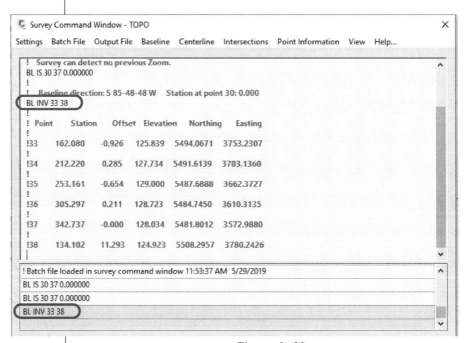

Figure A–23

The report for each inversed point is a distance that is either positive (i.e., to the right of the baseline) or negative (i.e., to the left of the baseline) and includes the point station relative to the baseline, as shown in Figure A–23.

When the query is run, the Autodesk Civil 3D software draws the baseline and zooms to it, as shown in Figure A–24. When you return to the baseline menu and its command list, you can select **Inverse point** to enter the beginning and ending points to inverse along the baseline.

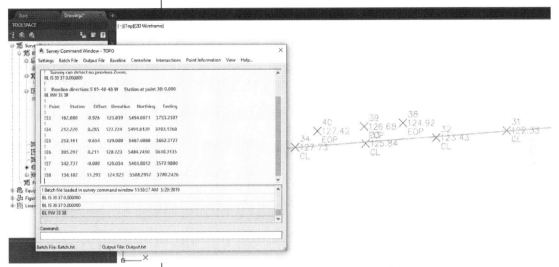

Figure A–24

The Output file records the answers given in the Survey Command Window, as shown in Figure A–25.

File Edit Format View Help

BL IS 30 37 0.000000

!

!   Baseline direction: S 85-48-48 W   Station at point 30: 0.000
BL INV 33 38

!

! Point   Station   Offset   Elevation   Northing   Easting

!

!33	162.080	-0.926	125.839	5494.0671	3753.2307
!34	212.220	0.285	127.734	5491.6139	3703.1360
!35	253.161	-0.654	129.000	5487.6888	3662.3727
!36	305.297	0.211	128.723	5484.7450	3610.3135
!37	342.737	-0.000	128.034	5481.8012	3572.9880
!38	134.102	11.293	124.923	5508.2957	3780.2426

Figure A–25

Connecting to Geospatial Data

In this appendix, you will learn how to easily connect to existing geospatial data and create a surface from it. This process enables you to easily determine which data should be collected during the field survey.

Learning Objectives in This Appendix

- Identify where tools are found in the Planning and Analysis workspace.
- Set the drawing coordinate system for a new drawing.
- Display the current conditions by connecting to GIS data.
- Create a surface from a shape file containing elevation data.

B.1 Introduction to the Planning and Analysis Workspace

The Planning and Analysis workspace in the Autodesk® Civil 3D® software contains tools that are also found in the AutoCAD® Map 3D® software. They help you to attach and analyze GIS data for more efficient planning of projects before starting a design.

Map Workflow

The following workflow is one of many workflows that can be used. It only covers a small portion of the AutoCAD Map 3D software capabilities.

1. Start a new drawing from a Civil 3D template that includes all of the required styles.
2. Assign a Coordinate System to the drawing file.
3. Attach Image and Digital Elevation Models (DEM) files using the **Data Connect** command.
4. Attach other source data using the **Data Connect** command. This includes file-based data sources (.SHP or .SDF files) and database data sources (Oracle or Microsoft SQL Server).
5. Create Autodesk Civil 3D surfaces from source data.
6. Style the layers for presentation or publication purposes.
7. Analyze the data.
8. Create labels and legends to annotate the drawing.

Data can be queried as it is added to the drawing file to ensure that only the area of interest or items of interest are incorporated into the drawing file. Once data is included in the drawing, it can be displayed using themes and symbols for correct representation of the entities. Analysis can be done on the entities to determine which entities are within a specific distance of another (buffer analysis) or which entities overlay another (overlay analysis).

The *Map Setup* tab>Coordinate System panel is used to assign a coordinate system to the drawing file, as shown in Figure B–1.

Figure B–1

The *Home* tab>Data panel is used to connect to source data, such as images, file sources, and database sources, as shown in Figure B–2.

Figure B–2

Creating a surface from source data is done using the Civil 3D workspace in the *Home* tab>Create Ground Data panel, as shown in Figure B–3.

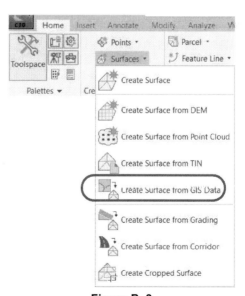

Figure B–3

B.2 Coordinate Systems

Coordinate systems are used in engineering and mapping to uniquely identify the position of geographical elements. Various systems project elements differently to accommodate the curvature of the earth's surface. Therefore, it is vitally important to set the coordinate system for the drawing in which you plan to work.

Coordinate systems communicate to the computer where the project is located in the world, along with mathematical equations used to account for the curvature of the earth. Once the drawing coordinate system has been set, any GIS or Survey data that is connected to the drawing automatically re-projects and lines up correctly in the current drawing.

How To: Set the Drawing Coordinate System in the Planning and Analysis Workspace

1. In the Quick Access Toolbar, change the workspace to **Planning and Analysis**, as shown in Figure B–4.

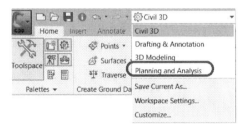

Figure B–4

2. In the *Map Setup* tab>Coordinate System panel, click

   (Assign) to assign a coordinate system to the drawing file, as shown in Figure B–5.

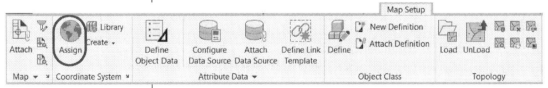

Figure B–5

3. Search for the code required by your project and select it, as shown in Figure B–6.

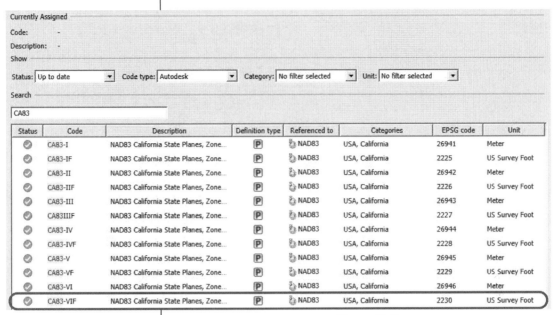

Figure B–6

4. Click **Assign**.

How To: Set the Drawing Coordinate System in the Civil 3D Workspace

1. In the Quick Access Toolbar, change the workspace to **Civil 3D**, as shown in Figure B–7.

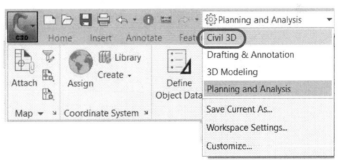

Figure B–7

2. In the Toolspace>*Settings* tab, right-click on the drawing name and select **Edit Drawing Settings**, as shown in Figure B–8.

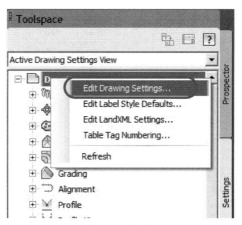

Figure B–8

3. In the Drawing Setting dialog box, in the *Units and Zone* tab, select the category and coordinate system for the drawing, as shown in Figure B–9. Click **OK**.

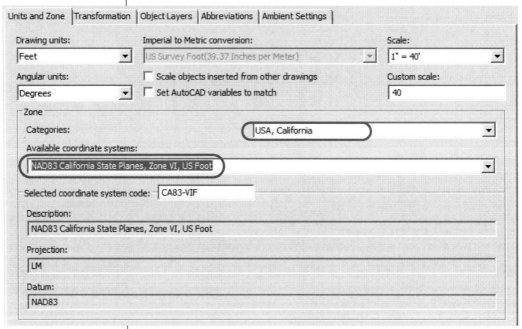

Figure B–9

- If the majority of your projects use the same coordinate system, you can set the Autodesk Civil 3D drawing template to use that coordinate system.

Practice B1 | Start a New Project

Practice Objective

- Display the current conditions by connecting to GIS data.

In this practice, you will create a new drawing and assign a coordinate system to the drawing.

1. Expand the 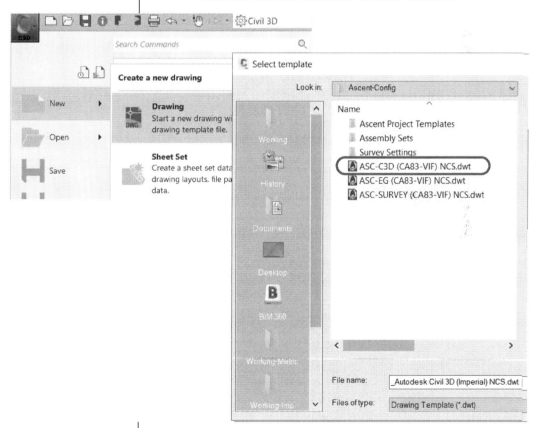 (Application Menu) and start a new drawing file. Browse to the *C:\Civil 3D for Surveyors\Ascent-Config* folder and select **_ASC-C3D (CA83-VIF) NCS.dwt**, as shown in Figure B–10.
   - This is a customized template file that is based on the **Autodesk Civil 3D (Imperial) NCS.dwt** template that is included with the Autodesk Civil 3D software.

Figure B–10

2. Expand 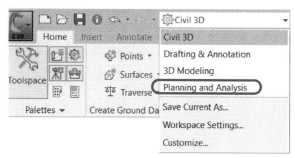 (Application Menu) and select **Save As**. Browse to *C:\Civil 3D for Surveyors\Working\Geospatial* and name the file **GEO-A1.dwg**.

3. Click **Save**.

4. In the Quick Access Toolbar, change the workspace to **Planning and Analysis**, as shown in Figure B–11.

Figure B–11

5. In the drawing, review the note shown in Figure B–12, which indicates that the drawing is already set to the required coordinate system. Erase the note.

DRAWING SET TO CA83-VIF COORDINATE SYSTEM. GO TO DRAWING SETTINGS TO MODIFY IF NEED BE. DELETE THIS MESSAGE.

Figure B–12

6. For the purpose of this practice, verify that the coordinate system is set up correctly. In the *Map Setup* tab>Coordinate

System panel, click (Assign) to assign a coordinate system to the drawing file, as shown in Figure B–13.

Figure B–13

7. In the *Search* field, type **CA83** and select **CA83-VIF** from the list of codes, as shown in Figure B–14. Click **Assign**.

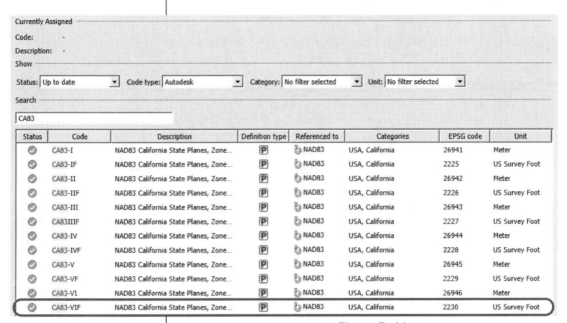

Figure B–14

8. Save the drawing.

B.3 Geospatial Data Connection

Geospatial data is collected and maintained by a large number of organizations using a variety of different software. The Autodesk Civil 3D software can connect to many of these data sources using the Feature Data Object (FDO) connection in *Display Manager* tab of the AutoCAD Map 3D Task pane or the *Home* tab in the Planning and Analysis workspace. The types of data that can be connected include:

- ArcSDE
- MySQL
- ODBC
- SQLite
- WFS
- WMS
- Oracle

- Enterprise Industry Models
- PostgreSQL
- Raster Image or Surface
- Spatial Data Files (SDF)
- ESRI Shape files (SHP)
- SQL Server Spatial

Connect to GIS Data

The process of connecting to GIS data is similar among data types. First, you must select the type of data to which to connect. Then, select the number of files that are going to be connected at the same time. You can connect to one file at a time or to an entire directory of files at the same time. If a database connection is selected (such as Oracle or ArcSDE) you might need to input your login credentials, as shown in Figure B–15.

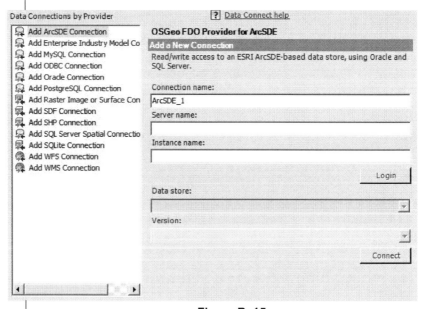

Figure B–15

Finally, you need to ensure that the coordinate system of the source file registers as you connect to it. If the coordinate system for the source file is listed as <unknown> (as shown in Figure B–16), it did not register correctly. Therefore, you need to assign the source coordinate system manually so that it re-projects automatically in the drawing and displays in the correct location.

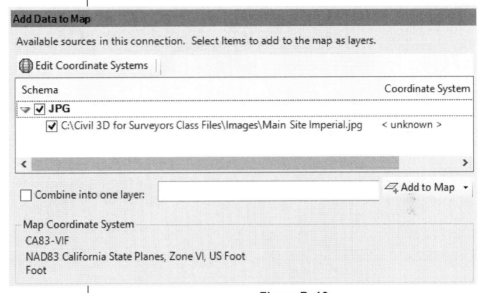

Figure B–16

How To: Connect to GIS Data

There are multiple locations in which you can access the Data Connection palette. The first is the *Home* tab in the Planning and Analysis workspace, the second is in the Map Task pane.

1. In the *Home* tab>Data panel in the Planning and Analysis workspace, click  (Connect), as shown in Figure B–17.

Figure B–17

Alternatively, you can do the following:

- In the *Home* tab>expanded Palettes panel in the Civil 3D workspace, click  (Map Task Pane), as shown in Figure B–18.

- In the *Display Manager* tab, in the Map Task Pane, click (Data) and select **Connect to Data**, as shown in Figure B–19.

Figure B–18

Figure B–19

2. In the Data Connect palette, select the correct connect type.

3. Type a name for the connection and click (Browse for source file) or (Browse for source folder), as shown in Figure B–20.

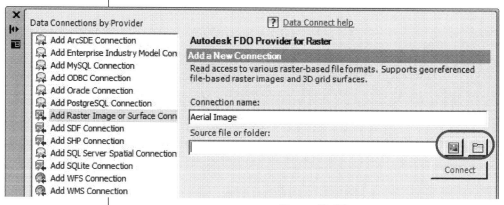

Figure B–20

4. Select the file or folder and click **Open**.

5. In the Data Connect palette, click **Connect**.
6. In the *Coordinate System* column, double-click on **<unknown>** to edit the coordinate system that is registered with the source file, as shown in Figure B–21.

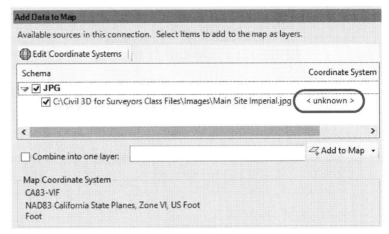

Figure B–21

7. In the Edit Spatial Contexts dialog box, select **<unknown>** and click **Edit**, as shown in Figure B–22.

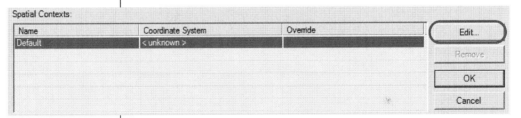

Figure B–22

8. Select the required coordinate system from the list of codes, as shown in Figure B–23. Click **Select**. Click **OK**.

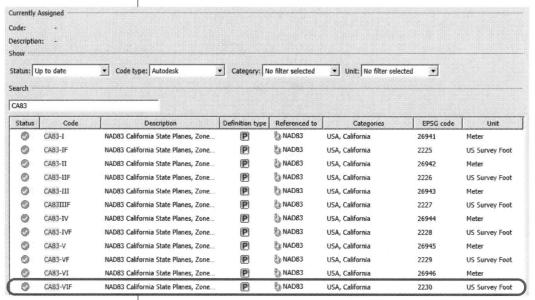

Figure B–23

9. In the Data Connect palette, click **Add to Map**.
10. Continue adding data sources, as required.

Autodesk Connector for ArcGIS

If you are using ESRI (R) ArcGIS Online or Enterprise portals, you can connect directly to the source using your ESRI ArcGIS login information. Your ESRI ArcGIS login credentials are required to enter the portal, as shown in Figure B–24.

Figure B–24

In the portal, you can navigate to your project site by entering an address, location name, or longitudinal and latitudinal coordinates, as shown in Figure B–25. You can also browse the available datasets that are contained in your organization's ArcGIS Online content that you can include in your project.

Figure B–25

Stylize GIS Data

The available styles for a GIS layer depend on the type of GIS data being displayed. Point features (such as points of interest in a city) can use block symbols as the point style while linear features (such as roads) use linetypes and linewidths to communicate differences between feature types. If an area feature (such as a city boundary or parcel) is used, both hatch patterns and linetypes/linewidths are used to communicate differences between feature types, as shown in Figure B–26.

Figure B–26

How To: Modify an Area Style

1. In the *View* tab>Palettes panel, click  (Map Task Pane), as shown in Figure B–27.

Figure B–27

2. In the Task Pane>*Display Manager* tab, double-click on the area layer.
3. In the Style Editor palette, in the *Style* column, click 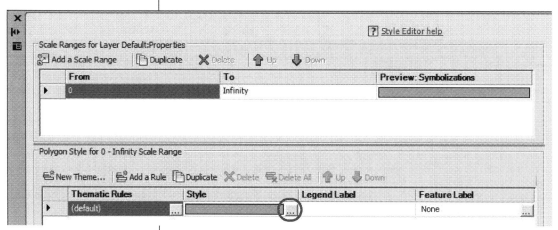 (Browse) as shown in Figure B–28.

Figure B–28

4. In the Style Polygon dialog box, change the border color and fill color or add additional borders and fills as required, as shown in Figure B–29. Click **Apply** and close the Style Polygon dialog box and Style Editor palette.

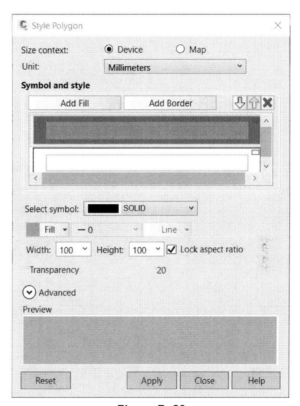

Figure B–29

Draw Order

Setting the drawing order of the layer determines which layer displays on top of another. If you use an aerial photograph or other raster file, it is useful to move it to the background so that other layers are able to display.

How To: Change the Draw Order of GIS Layers

1. In the Task Pane>*Display Manager* tab, select **Draw Order** and drag the layers above or below the others to ensure that they all display, as shown in Figure B–30.

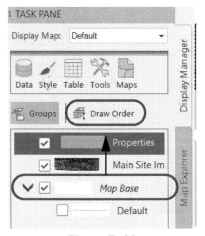

Figure B–30

2. In the Draw Order dialog box that opens, select **Continue action and allow Draw Order to control layer position from now on**.

Practice B2

Connect to GIS Data

Practice Objective

- Connect to an aerial image file using AutoCAD Map 3D tools.

In this practice, you will create a new drawing and assign a coordinate system to the drawing.

Task 1 - Connect to an image file.

1. Continue working with the drawing from the previous practice or open **GEO-B1-GIS.dwg** from the *C:\Civil 3D for Surveyors\Working\Geospatial* folder.

2. If required, change your workspace to **Planning and Analysis**.

3. In the *Home* tab>Data panel, click  (Connect), as shown in Figure B–31.

Figure B–31

4. In the Data Connect palette, select **Add Raster Image or Surface Connection**, set the *Connection name* to **Aerial Image** and click ⬛ (Browse for image file), as shown in Figure B–32.

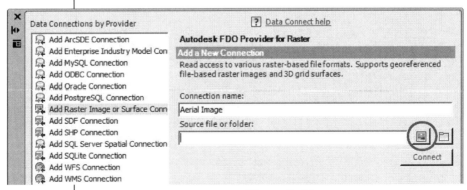

Figure B–32

5. Select the **Main Site Imperial.jpg** in the *C:\Civil 3D for Surveyors\References\Images* folder. Click **Open**.

6. In the Data Connect palette, click **Connect**.

7. In the *Coordinate System* column, double-click on **<unknown>** to edit the coordinate system that is registered with the image file.

8. In the Edit Spatial Contexts dialog box, select **<unknown>** and click **Edit**, as shown in Figure B–33.

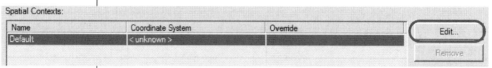

Figure B–33

9. In the *Search* field, type **CA83**, and in the list of code, select **CA83-VIF**. Click **Select**. Click **OK**.

10. In the Data Connect palette, click **Add to Map**, close the Data Connect palette, and save the drawing.

Task 2 - Connect to a shape file.

---

1. Continue working with the drawing from the previous task.

2. If you closed the Data Connect palette, in the *Home* tab>Data panel, click ![icon] (Connect).

3. In the Data Connect palette, select **Add SHP Connection**. Set the *Connection name* to **Parcels** and click ![SHP icon] (Browse for SHP file), as shown in Figure B–34.

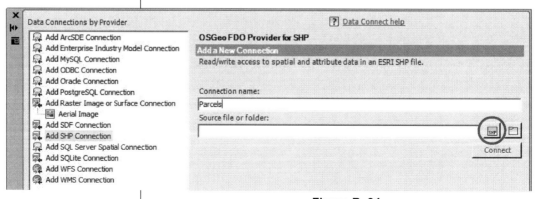

Figure B–34

4. Select **Properties.shp** in *C:\Civil 3D for Surveyors\ References\GIS* folder. Click **Open**.

5. In the Data Connect palette, click **Connect**.

6. In the Data Connect palette, click **Add to Map**. Close the Data Connect palette and save the drawing.

7. If the Map Task Pane is not open, click  (Map Task Pane) in the *View* tab>Palettes panel, as shown in Figure B–35.

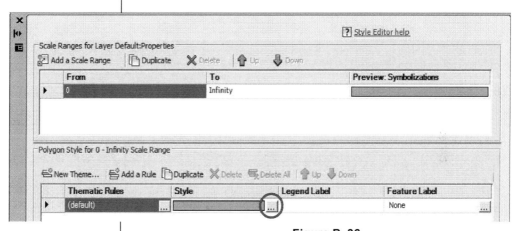

Figure B–35

8. In the Task Pane>*Display Manager* tab, double-click on the **Properties** layer.

9. In the Style Editor palette, in the *Style* column, click (Browse), as shown in Figure B–36.

Figure B–36

10. In the Style Polygon dialog box, change the *border color* to **Cyan** and the *fill color* to **No Color**, as shown in Figure B–37. Click **Apply** and close the Style Polygon dialog box and Style Editor palette.

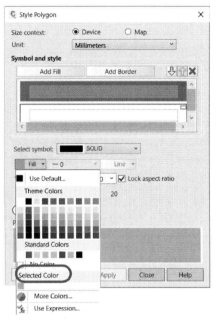

Figure B–37

11. In the Task Pane>*Display Manager* tab, select **Draw Order** and then drag the **Map Base** layer above the **Properties** layer, as shown in Figure B–38.

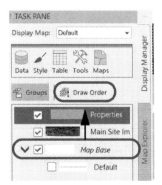

Figure B–38

12. In the Draw Order dialog box that opens, select **Continue action and allow Draw Order to control layer position from now on**.

13. Save the drawing.

B.4 Create a Surface from GIS Data

An Autodesk Civil 3D surface can be created from GIS data. Once created, the surface can be used to create surface profiles and act as a target for corridor models and grading groups. It is recommended that you request any available metadata when obtaining GIS layers that could be used for creating a 3D surface model. The metadata should indicate how accurate the data is and whether it can be used in detailed design drawings. GIS surfaces are not often used for detailed design because they are typically mapping grade rather than survey grade.

Having a surface from GIS data can be useful in the project planning phase of a project, even if it is not survey grade. Data source types that can be used to create a surface include: ArcSDE, Oracle, and ESRI Shape Files.

How To: Create an Autodesk Civil 3D Surface from SHP Files

1. In the Quick Access Toolbar, select **Civil 3D** for the workspace.
2. In the *Home* tab>Create Ground Data panel, expand the Surfaces drop-down list and click (Create Surface from GIS Data), as shown in Figure B–39.

Figure B–39

3. In the Object Options page, set the *Civil 3D object type* to **Surface**. Type a name and select the required styles for displaying the surface, as shown in Figure B–40. Click **Next**.

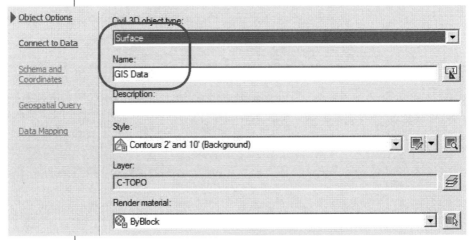

Figure B–40

4. In the Connect to Data page, for the Data source type, select **SHP**, click ... (Browse for file) and select a shape file that includes vector data for the contours and elevation data in the database file, as shown in Figure B–41. Click **Open** and click **Login**.

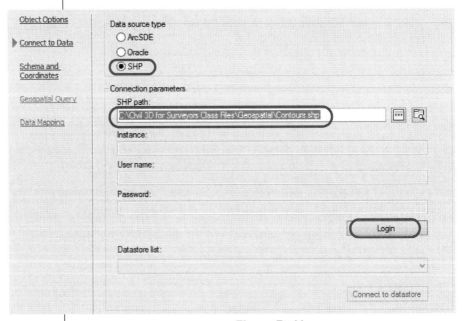

Figure B–41

5. In the Schema and Coordinates page, select the **Contours** feature class and ensure that the *Contours Coordinate system* is set, as shown in Figure B–42. Click **Next**.

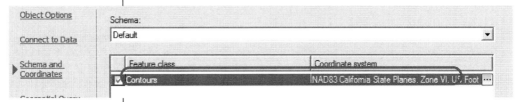

Figure B–42

6. In the Geospatial Query page, clear the **Define area of interest** option so that the entire Contours shape file is used to create a surface, as shown in Figure B–43. Click **Next**.

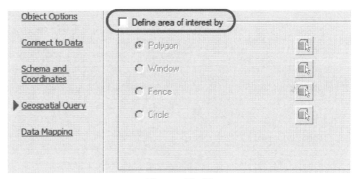

Figure B–43

7. In the Data Mapping page, expand the drop-down list and select the field that holds the surface elevation values, as shown in Figure B–44. Click **Finish**.

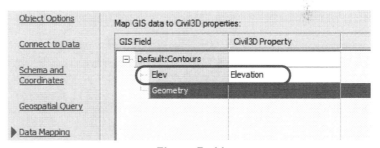

Figure B–44

Contour data is available from many sources. Large sites are often surveyed using aerial photogrammetry, which provides contour polylines and spot elevations. When contour data is used from other GIS data types, the Autodesk Civil 3D software interprets the imported linework as polylines with elevations.

In the Autodesk Civil 3D software, polylines with elevation are useful as custom contour objects. Whether using polylines or other GIS contour objects, the Autodesk Civil 3D software builds a surface by triangulating between contours. The end of each triangle side connects to a vertex of two different contours.

Contour Issues

Note the following issues when working with contour data: bays and peninsulas in the contours and the lack of high and low point elevations. These issues affect triangulation and the quality of a surface.

Bays and peninsulas in contours represent gullies or isolated high points on a surface. As long as there is data to work with, the Autodesk Civil 3D software builds a surface by triangulating between contours of different elevations. When the software cannot triangulate between different contours, the triangulation switches to connecting vertices on the same contour.

The **Minimize Flat Faces** command helps mitigate this situation by forcing the triangulation to target different contours, as shown in Figure B–45. However, this method, similar to the edge swap method, does not correct every problem on a contour surface.

- To launch the **Minimize Flat Faces** command, right-click on the *Edits* heading in the **Definition** collection of a surface and select the command.

The second issue with contour data regards the loss of high and low points. Contours represent an elevation interval (120, 122, 123, etc.). However, the top of a hill could be 123.04 or 136.92 and the only contours present are for the elevations of 123 or 136. Spot elevations are required in the surface data to help correctly resolve the high and low spots of a surface.

- Flat spots and the loss of high and low points affect the calculation of volumes for earthworks, as shown in Figure B–46.

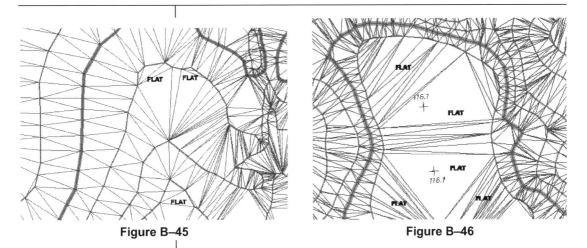

Figure B–45   Figure B–46

Minimizing Flat Triangle Strategies

By default, the **Minimize flat areas by:** options (shown in Figure B–47) are selected in the Add Contour Data dialog box.

Minimize flat areas by:
- ☑ Filling gaps in contour data
- ☐ Swapping edges
- ☑ Adding points to flat triangle edges
- ☑ Adding points to flat edges

Figure B–47

Together, these three methods attempt to detect and resolve peninsulas, bays, and other issues by adding additional points and filling in gaps based on surface trends. Generally, these provide the most expected results. The **Swapping edges** option is provided as a way of emulating how other terrain modeling software traditionally approached minimizing flat areas. The Autodesk Civil 3D software automatically applies three of the four Minimize flat area options as it creates the surface from GIS data.

Draping Images on a Surface

Images and other 2D linework can be draped on a surface. Draping a 2D image on a surface gives it the appearance of being 3D and provides a better visualization of what is happening on the project site.

How To: Drape an Image on an Autodesk Civil 3D Surface

1. In Model Space, select the **GIS Data** surface. In the contextual *Surface* tab>Surface Tools panel, click 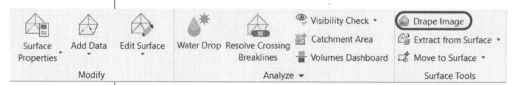 (Drape Image), as shown in Figure B–48.

Figure B–48

2. In the Drape Image dialog box, ensure that the **Main Site Imperial** image is selected and that the GIS Data surface is selected, as shown in Figure B–49. Click **OK**.

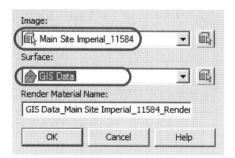

Figure B–49

Practice B3

Create a Surface from a Shape File

Practice Objective

- Create a surface from a shape file containing elevation data.

In this practice, you will create a new drawing and assign a coordinate system to the drawing.

Task 1 - Create a surface from a shape file.

1. Continue working with the drawing from the previous practice or open **GEO-C1-GIS.dwg** from the *C:\Civil 3D for Surveyors\Working\Geospatial* folder.

2. In the Quick Access Toolbar, select **Civil 3D** for the workspace.

3. In the *Home* tab>Create Ground Data panel, expand the Surfaces drop-down list and click  (Create Surface from GIS Data), as shown in Figure B–50.

Figure B–50

4. In the Object Options page, for the *Name*, type **GIS Data**. Leave all of the other settings as their defaults, as shown in Figure B–51. Click **Next**.

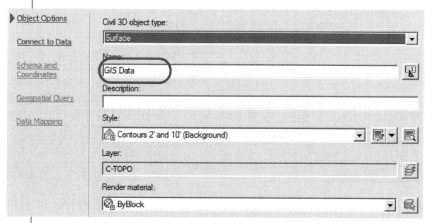

Figure B–51

5. In the Connect to Data page, set the *Data source type* to **SHP**. Click 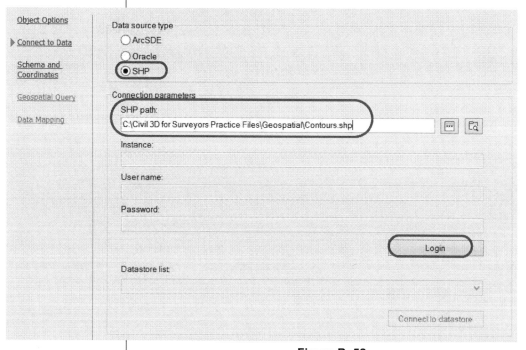 (Browse for file) and select **Contours.shp** in the *C:\Civil 3D for Surveyors\References\GIS* folder, as shown in Figure B–52. Click **Open**. Then, click **Login**.

Figure B–52

6. On the Schema and Coordinates page, select the **Contours** feature class and ensure that the *Contours Coordinate system* is set to **NAD83 California State Planes, Zone VI, US Foot**, as shown in Figure B–53. Click **Next**.

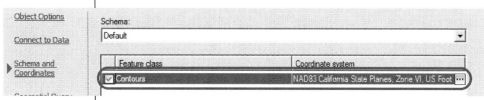

Figure B–53

7. In the Geospatial Query page, clear the **Define area of interest** option so that the entire Contours shape file is used to create a surface, as shown in Figure B–54. Click **Next**.

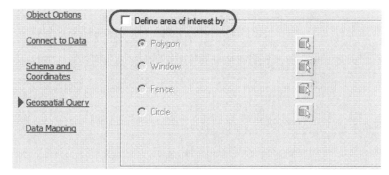

Figure B–54

8. In the Data Mapping page, expand the Elev drop-down list and select **Elevation**, as shown in Figure B–55. Click **Finish**.

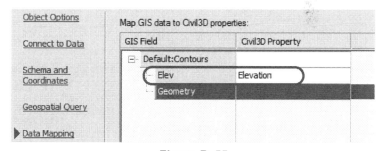

Figure B–55

9. Save the drawing.

Task 2 - Drape an image on the surface.

1. Continue working with the drawing from the previous task.

2. In the *View* tab, in the Visual Styles panel, select **Realistic** from the Visual Styles drop-down list. You can also access the Visual Styles through the *Modelspace Viewport Control* bracketed areas in the top left corner of the drawing window, as shown in Figure B–56

Figure B–56

3. In Model Space, select the **GIS Data** surface. In the contextual *Surface* tab>Surface Tools panel, click 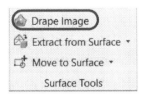 (Drape Image), as shown in Figure B–57.

Figure B–57

4. In the Drape Image dialog box, ensure that the **Main Site Imperial** image is selected and that the GIS Data surface is selected, as shown in Figure B–58. Click **OK**, then press <Esc> to clear the surface selection.

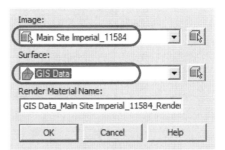

Figure B–58

The image might not look the same in the object view. Use 3D Orbit to display the results of draping an image.

5. In the *View* tab>Navigate 2D panel, click ⚓ (Orbit). Orbit the drawing as shown in Figure B–59. Press <Esc>.

Figure B–59

6. Save the drawing.

Chapter Review Questions

1. In which workspace is the Coordinate System panel located?

   a. Civil 3D

   b. 2D Drafting and Annotation

   c. 3D Modeling

   d. Planning and Analysis

2. What type of data cannot be connected using the Data Connection palette?

   a. ArcSDE

   b. Oracle

   c. Microstation DGN file

   d. ESRI Shape File

3. You have to be in the Planning and Analysis workspace to access the Data Connect palette.

   a. True

   b. False

4. In which workspace is the **Create Surface from GIS Data** command located?

   a. Civil 3D

   b. 2D Drafting and Annotation

   c. 3D Modeling

   d. Planning and Analysis

5. Which Toolspace do you need to be in to drape an image on a surface?

   a. Civil 3D

   b. 3D Modeling

   c. Planning and Analysis

   d. It does not matter because the *Surface* contextual tab displays when you select a surface no matter which workspace you are using.

Command Summary

Button	Command	Location
	Assign	• **Workspace**: Planning and Analysis • **Ribbon**: *Map Setup* tab>Coordinate System panel • **Command Prompt**: MAPCSASSIGN
	Create Surface from GIS Data	• **Workspace**: Civil 3D • **Ribbon**: *Home* tab>Create Ground Data panel • **Command Prompt**: CreateSurfaceFromGISData
	Data Connect	• **Workspace**: Planning and Analysis • **Ribbon**: *Home* tab>Data panel • **Command Prompt**: MAPCONNECT
	Drape Image	• **Ribbon**: Contextual *Surface* tab>Surface Tools panel
	Map Task Pane	• **Workspace**: Civil 3D, or Planning and Analysis • **Ribbon**: *Home* tab>Expanded Palettes panel, or *View* tab>Palettes panel • **Command Prompt**: MapWSpace

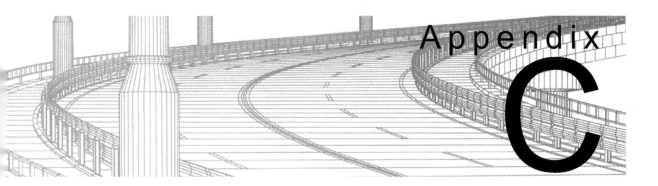

Additional Surface Tools

In this appendix, you will learn more about some of the additional tools that are available in the Autodesk® Civil 3D® software for working with surfaces.

Learning Objectives in This Appendix

- Calculate volumes between two surfaces.
- Create an AutoCAD 3D solid from an Autodesk Civil 3D surface.
- Create a 3D surface from a point cloud.

C.1 Surface Volume Calculations

You can generate volume calculations in the Autodesk Civil 3D software in many ways. Surface-to-surface calculations are often used to compare an existing ground surface to a proposed surface to determine cut and fill quantities. In the Autodesk Civil 3D software, quantities can be adjusted by an expansion (cut) or a compaction (fill) factor. Surfaces representing different soil strata can be compared to each other to determine the volume between the soil layers. There are multiple ways of comparing surfaces to each other in the Autodesk Civil 3D software.

Volumes Dashboard

In the *Analyze* tab>Volumes and Materials panel, click

(Volumes Dashboard). The Volumes Dashboard creates a volume surface based on a graphical subtraction of one surface from the other, as shown in Figure C–1.

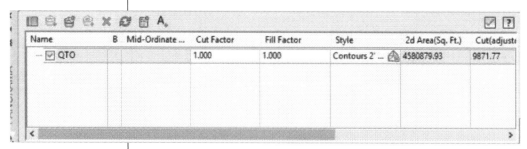

Name	B	Mid-Ordinate ...	Cut Factor	Fill Factor	Style	2d Area(Sq. Ft.)	Cut(adjuste
☑ QTO			1.000	1.000	Contours 2' ...	4580879.93	9871.77

Figure C–1

The *Net Graph* column color displays in red if the surface difference results in a net cut, and green if it is a net fill. You can have multiple volume entries listed if you are comparing multiple surfaces. If any surfaces change, return to this vista and click

(Recompute Volumes) to update the calculations. Alternatively, you can add another volume entry. Select the same two surfaces and compare before and after volume calculations.

Bounded Volumes

The area to calculate cut and fill can be limited by clicking

(Add Bounded Volume). This limits the calculations to the area defined by a polyline, polygon, or parcel.

Volume Reports

The dashboard's cut/fill summary contents can be placed directly into the drawing by clicking A_+ (Insert Cut/Fill Summary) inside the Volumes Dashboard. In addition, you can create a volume report from the dashboard contents to include in specifications or other project documents by clicking 🖹 (Generate Volume Report) inside the Volumes Dashboard.

Grid Volume or TIN Volume Surface

This method enables you to assign the surfaces you want to compare as object properties of a volume surface. The volume between the surfaces is calculated and included in the volume surface object properties. The TIN surface calculation is the same one conducted in the Volumes Dashboard. The Grid surface calculation is based on a grid of points interpolated from both surfaces, rather than all of the surface points of both. Grid surfaces tend to be less accurate, but faster to calculate and easier to prove by manual methods.

A grid of spot elevation labels that list the elevation differences between two surfaces can be generated from either a Grid Volume surface or TIN Volume surface. Once the volume surface is created, you can create the labels. In the *Annotate* tab>Labels & Tables panel, expand Add Labels, expand Surface, and select **Spot Elevations on Grid**, as shown in Figure C–2.

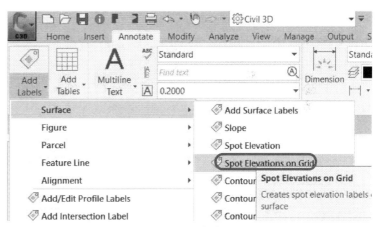

Figure C–2

3D Solid Surface from TIN Surface

The Autodesk Civil 3D software has the capability to extract a 3D solid surface from any TIN surface. During the extraction process, you can define the vertical properties, the output properties, and which surface to extract.

Vertical Definition

Three options are available for setting the vertical definition of a 3D solid from a TIN surface, as shown in Figure C–3.

1. The first option creates a solid with a consistent depth across the entire surface. This can be used to quickly calculate the volume of top soil to be removed.
2. The second options creates a solid with a fixed elevation. This option can be used to quickly calculate the water volume of a pond, which has a consistent water elevation.
3. The last option creates a solid between two surfaces. This could be used to create various solids from soil report point. Doing so provides a solid for each type of material.

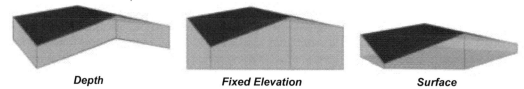

Depth   **Fixed Elevation**   **Surface**

Figure C–3

Output Properties

Multiple output settings enable you to define where the solid is created during the extraction process. The layer and color for the solid can also be set. Then, you can create the solid in the current drawing or in a new drawing. If you select a new drawing, you can set the file path and name of the new drawing by clicking

 (Browse).

How To: Create a 3D Solid Surface

1. In the model, select a TIN surface.
2. In the contextual *Surface* tab>Surface Tools panel, expand ![icon](Extract from Surface) and select ![icon](Extract Solids from Surface).
3. In the Extract Solid from Surface dialog box, shown in Figure C–4, set the vertical definition and the required drawing output.

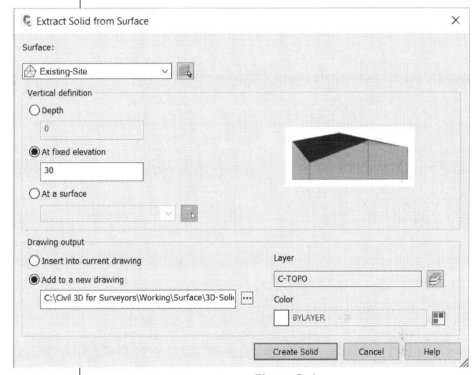

Figure C–4

4. Click **Create Solid**.

Practice C1 | Create a 3D Solid

Practice Objective

- Create a 3D solid from a surface.

1. Open **SUF1-Finished.dwg** from the *C:\Civil 3D for Surveyors\Working\Surface* folder.

2. Select the **Existing-Site** surface in Model Space. In the contextual *Surface* tab>Surface Tools panel, expand (Extract from Surface) and select (Extract Solids from Surface).

3. In the Extract Solid from Surface dialog box (shown in Figure C–5), set the following:
    - *Surface:* **Existing-Site**
    - *Vertical definition:* select *At fixed elevation*: **100**
    - *Drawing output:* select *Add to a new drawing* and save it to *C:\Civil 3D for Surveyors\Working\Surface\\3D-Solid.dwg*.

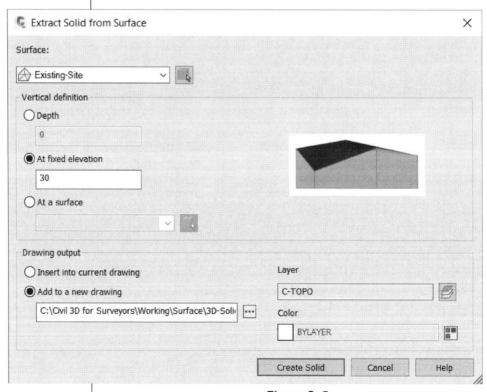

Figure C–5

4. Click **Create Solid**.

5. Click **OK** when prompted.

6. Open **3D-Solid.dwg** from the *C:\Civil 3D for Surveyors\ Working\Surface* folder. Orbit the model, and verify that the bottom of the solid surface is at elevation **100**, as shown in Figure C–6.

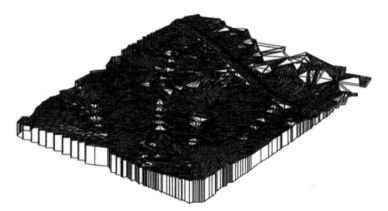

Figure C–6

7. Close the drawing without saving.

C.2 Point Cloud Surface Extraction

Point clouds are dense groupings of points created by 3D scanners. The AutoCAD software has been capable of working with point clouds from its previous versions. The accepted point cloud file formats are .RCP and .RCS. They are faster and more efficient than the previous file formats and are created using the Autodesk Recap software.

- As with cross references, images, and other externally referenced files, you can attach and manage point clouds using the External References Manager.

- Point cloud object snaps have been added to the *3D Object Snap* tab in the Drafting Settings dialog box and the 3D Object Snap options in the Status Bar.

- In a point cloud, you can use the **Object** option in the **UCS** command to align the active UCS to a plane.

- Dynamic UCS now aligns to a point cloud plane according to point density and alignment.

Attach Point Cloud

In the Attach Point Cloud dialog box, you can preview a point cloud and its detailed information (such as its classification and segmentation data) before attaching it, as shown in Figure C–7. You can also use a geographic location for the attachment location (if the option is available).

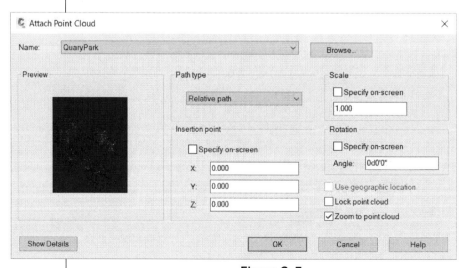

Figure C–7

How To: Attach a Point Cloud

1. In the *Insert* tab>Point Cloud panel, click 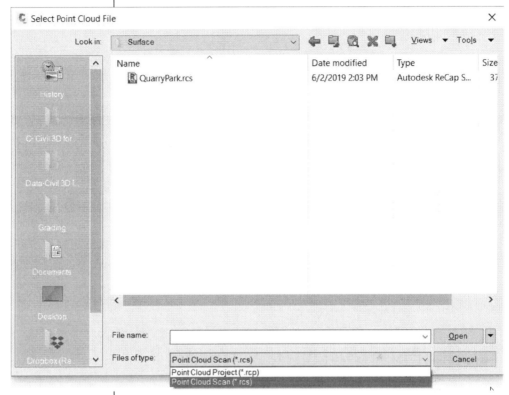 (Attach).
2. In the Select Point Cloud File dialog box, expand the Files of type drop-down list and select an option, as shown in Figure C–8. In the *Name* area, select a file and click **Open**.

Figure C–8

- The AutoCAD software can attach Point Cloud Project (RCP) and Scan (RCS) files (which are produced by the Autodesk ReCap software).
- The Autodesk ReCap software enables the creation of a point cloud project file (RCP) that references multiple indexed scan files (RCS). It converts scan file data into a point cloud format that can then be viewed and modified in other products.

3. In the Attach Point Cloud dialog box, click **Show Details** to display the point cloud information.

4. In the *Path type*, *Insertion point*, *Scale*, and *Rotation* areas, set the options that you want to use to attach the point cloud, as shown in Figure C–9. Click **OK**.

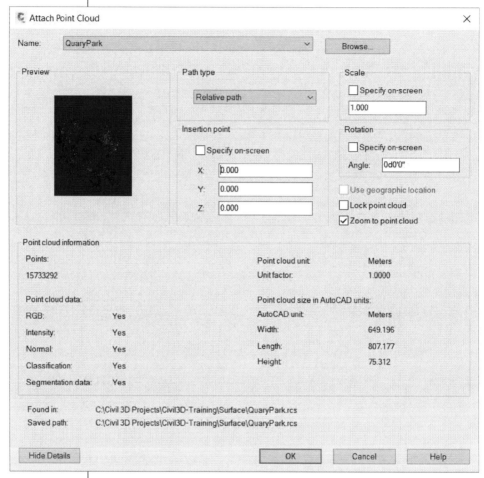

Figure C–9

5. At the *Specify insertion point* prompt, click in the drawing to locate the point cloud.

Point Cloud Transparency

When point clouds exist in a drawing with other geometry, it can be difficult to see anything behind the point cloud. A new tool in the *Point Cloud* contextual tab>Visualization panel enables you to adjusts the transparency of the point cloud, as shown in Figure C–10. Alternatively, you can adjust the point cloud transparency in the Properties palette, as shown in Figure C–10.

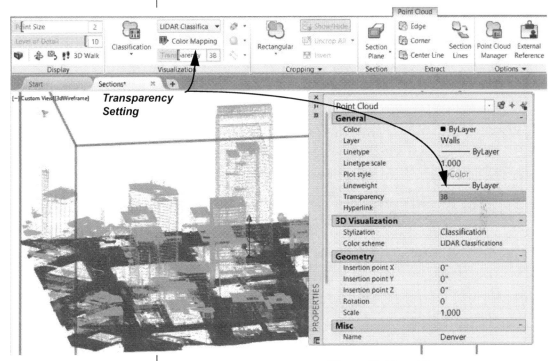

Figure C–10

Cropping Point Clouds

Displaying the bounding box around the point cloud data enables you to determine its position in 3D space relative to the other objects in the drawing. The cropping tools in the Cropping panel enable you to display only the information that is required for your project, as shown in Figure C–11. The cropping boundary can be rectangular, circular, or polygonal and is normal to the screen. You can use ⊞ (Invert) to reverse the points from inside to outside the boundary.

Figure C–11

A new tool in the Cropping panel (displayed by expanding the panel) enables you to save and restore named cropping states. Both the visibility of the scans and regions as they are displayed and the cropping boundary are maintained in named cropping states, as shown in Figure C–12.

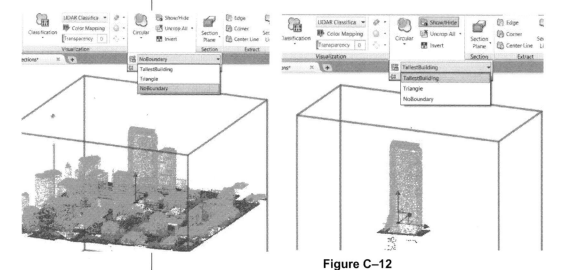

Figure C–12

Hint: List Crop States

The new command **POINTCLOUDCROPSTATE** can be used to **S**ave, **R**estore, and **D**elete crop states, as shown in Figure C–13. Using the **?** option lists all of the available crop states.

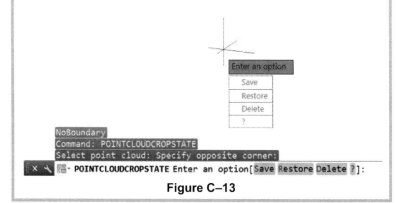

Figure C–13

How To: Save a Named Crop State

1. Once a point cloud has been attached, select it in the model.
2. In the *Point Cloud* contextual tab>Cropping panel, select an appropriate crop boundary, as shown in Figure C–14.

Figure C–14

3. In the model, pick points to draw the boundary. If a Polygonal boundary was selected, press <Enter> when done.
4. At the cursor, select either **Inside** or **Outside** to indicate which points to keep.
5. Expand the *Point Cloud* contextual tab>Cropping panel, click (New Crop State).
6. Enter a name for the new crop state.

Surfaces from Point Clouds

Point clouds can be used to create Autodesk Civil 3D surfaces. Once a point cloud has been attached to the drawing, it can be used to create a surface. In the *Home* tab>Create Ground Data panel, expand Surfaces and select (Create Surface from Point Cloud), as shown in Figure C–15.

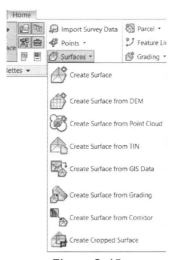

Figure C–15

The 🐾 (Create Surface from Point Cloud) tool extracts point data from the point cloud to create a TIN surface. During the surface creation process, you can:

- Name the surface.

- Select a style for the surface.

- Select a render material.

- Select part or all of a point cloud.

- Select a filter method for Non-Ground points.

Point Cloud Selection

If there are one or more point clouds in the model, it is important to communicate to the software which points from the point clouds to use in the surface. The three available options for this are described as follows:

- ⬜ : Add an entire point cloud.

- ⬜ : Remove a selection from the list.

- ⬜ : Add a selected area of a point cloud.

Non-Ground Point Filtering

When point clouds are created, they create points on any and every object visible in the scan area. This means that points can fall at the tops of buildings, trees and other structures. To create a surface that represents the ground terrain, the points that are not on the ground must be filtered out.

Three filter methods exist when creating a surface from point clouds:

1. **Planar average:** Predicts the elevation of a surface by finding the average elevation of a plane of points. An example is shown in Figure C–16.

2. **Kriging interpolation:** Predicts the elevation of a surface by computing a weighted average of the elevations of neighboring points. An example is shown in Figure C–17. This is usually the most accurate option.

3. **No filter:** Uses the point cloud point elevations for the surface elevations. An example is shown in Figure C–18.

    Figure C–16   **Figure C–17**   **Figure C–18**

How To: Create a Surface from Point Clouds

1. In the *Home* tab>Create Ground Data panel, expand **Surfaces** and select ✺ (Create Surface from Point Cloud).

2. In the model, select the point cloud or select any of the following options in the command line, as shown in Figure C–19.
   - Window
   - polyGon
   - polyLIne

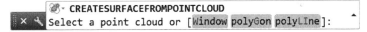

Figure C–19

3. In the Create TIN Surface from Point Cloud dialog box - General page, type a surface name, set the surface style, and render material, as shown in Figure C–20. Click **Next>**.

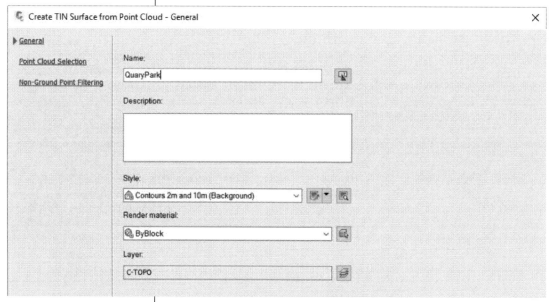

Figure C–20

4. In the Create TIN Surface from Point Cloud dialog box - Point Cloud Selection page, select the Point clouds or parts of the Point clouds, as shown in Figure C–21. Click **Next>**.

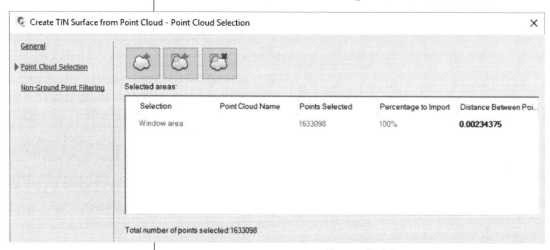

Figure C–21

5. In the Create TIN Surface from Point Cloud dialog box - Non-Ground Point Filtering page, select a filter method and click **Create Surface**, as shown in Figure C–22.

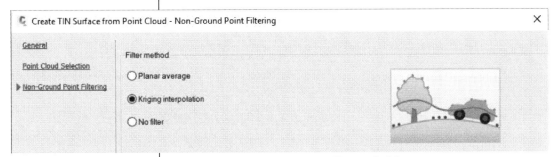

Figure C–22

6. In the Point Cloud Processing in Background message box, click **Close**.

Practice C2	# Create a Point Cloud Surface

Practice Objective

- Communicate information about a surface by labeling and analyzing it.

In this practice, you will attach a point cloud to a new drawing file, as shown in Figure C–23. You will then create a surface from the point cloud.

Figure C–23

Task 1 - Attach a point cloud.

1. Start a new drawing from the **_AutoCAD Civil 3D (Imperial) NCS.dwt**.

2. In the *Insert* tab>Point Cloud panel, click (Attach).

3. In the Select Point Cloud File dialog box, navigate to the *C:\Civil 3D for Surveyors\References\PointCloud* folder. In the *Name* area, select **Quarry Park.rcs** and click **Open**.

4. Accept the default options in the Attach Point Cloud dialog box, click **OK**, and use an insertion point of **0,0**.

5. Save the file.

Task 2 - Analyze the point cloud.

1. Select the point cloud. In the *Home* tab>Create Ground Data panel, expand **Surfaces** and select  (Create Surface from Point Cloud).

2. In the model, select the point cloud.

3. In the Create TIN Surface from Point Cloud dialog box> General page, type **Quarry Park** for the surface name. Leave all other defaults and click **Next>**.

4. In the Create TIN Surface from Point Cloud dialog box>Point Cloud Selection page, select the point cloud and then click

    (Remove a selection from the list).

5. On the same page, click (Add a selected area of a point cloud). In the model, draw a window around the area indicated in Figure C–24 and click **Next>**.

Figure C–24

6. In the Create TIN Surface from Point Cloud dialog box> Non-Ground Point Filtering page, select **Kriging interpolation** and click **Create Surface**.

7. In the Point Cloud Processing in Background message box, click **Close**. It might take a few minutes to process the points.

8. Close the file without saving.

Index

A

Assign a Coordinate System **B-3**, **B-4**

B

BIM 360 **1-4**

C

Coordinate Geometry Editor **3-25**

D

Draw Order **B-18**
Drawing Settings **1-33**
    Abbreviations **1-38**
    Ambient Settings **1-38**
    Object Layers **1-36**
    Transformation **1-36**
    Units and Zone **1-34**

G

Geospatial Data Connection **B-10**, **B-19**, **B-20**

M

Map Workflow **B-2**

N

Network Groups **4-30**

O

Object Viewer **7-42**

P

Panorama **1-24**
Places **1-14**
Point Cloud **C-8**
    Attach **C-8**
    Create Surface from Point Cloud **C-14**, **C-19**
    Cropping **C-12**
    External References **C-8**
    Object Snap **C-8**
    Transparency **C-11**
    UCS **C-8**

Points
    Create **6-4**, **6-7**, **6-46**, **6-47**
    Description Key Set
        Apply **6-9**
    Description Key Sets **2-42**, **2-46**
    Duplicate Point Numbers **6-14**
    Edit **6-40**, **6-44**
    Export **6-12**, **6-16**
    Identity **6-3**
    Import **6-12**, **6-16**
    Lock/Unlock **6-46**, **6-48**
    Overview **2-22**
    Point File Format **6-19**
    Point Groups **6-28**, **6-35**
    Reports **6-54**
    Transform **6-16**
    Values **6-3**

S

Settings **1-21**
    Command **1-42**
    Drawing **2-11**
    Feature **1-41**
    LandXML **1-40**
    Overrides **1-43**
    Point **6-2**
    Survey Database **2-6**
Styles **1-44**
    Import **1-52**, **1-63**
    Label **1-39**, **1-49**, **1-59**
    Object **1-46**, **1-57**
    Point Label **2-28**, **2-37**
    Point Marker **2-24**, **2-35**
    Purge **1-54**, **1-63**
    Reference **1-56**
    Surface Contour **7-28**
Stylize GIS Data **B-15**
Surface
    3D Solid Surface from TIN Surface **C-4**, **C-6**
    Analysis **7-42**, **7-56**
    Boundaries **7-24**
    Breaklines **7-20**, **7-29**, **7-32**, **8-25**
        Survey Figures **7-22**

Drape Images On a Surface **B-28**, **B-31**
Edit **7-35**, **7-44**
    Copy Surface **7-39**
    Line Edits **7-36**
    Point Edits **7-36**
    Raise/Lower **7-40**
    Simplify **7-37**
    Smooth Contours **7-38**
    Smooth Surface **7-39**
    Surface Paste **7-40**
From DEM Files **7-14**
From Drawing Objects **7-14**
From GIS Data **B-23**, **B-29**
From Point Files **7-14**
From Point Groups **7-14**
Labels **7-54**
Process **7-2**
Properties **7-8**, **7-41**
Quick Profile **7-43**
Rebuild **7-10**
Volume Calculations **C-2**
Survey
    Blunder Detection Analysis **A-10**
    Database **2-50**
        Import Points **6-22**
    Database Editing **2-56**
    Field Book
        Edit **4-45**
        Edits **4-29**
        Import **2-4**, **4-4**, **4-7**
        Re-import **4-46**
    Figure Prefix Database **2-13**
    Figures **2-10**, **4-42**, **7-32**
        Create Manually **4-47**, **5-14**
        Insert **5-15**
    Import Points **5-9**
    Least Squares Adjustment **A-2**, **A-8**, **A-13**
        Analysis **A-9**
        Blunder Detection Analysis **A-10**
        Update the Survey **A-12**
    Line Code Errors **5-13**
    Linework Codes **5-3**
        Coding syntax **5-3**
        Curve Segment Codes **5-5**
        Fix **5-30**
        Line Segment Codes **5-4**
        Special Codes **5-3**
    Missing Figure **5-13**
    Multiple Network Surveys **4-28**
    Network **4-2**
    Open a Survey Database **2-56**
    Translate a Database **5-34**

Traverse **4-14**, **4-19**
    Adjustment Reports **4-17**
    Closed Connected **4-29**
    Define **4-16**, **4-21**
Workflow **2-2**

T

Template **1-33**, **2-9**
Toolspace
    Prospector tab **1-18**, **1-26**
    Settings tab **1-20**, **1-27**
    Survey tab **1-21**, **2-6**
    Toolbox tab **1-22**
Transparent Commands **3-5**, **6-6**
    Bearing and Distance **3-5**
    Point Number **3-5**
    Profile Grade and Elevation **3-6**
    Profile Station and Elevation **3-6**
    Profile Station at Grade **3-6**
    Station and Offset **3-6**
    Zoom to Point **3-5**

U

User Interface **1-7**
    Application Menu **1-8**
    Command Line **1-12**
    InfoCenter **1-9**
    Quick Access Toolbar **1-8**
    Ribbon **1-10**
    Status Bar **1-12**

W

Workspaces **1-5**
    2D Drafting & Annotation **1-6**
    3D Modeling **1-6**
    Civil 3D **1-6**
    Planning and Analysis **1-6**, **B-2**